M42 ESO/J. Emerson/VISTA. Acknowledgment: Cambridge Astronomical Survey Unit

VOYAGER

101 WONDERS BETWEEN EARTH AND THE EDGE OF THE COSMOS

CALLISTO

0 Light Seconds

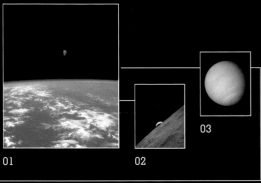

01

02

03

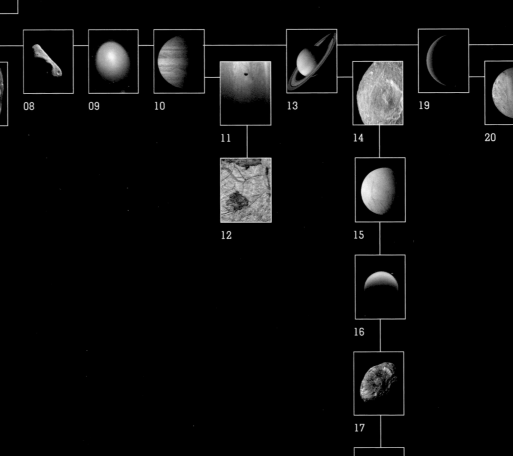

04

05

06

07

08

09

10

11

12

13

14

15

16

17

18

19

20

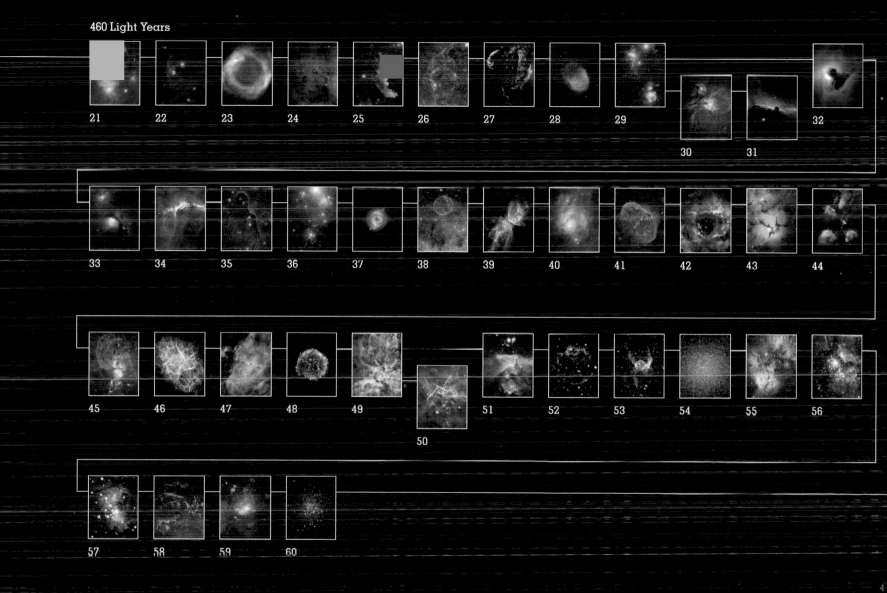

460 Light Years

160 Kilo Light Years

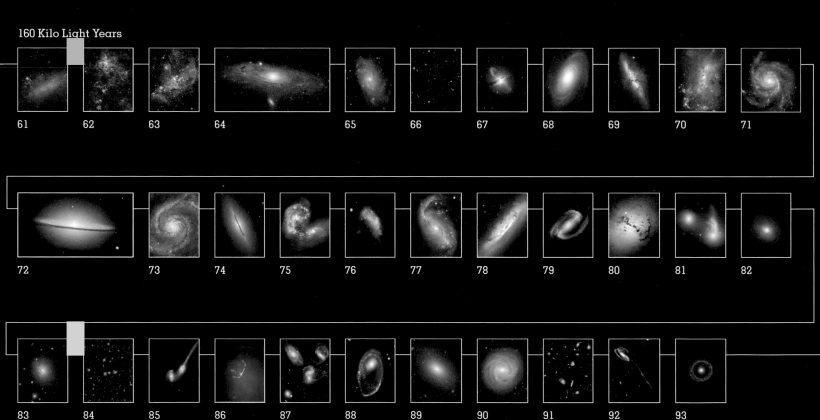

61   62   63   64   65   66   67   68   69   70   71

72   73   74   75   76   77   78   79   80   81   82

83   84   85   86   87   88   89   90   91   92   93

04 INTERTEMPORAL

1 Giga Light Year

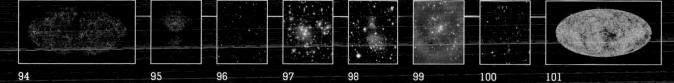

This is a journey through space and time. The Universe that surrounds us is vast beyond comprehension and a testament to both titanic forces and cosmic timescales. From the simplest of beginnings to the complex tapestry of celestial objects that surrounds us now, space is filled with wonders. On this journey we will encounter grandeur on an astonishing scale, beauty in the most unexpected places, and the most shocking natural violence.

We will see sand dunes weaving across the northern plains of Mars, driven by the winds of Martian spring and the icy surface of Enceladus cracking like an egg to blast geysers of water into space, feeding Saturn's rings. We will soar above alien cloudscapes of fluorescing gases, and burrow into the secret nests of new stars hidden within. We will marvel at the way stars sweep themselves into graceful spiral forms across vast tracts of space, and how galaxies string themselves into filaments to create a cosmic web that stretches from one side of the Universe to the other.

___The journey is organized into four distinct sections each representing a cosmic dominion: interplanetary, interstellar, interglalactic and finally, intertemporal. As we move from zone to zone, so the pace of our journey increases. Our first interplanetary steps are measured in light seconds, our final strides in the intertemporal zone are measured in giga light years. The transition from zone to zone also represents a leap in scale where we see how the components of the previous zone band together to create an altogether more monumental assemblage. What is striking about each zone is that it possesses its own character. Each is a unique realm that functions almost like an ecosystem in its own right, with hierarchies populated by dominant and subservient celestial objects, cycles of life and death, and evolution on the long scale of cosmic time.

___We start on Earth, in orbit around the Sun, a typical middle-aged star. At 4.6 billion years old, it is about halfway through its lifespan and comfortably stable in both the light it puts out and the magnetic activity that spits giant gouts of its superheated atmosphere into space.

___We shelter from this rain of particles on the Earth, protected by our magnetic field, while we watch the rest of our sibling planets. From the furnace of rocks on Mercury's airless wastes to the ephemeral clouds of Saturn's upper atmosphere, they exhibit different temperaments and personalities just like the brothers and sisters of a human family. Yet all were born from the same cloud of dust and gas that surrounded the young Sun.

___There are rocky planets like the Earth, with surfaces to be explored and in some cases clouds to soar through, and there are bloated giants with soupy atmospheres and no appreciable solid surfaces. These are alien dominions that strike few resonances with what we think of as a planet based on the world around us.

___There are ten times as many moons in the Solar System as planets, and that means ten times more worlds of wonder to behold. Jupiter's moons have a special place in history, as they were the first to be discovered beyond our own moon, and are wildly divergent from one another. Io and Europa are worlds of fire and ice respectively with the sulphur volcanoes of Io contrasting with the ice floes of Europa.

___These days the planets live in isolation – like neighbours that never talk – unless it is to exchange the odd meteorite. Interspersed with the planets and moons are the asteroids and the comets. Smaller, mountain-sized worldlets, they remind us of the formation of the Solar System, when a prodigious number of these objects formed the building blocks of the bigger things. They smashed together, melting into one another and solidifying into the planets of today.

___Each object in interplanetary space is unique and striking, but one stands out above all the others. To our knowledge, it is the one place in the Universe where matter organized itself well enough for conscious minds to be able to peer out across the heavens and attempt to comprehend it all. It is our home and the start of our journey, Earth.

___How did Earth become so privileged that life became widespread across its surface? Its distance from the Sun and its size certainly play a part, but how life actually started and whether these conditions have been replicated elsewhere in the Universe are questions that tantalize.

___In the interstellar zone, the planets disappear from view and are replaced by the burning orbs of light that are the stars. The Sun's soft yellow glow blends with the light from its companions. Around each star, there may well be planets but for now they are mostly lost to our view on this scale. Here the stars are the individuals, with differences in brightness, colour and activity to distinguish them.

___Unlike planets, stars can be identical twins. The defining property of a star is its mass. This determines how fast the nuclear reactions run in its core, and therefore how much energy it produces. In turn, the energy determines the surface temperature and brightness of the star. So two stars with the same mass will have the same brightness.

___The unit of currency used to compare stars is the solar mass: 2×10^{30} kg. The Sun is outshone millions of times by the Galaxy's most massive stars. With masses of ten times or greater that of the Sun, and surface temperatures higher than 10,000°C, these heavyweight stars consume their fuel of hydrogen and other gases and live short, profligate lives that enliven space but are doomed to end in disaster. Each one ruptures as the result of an almighty implosion in its core: a supernova.

___But the giants are outnumbered. The Galaxy has many more stars with masses less than the Sun than those with more. These smaller stars are little more than embers on the stellar scale, burning a miserly red light that they can kindle for tens of billions of years, sometimes longer.

___The stars inhabit an interstellar dreamscape of bright hues and swirling contours. These are the nebulae from which the stars are born, and back into which they will pass when their lives are done. Between one and ten new stars are born every year from these celestial wombs, most of them common or garden low mass stars, but occasionally a giant is produced. As the giant's nuclear furnaces ignite, its scorching radiation pours into the birth cloud, lighting it up with the boiling glow of fluorescing gasses while a fierce stellar wind carves out great caverns within the surrounding nebula – complete with towering stalagmites and stalactites.

___Will these nebulae produce more stars before starlight disperses them forever? What happens to the stars after they are born? How do they end their days? These are the questions that predominate in the interstellar zone.

___By taking a 100,000 light year step, we arrive in the intergalactic zone, where the stars are hard to distinguish as individuals – mere grains of sand on the galactic beach. A few hundred billion stars combine their light to make the hazy grouping that is our Galaxy. From this vantage point, we can see Milky Way's grand design. Its stellar denizens are marshalled and corralled by the opposing forces of gravity and rotation. Gravity pulls them together, whilst rotation drives them apart. Eventually they reach equilibrium, and a flat disc of stars circulates around a central stellar hub.

___In the disc are spiralling waves of stellar creation, outlined by the burning blue light of the short-lived stars. These arms sweep around the Galaxy every few hundred million years, sparking new bouts of star formation in their wake.

___As we turn our gaze outwards, we see this glorious display repeated across intergalactic space, with galaxy after galaxy punctuating the otherwise eternal night. The drama of the Milky Way with its bursts of new stars, its cataclysmic stellar explosions and its rippling shockwaves of gas is repeated over and over again. Sometimes it is played out in other spiral galaxies, and sometimes in galaxies of different shapes and sizes such as giant elliptical collections or even poorly stocked, irregularly shaped assemblages.

___As these other galaxies come into range, so the Milky Way begins to lose its overwhelming importance. This is a dizzying height from which to contemplate the Universe, and we can catch our first glimpse of the true scale of creation.

___The Milky Way is just one participant in a small collection of thirty or so galaxies. Beyond the 'Local Group' lie other collections of galaxies, some bigger, others of similar size. Many galaxies cluster together in this way, whilst others are loners; between a third and a half of them are content to wander the intergalactic void in isolation. Those in groups and clusters tend to accumulate into even larger groupings, forming superclusters that stretch tens of millions of light years across space.

___Within these giant flocks, the galaxies all rotate whilst circling each other. Occasionally they will clash, igniting ferocious conflicts in which the galaxies pit themselves against one another for gravitational supremacy. During these bouts, they rip each other's stars out, tussling for control of the stellar cargo because each new influx promises to make the winning galaxy larger and more powerful. They persist until one or the other, or sometimes both, are destroyed, leaving behind a wrecked assemblage of confused stars.

___As at all the scales of the Universe, there are new questions to be answered. What sets the spiral pattern of arms going? Can galaxies recover from direct hits from other galaxies? Is the rotation of each galaxy driven by a form of invisible matter as yet undiscovered in Earthly laboratories?

___At the greatest scales, space and time become intertwined. This is what we have termed the intertemporal zone, where the galaxies themselves are the grains of sand. There could more galaxies in the Universe than stars in the Milk Way: hundreds of billions or even more. Trillions of galaxies, in fact, many gathered into clusters, which themselves assemble into superclusters. Nature has strung these superclusters out into filaments, stretched across the Universe like bunting. In between the filaments are gigantic voids, intertemporal deserts with only the odd galaxy acting as an oasis of light.

___With each step taking us billions of light years further from home, whole clusters of galaxies are now the building blocks, and the galaxies themselves are reduced to mere pinpricks of light. You would be forgiven for thinking that you were looking at single stars but no, these are stellar metropoli containing millions or billions of individual stars.

___On these scales, things can easily become confusing. You cannot rely on time as you do in the everyday world because the presence of matter slows it down. This means that time must be travelling more slowly in the superclusters than in the giant voids. Truly we run into the concept of space and time as conjoined realities: where you are in space affects how time runs. They are flipsides of the same coin rather than entirely separate entities.

___There is movement here, too. In the spaces between the clusters of galaxies, space itself is expanding like a never-ending piece of elastic. If space is growing ever bigger, it means that the Universe must have been smaller in its earlier days. Running the cosmic clock backwards tells us that everything we can see today would have been concentrated into a single point-like mass about 13.7 billion years ago. So this is assumed to be the age of the Universe, and the event that gave birth to it is called the big bang.

___No one knows what happened during the big bang, it is the ultimate enigma. Our knowledge of physics has yet to be developed sufficiently. However, at that time, something created all matter and energy, space and time, and sent it hurtling across space. The expansion of space is a remaining vestige of the magnificent fury unleashed during this extraordinary creation event.

___Light is our messenger for scanning the heavens. It is a wave of energy that rolls through space, just like a wave of water rolls across the sea. Matter creates light and matter absorbs light. It does this by juggling the positions of the outer particles in its atoms, allowing them either to expel excess energy or to absorb a new delivery. If the matter doing the absorption happens to be in the retina of our eyes, so we perceive the light and see the object. These days, telescopes act as our proxy eyes. They can be much larger than our biological ones, having mirrors 10 metres across compared to our pupils of a few millimetres.

___They are sited in high places, on mountaintops and plateaux above most of Earth's thick atmosphere that blurs the images of the celestial objects. This is where the Hubble Space Telescope reigns supreme. Although modest in size, just 2.4 metres across, it is in orbit above the turbulent atmosphere.

___There is a lot more to light than meets the eye.

We are all familiar with the rainbow spectrum of visible light, but it forms only a tiny band in the middle of the overall electromagnetic spectrum. Most light exists in forms that are invisible to us, our human eyes having evolved to see just the most plentiful wavelengths given out by the Sun. Across the Universe as a whole, objects radiate in all the other wavelengths, and we need mechanical eyes to help us see.

___The names of these other wavelengths are familiar: radio waves, microwaves, infrared, ultraviolet, X-rays and gamma rays. All are fundamentally the same as visible light, which lies between infrared and ultraviolet on the spectrum, but with longer or shorter wavelengths. All carry energy and are one of means by which widely separated concentrations of matter can communicate with each other, because all atoms have the ability to absorb or emit light of these various wavelengths.

___Without the help of artificial eyes sensitive to the hidden wavelengths of electromagnetic radiation, most of the Universe would remain invisible to us. It would be the equivalent of approaching a city at night and seeing only the streetlights, while the main bulk of the buildings remained invisible all around us.

___Using specialized telescopes we can tease out the hidden messages from the celestial objects. In the same way that a bat detector transforms ultrasonic utterances into chirps that human ears can register, so we have to colour-code invisible radiations – be they radio or X-rays – into visible images. In all cases, the longest wavelengths are coloured red and the shortest blue, to mimic the sweep of the rainbow.

___The most plentiful form of electromagnetic radiation is at microwave wavelengths. There are a billion photons of microwave energy for every single atom; they were created during the fireball of the big bang, and now they bathe all of space in a perpetual sleet.

___As we delve ever deeper into the Universe, so we will be travelling back through time. This is because light travels faster than anything else through space. Racing at almost 300 million metres a second, it could circumnavigate the Earth's equator seven and a half times in that second. And it never tires. Light will always travel at this speed through space, regardless of the distance it has covered, or the colour it contains. Truly light is the fleet-footed messenger of the heavens, carrying with it most of the knowledge we can gather about the Universe.

___At this speed, it can cross approximately 9.5 trillion kilometres every year. So, this is the distance called a light year. For example, our nearest large galactic neighbour, the Andromeda Galaxy is 22 million trillion kilometres or 2.3 million light years away. In our everyday world, light travels so quickly it can be thought of as travelling instantaneously from one place to another. In the Universe at large, however, the distances can be so vast that even light will take millions or billions of years to cross the firmament and deliver its cargo of information. So we see celestial objects the way they appeared when they released their light, which is not necessarily as they would look now. We see the Andromeda Galaxy as it was 2.3 million years ago, and won't know what it looks like right now for another 2.3 million years.

___Like an archaeologist digging down through successive rock strata, this means that the further we peer into space, the further we look back through time because it has taken longer for the light to reach us.

___We will measure our journey against light speed, giving us an easy way of judging both distance and this look-back time. A distance in light units, be they seconds, minutes, hours or years, instantly tells us how far back in time the object is located. Across the interplanetary realm we will measure our journey in light seconds and light minutes. These are but small steps through our cosmic garden. Within interstellar space, our yardstick will become the light year. As we press on into intergalactic space, the ruler extends to millions of light years – mega light years. Eventually we reach the billions of years light – giga light years – that correspond to the intertemporal zone and the effect of look-back time will become extreme.

___Most of the objects we see in this realm are long gone today, evolved into new forms, or rendered extinct by the changing universal environment. Many of them are just distant memories; they exist now only as long as light carries their song across space. By studying this light, we can chart the course of celestial evolution.

___This new image from the European Space Agency's spacecraft Planck shows all of creation [1]; from the very first microwave light to enter the Universe to the very latest created just a few scant light years away.

___The oldest light appears at the top and bottom of the image as the mottled pattern of magenta, gold and purple. It reveals subtle differences in the density of the atoms that pervaded the whole Universe just 400,000 years after the big bang. This gas was composed of the atoms that we now see corralled into planets, stars and galaxies. Where the microwave background radiation is densest, in the gold spots, so the likelihood of galaxies forming is greatest. The opposite is true for the purple patches, where the gas was sparse. In short, this pattern represents the cosmic blueprint for the web of galaxies found today.

___Across the middle of the image, superimposing themselves on top of the ancient light, are the braided filaments of cold dust that thread the Milky Way. Our Galaxy is a flat twist of stars 100,000 light years across, when viewed from above. Situated in one of the spiralling arms, we view the Galaxy as a thin band of stars that crosses the night sky. This view is echoed in microwaves but with embellishments. The pink band is the disc of the Galaxy, suffused with dust and then streamers of dust-laced gas reach upwards and downwards to surround us with a 'cat's cradle' of matter.

___The dust itself exists at a temperature of –261°C, only about 12 °C above absolute zero. At such frigid temperatures, it is sluggish and almost completely at the mercy of gravity. Almost.

___To the right of the image, just below the main disc of the Galaxy is the mighty Orion cloud of molecular gas. Surrounding this region is an arc of pink light, which is the shockwave of a star that exploded 2 million years ago. It has snowploughed dust in its path, creating the bubble. Other areas show similar activity, such as the arcs that sit above and below the plane of the Galaxy, just to the left of Orion. These mark the region of the Vela supernova, another exploded star. Over on the opposite side of the Galaxy, much smaller pink bubbles show younger stellar explosions. These cataclysms keep the dust moving, stirring the Galaxy and ensuring that gravity does not have its own way all the time.

___Resting in space, between the Milky Way and the background radiation are over hundred billion other galaxies. A few of them show up in this image. The nearest are the two knots of white light below the centre right of the image. These are the small nearby galaxies, known as the Magellanic Clouds. The Andromeda Galaxy shows up in the lower left quadrant of this image as a diagonal sliver of microwave light. At 2.3 million light years away, it is the most distant object he unaided eye can resolve from the surface of the Earth with.

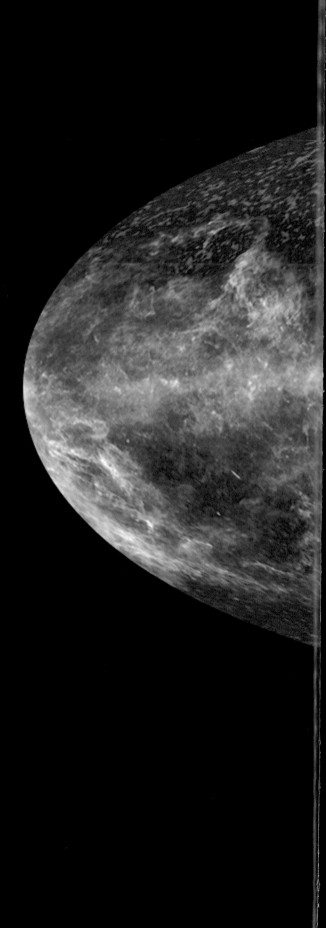

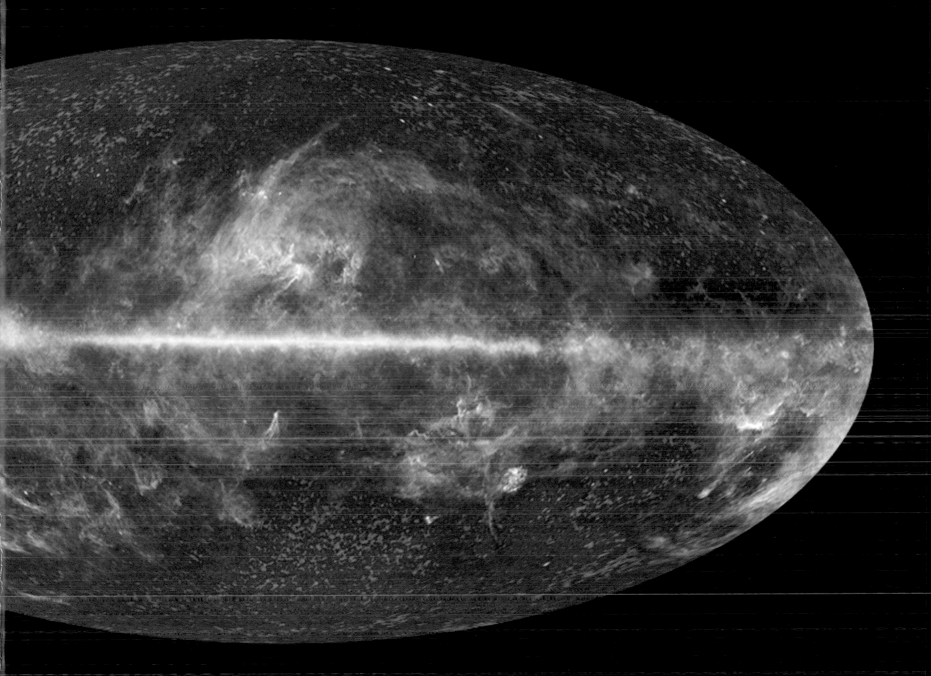

The bright diagonal stream to the upper right of the centre is the active galaxy Centaurus A, 11 million light years away. Here two mature spirals have collided, one scything into the other. Copious quantities of matter have been forced into the clutches of a supermassive black hole. These lurking gravitational ogres are destroyers, gripping nearby celestial objects and crushing them out of existence. In the process, they wring out energy from the captured atoms and the outpouring of X-rays catapults other matter to safety. What is shining here is the ejected dust, now rapidly cooling off in the frigid depths of intergalactic space.

___If light is the messenger, then gravity is the architect. In absolute terms, gravity is the weakest of the forces of nature but it does have the longest range. Created by every object that has mass, its real strength lies in the fact that it is purely attractive. Gravity never repels. It helps to sculpt the great sweep of the Universe on its grandest scales and provides much of the details on the finer scale too.

___All celestial objects are formed because of the action of gravity pulling matter together while other forces rise to challenge its supremacy. At the smallest end of that scale, planets and asteroids are the result. Here the amounts of matter squeezed together are small enough that the strength of chemical bonds is able to halt gravity in its stride. The atoms in the rocks cast themselves into a crystalline lattice that provides an unbreakable scaffolding to prevent further collapse.

___On the interstellar scale, gravity can break these bonds. It squeezes larger volumes of matter together and heats them as it does so. As the temperature rises, so solid chunks of matter are vaporized; even molecules of gas are ripped apart. All the while, gravity is squeezing the matter into a smaller and smaller volume of space. It ends when the temperature of the gas cloud reaches around 15 million °C. At that point collisions between hydrogen atomic nuclei are so fast they fuse together.

___This unleashes energy from the nuclei, which starts to fight its way out through the surrounding mass of matter. As it repeatedly collides with atoms on its outward journey, so it provides support, helping to shore up the collapsing matter from the relentless pull of gravity. This is the situation inside a star; it is a delicate balance of light versus gravity and, for as long as the star has fuel to fuse, it will remain a stable celestial object.

At the end of a star's life, gravity will triumph

The object's complement of matter will be pulled ever denser, until either the atoms are compressed into a new stable configuration – such as a neutron star – or it collapses completely into that most mysterious of objects: a black hole. No one truly knows what happens to the matter inside a black hole. Can it really disappear out of existence? It remains an enduring celestial conundrum.

___A journey through the Universe, from familiar shores to distant realms is the perfect way to explore space because the history of astronomy has been one of ever-expanding horizons. Every great advance in our understanding has been at the price of divesting the Earth of another level of assumed importance and each time this has happened, the reward has been a greater cosmic perspective over a wider Universe.

___For two millennia, from the time of the ancient Greeks until the 16th century, Earth was considered to be the centre of the heavens, the focus of creation. Yet, while trying to understand the movement of the planets through the night sky, Copernicus and Kepler were forced to demolish this cherished view. The former proposed that the Sun was the centre of everything and Kepler made the system work by showing that the planets did not all follow perfect circular orbits, as had been assumed, but elliptical paths.

___The next great leap was into the stellar universe, when the true distance of the stars was finally revealed in the 19th century. Now, clearly shown to be tens of thousands of times further away than the planets, the stars were unmasked as anything but fixed in space in the way the apparently immortal constellations had suggested. Instead all stars move through space and our Sun is not even near the centre of rotation but just one of the massed ranks out in the boondocks of the Galaxy. In time, the constellations will deform as the stars move.

___The greatest leap outwards took place during the early 20th century, when indistinct smudges of light revealed themselves in the telescopes of the day as whole galaxies. The Universe was not only larger than we had imagined, it was vastly larger than we could imagine, stretching for some 90 billion light years in diameter. Fortunately, this was the moment in human history when Albert Einstein developed General Relativity, the mathematical tools by which we can investigate the Universe as a whole. It was the moment we realized all of space was expanding, driving clusters of galaxies ever further away from each other

and forever banishing the idea that the Universe was eternally static.

___Today, we are grappling with the very largest scales of the Universe and realizing that, at such enormous distances, space and time become inextricably linked both through the concept of look-back time and the way gravitational fields make time pass more slowly. As well as living in a cosmic landscape, we may also be living in a cosmic timescale, with time running at different speeds in different parts of the Universe.

___Take your own journey across these fascinating reaches. There are billions of light years of space represented here, flip through, stop anywhere that takes your fancy. The book can be read in any order but, taken sequentially, it works from the Earth outwards. The positions of the objects have been frozen in time on 25 December 2010. This particularly affects the Solar System objects, and specifically those closest to Earth, as they doggedly follow their orbits. If our growing understanding of the Universe has taught us anything, it is that the Universe is a dynamic place of perpetual movement.

___Every second, the Earth covers 34 more kilometres in its orbit around the Sun, which itself speeds 269 kilometres in its orbit around the centre of the Milky Way, whilst the whole Galaxy moves 121 kilometres closer to the Andromeda Galaxy. The Local Group, containing the Milky Way and Andromeda, have moved away from the nearby Virgo cluster of galaxies by 965 kilometres in that second.

___Over the average human lifespan of 70 years, the Sun will have carried you on a journey 500 billion kilometres through the Galaxy, and the Galaxy will have taken you 267 billion kilometres closer to Andromeda.

___Yet these are small steps in the grand scale. Over its lifetime, the Sun has completed around 21 orbits of the centre of the Galaxy, each turn taking some 200 million years. Although these distances and times sound vast, from interplanetary space outwards the slow clockwork of the Universe will make little difference if you are reading this a year, a decade or a century from publication. But don't dally too long. The grand sweep of the Universe will not last forever!

___Perhaps the biggest of the cosmic mysteries, if indeed there is something more to it than just random chance, is that there will never be a better time to see the Universe than in the next billion years or so. This is its heyday.

___It has taken 13.7 billion years to finesse itself to this standard but it will not last much longer. The rate of star formation is dropping as reserves of gas run out and the clusters are gradually destroying their individual galaxies in favour of much larger, less elegant conglomerations. And even the superclusters are doomed.

___They could perhaps have survived the gradual expansion of space for aeons yet to come. However, with space accelerating constantly, they will be torn apart, their galaxies orphaned and then shredded as the dark energy of expansion builds up its strength. There may not be any end to this acceleration. As time passes, it might simply grow stronger and stronger.

___In this nightmare scenario, stars are the next to disintegrate, then planets, people and eventually even the atoms themeselves will surrender to the boundless rise of dark energy.

___Its ultimate battle will be with black holes. These all-powerful destroyers were once thought to be impervious to external forces. But if the cosmic acceleration just keeps growing, how soon before even the black holes are ripped to shreds? We simply have no idea.

___But enough of the speculation, there is enough real wonder in the heavens that humankind will never run out of targets for its telescopes. Take the stars in our Galaxy. Two hundred billion incandescent orbs, each one tens or hundreds of times larger than our home planet. Yet each one reduced to a mere speck in our cameras [1].

___Now jump to the largest scales and the pattern repeats itself only this time the specks are not individual stars but mammoth collections of hundreds of billions of stars: whole galaxies in their own right [2]. There are as many galaxies in the Universe as there are stars in the Galaxy. And every galaxy is creating new stars at a rate of between one and a thousand per year and each star is waiting for us to know it.

___This book is a journey into these extraordinary realms. You start here, on Earth, nestled in the Orion Spur of the Milky Way Galaxy, near the centre of the Local Group, gravitationally bound to the Virgo Supercluster, but the entire night sky is now yours to explore. You have 45 billion light years to travel and 13.7 billion years of time to traverse. So, with the clock set to zero, let the journey commence!

1

2

LIGHT SECONDS
LIGHT MINUTES
LIGHT YEARS
KILO LIGHT YEARS
MEGA LIGHT YEARS
GIGA LIGHT YEARS

INTER
PLANETARY

The worlds of the Solar System provide the stepping-stones for the first stage in our journey. Each world, be it a planet or moon, although often mixed from a common set of ingredients has its own unique characteristics. From the airless hunk of Mercury to the toxic atmosphere of Jupiter, from the barren magnificence of the Moon to the ice mountains of Mimas, the landscapes are all expressions of possibility. It seems as if all of nature's myriad permutations occur somewhere.

There is a remarkable dichotomy of planetary types. In the inner regions, the four planets are closer together. Mercury, Venus, Earth and Mars share properties in common. They are relatively small, made predominantly of dense material such as rock, and possess relatively thin atmospheres, if any at all. These are called the terrestrial worlds or simply the rocky planets.

___In the outer Solar System, the type of planet changes dramatically. Taking Jupiter as their role model, Saturn, Uranus and Neptune are much larger worlds. They are made largely of gases with extensive atmospheres sitting on cores of crushed rocks and metal. These solid hearts are buried so deeply beneath their atmospheres that these planets have no solid surfaces of which to speak. They are known appropriately as the gas giants.

___Then there are the vagabonds: the asteroids and the comets. These are the smallest of the celestial objects, just hunks of rock and ice hurtling through space. The majority of the asteroids are made of rocks and metal, and shepherded within a wide belt around the Sun between Mars and Jupiter. The comets on the other hand have free range. They wheel through the Solar System, swooping from above or climbing from below to dart briefly round the Sun like birds hunting on the wing. They mark their paths with trails of dust and gas that were once part of these small bodies. Eventually they deplete themselves so much that they disintegrate, or they develop a layer of carbonaceous scarring that seals in the remains of the ice. In either case, the comet fades from further view.

___And, at the centre of it all, presiding over this retinue is the Sun. It accounts for 99 percent of the mass in the Solar System and provides the gravitational hub around which everything turns. Its energy drives the atmospheres of the planets, conjuring impressionistic storms and vortices, cloud belts and blankets of chemical smog. It launches a constant wind of particles that flows past the planets, sparking dancing aurorae on those planets with any atmosphere.

___The worlds of the Solar System follow a hierarchy. In the kingdom of the Sun, there are eight fiefdoms, each belonging to one of the orbiting planets. In each of these domains, the planet exerts control over its moons. These smaller celestial bodies orbit the planets, as the planets orbit the Sun. The moons are as individualistic as the planets.

___There is infernal Io, which is in a perpetual state of catastrophic eruption; twilight Titan with dense clouds that prevent most sunlight reaching its surface; and hypnotic Hyperion, which tumbles through its orbit with no predictable pattern to its day and night cycle.

___Jupiter itself is so large that it extends its dominion over the asteroid belt as well as its moons. Although the asteroids go around the Sun rather than circling the giant planet, nevertheless Jupiter's gravity keeps them in regimented orbits, allowing some gatherings but dispersing others.

___Then there are the dwarf planets, such as Pluto. These are worlds that orbit the Sun yet cannot muster the gravity to control their wider environments. In the case of Pluto, a swarm of smaller asteroid-like objects called the plutinos share similar but independent paths. Pluto even blurs the definition of what should be considered a planet and a moon because its largest companion, Charon, is half its size, prompting some to think of them as a double dwarf planet system, rather than a planet and moon. In the asteroid belt, the biggest member is called Ceres. At 975 km in diameter, it too is a dwarf planet.

___The segregation of the planets, from rocky worlds to gas giants, lends itself to a simple formation scenario in which the planets coalesced from a rotating disc of matter that was heated from the centre to the edge by the nascent Sun. Such a disc would be formed naturally as a gas cloud fell together, because of the way the cloud's rotation resisted the collapse around its equator.

___In the inner portion of the disc, where the temperatures would have been greatest, only the high temperature chemicals such as silicon and iron would have found it possible to solidify. The more volatile material such as water ice would have been forced to remain in gaseous form. So the planets in the inner Solar System would have had a restricted diet from which to feed. This is now reflected in their composition and relatively small sizes.

___Further out the temperature of the disc dropped, creating a 'snow line' beyond which water and other volatile chemicals such as ammonia and methane could become solid. These increased both the amount and variety of the building blocks available to the embryonic gas giants, ensuring their magnified size. Occasionally one of the icy building blocks slid through the inner Solar System, creating

the first rain of comets that helped fill the oceans of the inner planets. Venus, Earth, Mars – all would have received their quota. Yet only Earth jealously protected it, hiding it under a shield of magnetism from the ravages of the Sun's young light. Now, of course, Earth is the only world that retains an abundance of liquid surface water. Venus and Mars show evidence of formerly being lush, but Mercury displays no signs of ever having been hydrated. This is probably due to its ringside seat by the Sun.

___As the matter thinned out with ever-increasing distance, so the icy worlds of Pluto, Charon and myriad other dwarf planets that probably exist at extreme distances from the Sun, could form. Only a handful of these distant outposts have been found so far. Many may have been exiled there by gravitational slingshots during close encounters with the gas giants billions of years ago.

___As sensible as this pattern of planets appears to be, we know it is not the only possible one. Planets around other stars, known as exoplanets, have been sensed by the way they cause their parent stars to wobble. Of the 400 plus that have been detected, most are gas giants locked into orbits even tighter than Mercury's around the Sun; some much tighter. The closest planets whip around their stars in just a few days, making Mercury's 88-day orbit look leisurely.

___It is thought that such gas giants form far from their sun as expected but then migrate inward as the pressure of their remaining natal clouds sap them of orbital energy. As they begin the long march towards their star, they sweep ahead of them any smaller planets that get in the way. One by one these are forced into the fires of the central orb and lost forever, as the gas giant manoeuvres into its final resting orbit.

___Given the proximity of these gas giant exoplanets to their stars, the input of heat would be enormous, rousing storms of immense ferocity. Winds up to 10,000 km/h power through the atmosphere as blistering gas races from the glare of the star to the night-time side of the planet.

___While, in time, we may well find solar systems similar to our own, at the moment it remains a unique crown bedecked with a diverse array of planetary jewels.

Right: the Sun rises behind the International Space Station

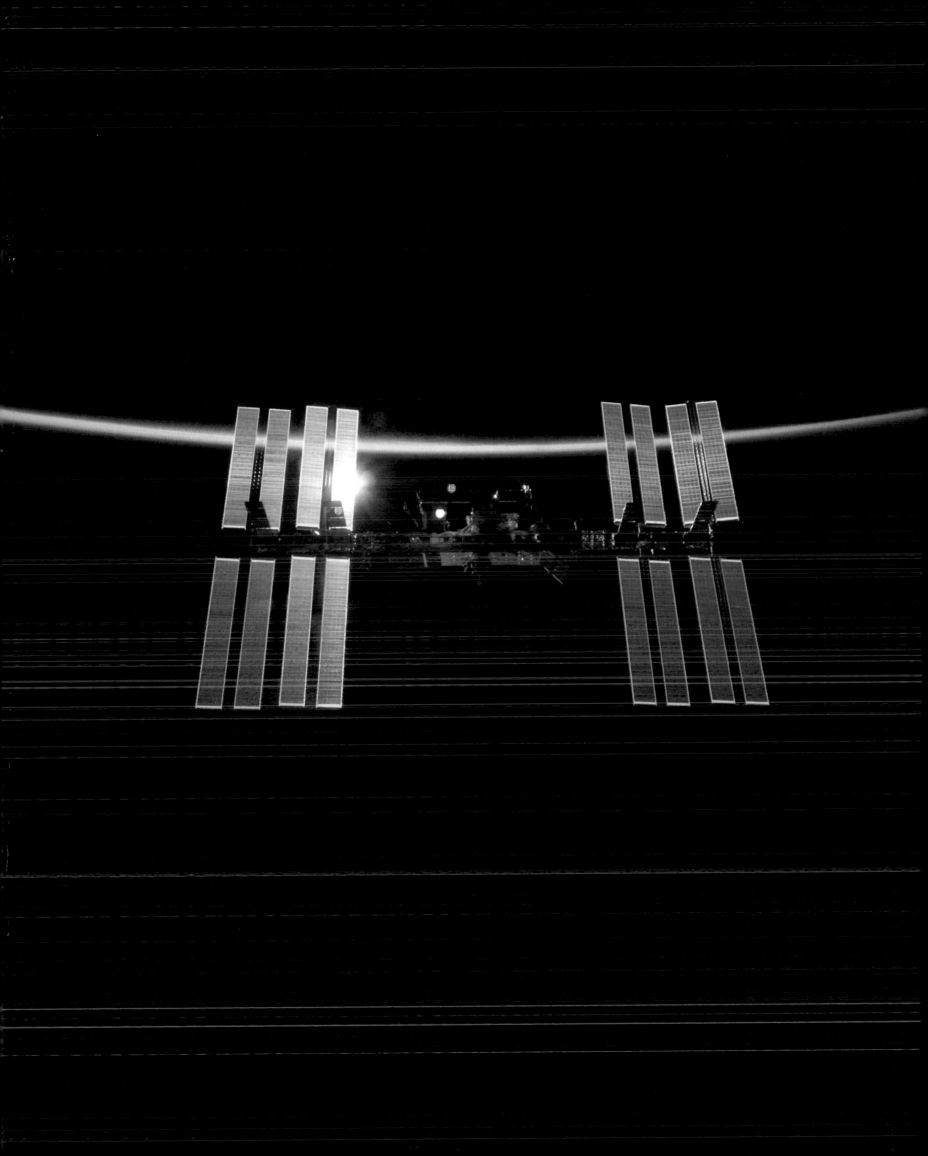

1

2

A planet called home

We live on a world of many hues and many faces:
from the lush green of the forests to the burnt ochre
of the deserts; from the silver tint of stone and metal in
the cities, to the gleaming white of the Arctic wastes.
Yet from space, one colour overwhelms them all: blue.

'How inappropriate to call this planet Earth when it is quite clearly Ocean', said the science fiction author Arthur C Clarke. It is a sentiment easy to concur with from space. More than seventy percent of Earth's surface is covered in water. The restless bulk of the great seas ebbs and flows in synchrony with the Moon, lapping at the shoreline and stirring our adventurous hearts.

___The molecular basis of life depends so much on water, maybe the oceans stirred life into the Earth in the first place. On the sea floor there are powerful volcanic vents that jet scalding water into the otherwise frigid depths. The dissolved chemicals and abundant microbes clustering around these today suggest they may have been good sites for early life. But exactly what transforms a collection of chemicals into life is something that continues to elude us.

___Earth is the largest rocky planet in the Solar System, and our home. Its great age is measured at 4.6 billion years, or about one third of the total age of the Universe. Yet our tenure on this world has so far been but the merest blink of a cosmic eye. Humans became distinct from their genetic ancestors some 200,000 years ago, emerging from the African savannah.

___Life transforms our planet into a vibrant, changeable place yet it is not omnipotent. Today, large swathes of the planet are excluded from our habitation, and they always have been. The mighty desert wastelands offer barren comfort to humans but glorious sights from space [1]. The swirling hurricanes of water vapour that grip the atmosphere every year terrorize us but take on a serenity from on high [2].

___Taken over the sweep of cosmic time, only a tenth of a percent of the planet's entire lifespan will afford what we think of as habitable conditions. Nevertheless, Earth is all we have. No other place in the Solar System comes close to replicating its 'Goldilocks' nature: not too hot, not too cold, but just right. The more we look into the Universe, the more we realize our luck.

___In the same way that the early mariners were inspired to cross the oceans, so our celestial observations draw our minds upwards. Where once it was the promise of distant continents that lured us, now it is the stars that are our destination.

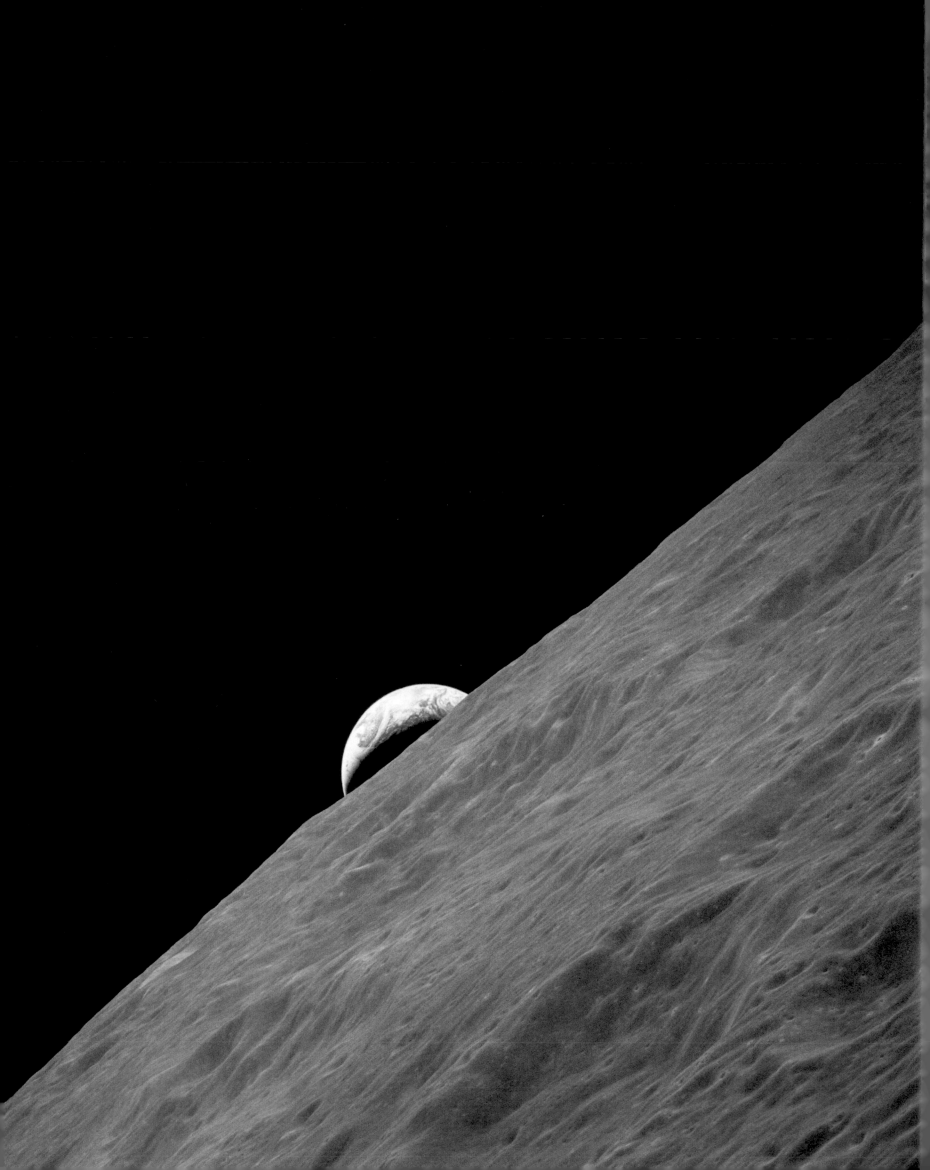

The Moon
MOON of EARTH

DIAMETER: 3,500 KM

LIGHT SECONDS
LIGHT MINUTES
LIGHT YEARS
KILO LIGHT YEARS
MEGA LIGHT YEARS
GIGA LIGHT YEARS

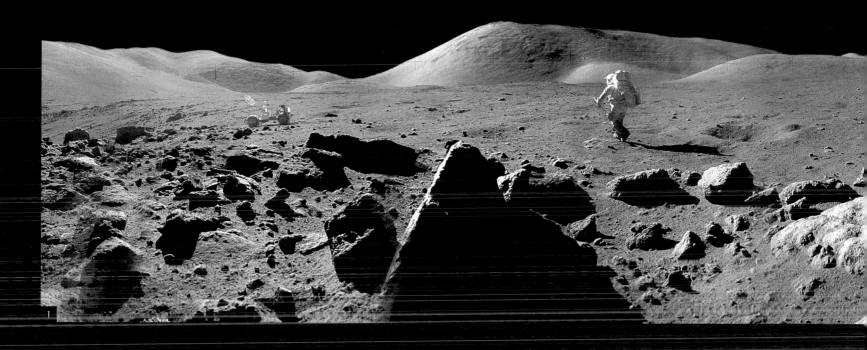

1

One small step

Earth's fixed companion, the Moon sits on our cosmic doorstep. Yet it took millennia of human technological development to get us there in rocket ships. Now awaiting our return, the Moon may hold the secret to why there is life on Earth.

The surface of the Moon is pure in a way that no stone on Earth can ever be. Untouched by wind or rain, there is nothing to alter the lunar rocks in any way. The face that we see today, the ridges and the craters, and the solidified lava seas, are all the same as they were billions of years ago.

___Our Moon is by no means the largest in the Solar System. It ranks only fifth, but it is the largest moon in relation to its parent planet, containing about one eighteenth of the mass of the Earth. Now the Moon watches over us, stirs our oceans into tides with gravity, and keeps her silent counsel.

___Time has stood still for the Moon, giving us a snapshot of forces no longer at play in the Solar System. In particular, the craters mark the final act of formation, speaking of a nightmarish era when mountain-sized rocks rained down on the newly forged worlds.

___Today little hits the Moon, or any other celestial body in the Solar System. The leftovers from the era of planetary formation have largely been mopped up. Go back 4 billion years and the environment was entirely different. The nascent Solar System swarmed with asteroids, colliding with the planets and the moons, blasting out titanic impact craters. Through it all, the Moon endured.

___On Earth, this bombardment brought with it the raw chemical ingredients that went on to form life. Today, the evidence is long gone from our planet: either transformed into life, eroded away by the weather, or melted into the planet's depths by the movement of the continents. Not so on the Moon.

___Until the six Apollo landings [1], the Moon's silver surface had lain virtually untouched for aeons. Although the astronauts did not find these most ancient of rocks, future lunar missions could finally reveal the chemical building blocks supplied to Earth that made life possible. It is a tantalizing possibility, perhaps even the best reason to return to our nearest celestial neighbour.

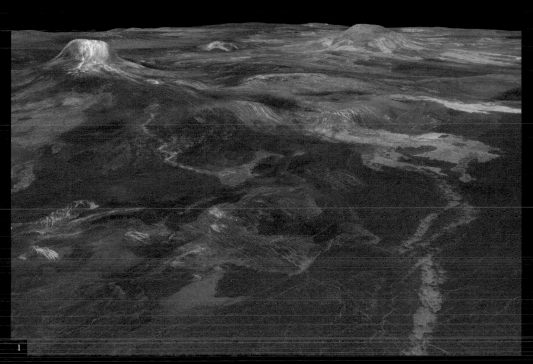

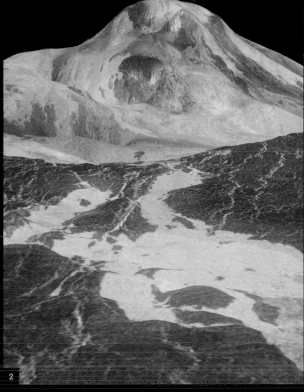

Welcome to hell?

Venus is hell: hotter than a kitchen oven, sulphuric acid rain, and winds that tear through the atmosphere at 400 km/h. Yet despite all that, Venus is the only other place in the Solar System where pockets of Earthly conditions prevail. Forget Mars, Venus is the place to search for extraterrestrial life.

Of all the planets, Venus is the one most reluctant to yield its secrets. Despite drawing closer to Earth than any other planet, a mere 38 million kilometres, its blankets of cloud mask the surface from direct view. Only by using radar can we see the ground from orbit [1].

___Occasionally sky watchers have reported glimpsing an 'ashen light' from the night-time side of the planet. While the reality of this phenomenon is debated, if true it could be caused by lightning in the Venusian atmosphere, or temporary partings in the clouds, allowing the light from the hot rocks below to escape.

___The surface is littered with volcanoes like Maat Mons [2], some thought to be still active and belching plumes of sulphur dioxide into the atmosphere. Lava flows have been spotted that look remarkably young, maybe even created in the recent past. While such volcanoes are another fitting contribution to

the Hadean landscape, drift upwards into the atmosphere and remarkable changes begin to occur.

___First, things get even worse. There are the clouds of sulphuric acid that drape themselves across the atmosphere. But above these, the conditions become more familiar, clement even.

___Between 50 and 60 km above the hellish surface, sunlight is streaming in providing a source of ready energy. The atmospheric pressure is the same as at sea level on Earth, and the temperature lies between 0–100 °C, in other words within the range where liquid water droplets could condense. And, perhaps crucially, all the chemicals necessary for life on Earth are also found here in the atmospheric gases: nitrogen, carbon, oxygen, and hydrogen.

___The only problem is the wind. At the surface, it is little more than the lightest of

breezes but it picks up relentlessly with altitude until at this otherwise clement height, it is tearing past you at 360 km/h.

___Nevertheless, this layer of the Venusian atmosphere is the only other place in the Solar System that replicates the life-bearing conditions of Earth – minus the surface of course. Not even Mars is this similar: it is too cold, the atmospheric composition isn't right and the pressure is too low. There is no guarantee that life is present in the atmosphere of Venus but it is surely worth a look. Some have even suggested that the dark swathes seen in ultraviolet images of Venus are concentrations of airborne bacteria, harvesting the ultraviolet light from the Sun and using it to metabolize chemicals for food. Most believe that these markings are ultraviolet absorption by molecules in the atmosphere but, until we visit the atmosphere with scientific equipment, we cannot be sure one way or another.

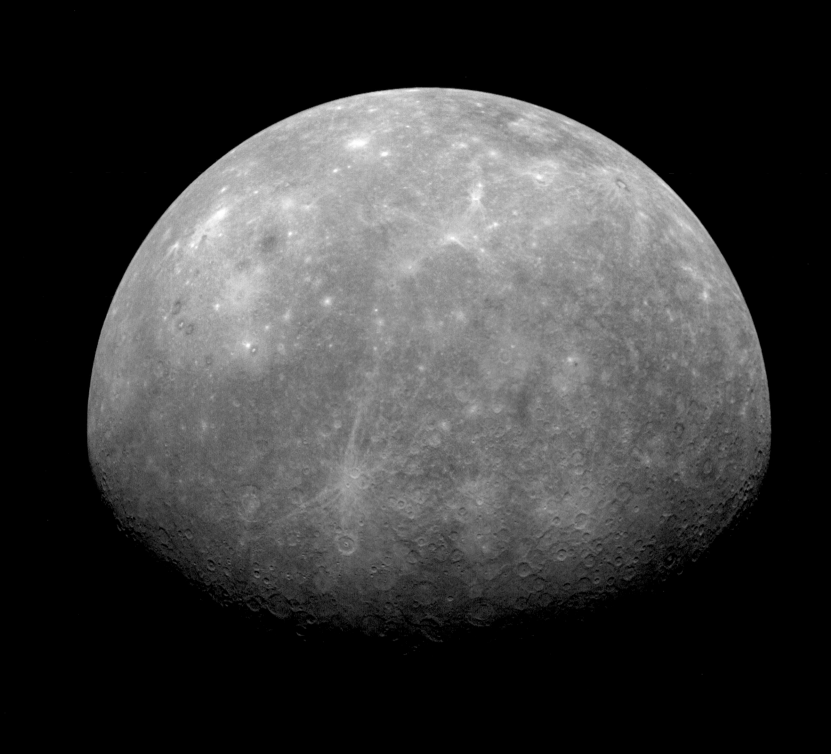

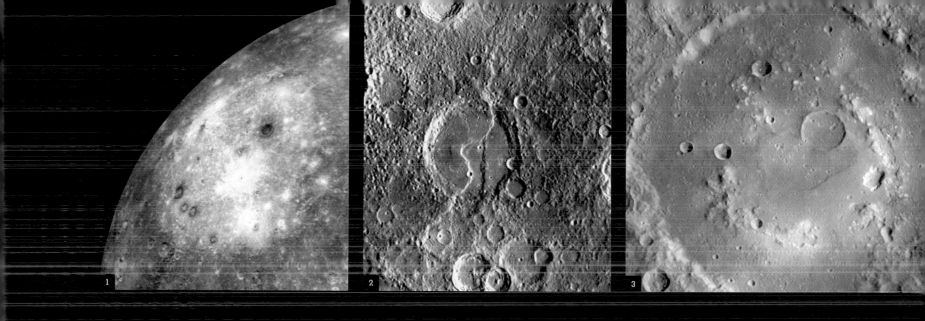

Mystifying Mercury

At first glance, you'd be forgiven for thinking we have returned to the Moon with its silver grey landscape of barren desolation. But look closer: no dark lava plains. This is Mercury, a world that does not make sense.

Perhaps Mercury should have been called Icarus. Lying closer to our Sun than any other planet, by mid afternoon Mercury's temperature has soared higher than 350 °C, hot enough to melt lead. Then at night, with no blanketing atmosphere, the temperature plunges to –200 °C.

___Up near the poles, there are deep craters where the Sun's burning rays can never penetrate. Inside these dark traps, the ground is so cold that it will snare any passing water molecule, creating a permanently icy floor. But that's not what makes Mercury a mystery.

___Icarus lost his wax and feather wings by flying too close to the Sun. Mercury may have lost its entire outer layers of rock, irradiated away by the fearsome light from the newborn Sun. The clues lie hidden inside the planet.

___Mercury is the smallest planet but it possesses a metal heart larger than that of Mars. This swollen core accounts for 40 percent of the planet's volume, more than twice the percentage taken up by the Earth's core, and signals that Mercury may once have been twice its present size. If the planet pulled itself together quickly, then the young Sun's X-ray birth pangs may have been sufficient to evaporate half of it away.

___Or perhaps the impacts that scarred the Moon were so much worse at Mercury that they blasted away the outer rocky layers, allowing the original core to dominate. There is certainly good evidence of calamity.

___The Caloris Basin [1] is a giant impact scar measuring 1,550 km across. On the other side of Mercury, directly opposite, is a region of chaotic terrain. It is as if a giant has scooped up a handful of the planet, crushed it and patted it back into the ground. In this case, the giant was the Caloris Basin impact, sending shockwaves ricocheting through Mercury's body. When they reached the other side, they pulverized the surface layers. Huge fault lines disect the surface [2] and sunken pits tinged with yellow minerals hint at past volcanic episodes [3].

LIGHT SECONDS
LIGHT MINUTES
LIGHT YEARS
KILO LIGHT YEARS
MEGA LIGHT YEARS
GIGA LIGHT YEARS

The Sun

STAR

DIAMETER: 1,400,000 KM

Brilliant fury

It is the heart of our Solar System. The Sun is both the hub around which the planets orbit, and the furnace that creates the energy for life on Earth. Millions of tonnes of matter are transmuted into energy every second but the sunlight reaching Earth is hundreds of thousands of years old. Where has it been?

Talk to an astronomer and they are likely to tell you that the Sun is an unremarkable, middle-aged star orbiting in a stellar backwater of the Galaxy. But we know better. The Sun is the beating heart of our existence. It provides the gravitational glue to keep the planets in orbit and the energy to maintain life on Earth.

___No wonder then that it was once thought a god, its divine radiance cascading into space. Now we know that the fire is generated in a nuclear furnace, concealed in the very heart of the Sun. At these great depths, 522,000 km from the surface, the crushing weight of the Sun's outer layers raises the temperature higher than 13 million °C and the density to 150 times that of water. At these extremes, atoms are first stripped of electrons, their outermost particles

and then the nuclei are slammed together.

___The pummelling drives many nuclei to overcome their mutual repulsion and they fuse with one another. Once joined, they transform into a new chemical species, releasing floods of energy. Inside the Sun, it is the creation of helium from hydrogen that keeps the energy pouring out.

___Released initially as gamma rays, this powerful radiation is swiftly absorbed by other nuclei within the dense surroundings. But they cannot contain their newly found energy and so hand it on, shooting the rays back out into the gas in random directions where they are absorbed again, this time by other, nearby atomic nuclei. This chaotic absorption and re-emission takes place repeatedly, sapping

the gamma rays of energy and working them into visible rays of light.

___The torturous journey from core to surface takes hundreds of thousands of years. The surface is a roiling mosaic of convection cells heated to 6,000 °C, spotted with cooler dark blemishes, or sunspots [1], where giant magnetized arcs puncture the surface. Free at last, light catapults from the surface at breakneck speed, covering 300 million metres every second.

___If it happens to be heading for Earth, it arrives just over eight minutes later. Each Earthly dawn, we bathe in the energy of the Sun, but it is old stock, manufactured hundreds of thousands of years ago deep in the Promethean heart of our central star.

0016.0

LIGHT SECONDS
LIGHT MINUTES
LIGHT YEARS
KILO LIGHT YEARS
MEGA LIGHT YEARS
GIGA LIGHT YEARS

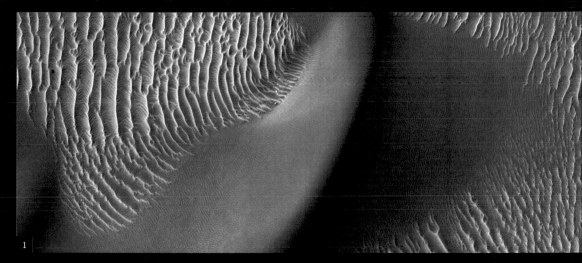

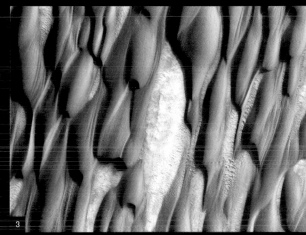

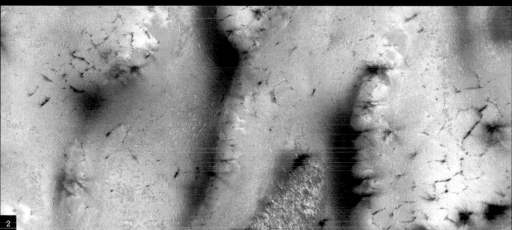

Sands of Mars

Alien trees seem to sprout upwards from the Martian
sand dunes. But look again: these tendrils run not
upward but downhill. They are mini landslips caused
by the planet belching out frozen gases as the
atmosphere stirs from its winter hibernation.

Winters are harsh on Mars, so cold that
they sap the planet's atmosphere, leaving
the surface exposed to the vacuum of space.
Mars's atmosphere, which is tenuous at best,
freezes to the surface, binding into the planet's
fine sands [1] and covering them in a frosty
pink layer that looks eerily organic [2].

___As spring dawns in the northern
hemisphere, so the temperature begins to
climb from a low of –150 °C, to a Martian balmy
–17 °C, and the frozen atmosphere stirs back
into life. Composed chiefly of carbon dioxide,
which has a melting point at –78 °C, the
atmosphere thaws, turning straight from
ice into gas.

___The bubbles of gas burst upwards through
the sands, creating dark spots across the dunes
[2] as the sheen of frozen gas is popped back

into the atmosphere, revealing the true colour
of the Martian sand. Where these blisters break
on slopes, they push the sand tumbling down,
creating the streaks. By summer, these dunes
will all be as dark as the streaks and spots, and
the atmosphere will be returned to its gaseous
state, veiling the planet.

___As the gas liberates itself, like invisible
mayflies escaping their cocoons, so it rushes to
populate the entire atmosphere. It whips across
the surface of the planet at speeds of several
hundred kilometres per hour and lifts the fine
sand into the air creating billowing clouds of
dust and setting columns of dunes marching
across the Martian plains [3].

___In the most extreme cases, the entire planet
can become smothered in the dust. Even the
volcanic spires are lost from view, as the dust

reaches up many kilometres into the
atmosphere. As the summer months progress,
so the dust settles again and one by one the
volcanoes come back into view. Then the
smaller peaks, the craters and the rifts all
materialize once more. The planet settles,
morning mist hugs the slopes, the polar caps
shrink away and Mars bathes in the sunlight.

___But it is temporary respite. As the planet
climbs away from the Sun, so the temperature
drops again. The atmosphere becomes
sluggish and the molecules sink to the ground.
The dune fields in the far north and the icy
plains of the south become cold traps, instantly
freezing any gas that touches the surface, and
the seasons start all over again.

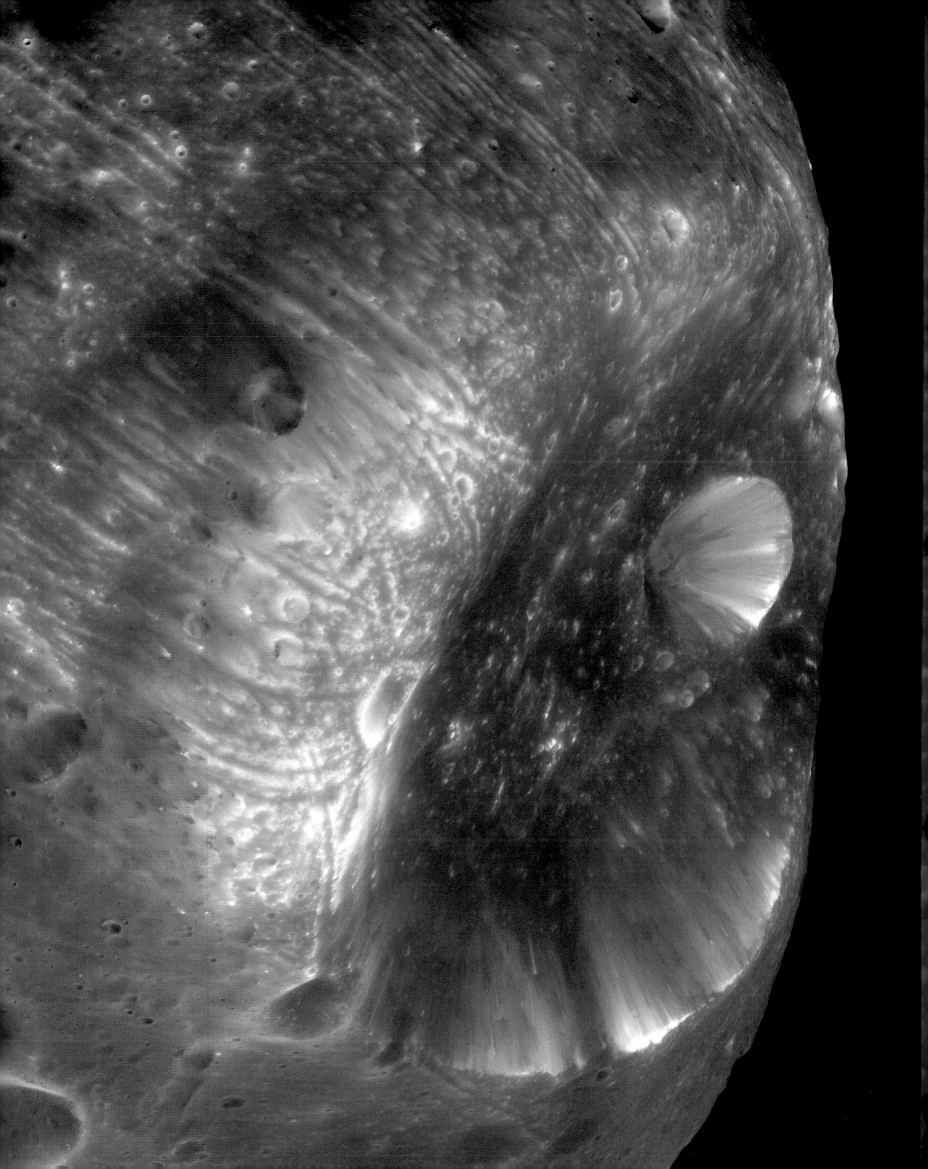

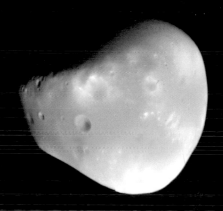

Phobos

MOON of MARS

DIAMETER: 22.4 KM

LIGHT SECONDS
LIGHT MINUTES
LIGHT YEARS
KILO LIGHT YEARS
MEGA LIGHT YEARS
GIGA LIGHT YEARS

1

2

Puzzling Phobos

It is Mars's largest moon but don't let that fool
you, Phobos is still little more than an asteroid. Just
two-billionths of the Earth's mass, it has no atmosphere
and hardly any gravity. Yet it could be an easier
destination for exploration than our own Moon.

Phobos [1] is an elongated rock measuring just
26.8 x 22.4 x 18.4 km. Its sister moon, Deimos [2],
is even smaller at 15 x 12.2 x 10.4 km. Both
resemble asteroids and so can be thought of
as just that: small space rocks that wandered
too closely and were captured by the gravity
of Mars.

___Phobos is dark, almost black, absorbing
more than 90 percent of the sunlight that strikes
its surface and resembling the meteorites known
as carbonaceous chondrites. These ancient
celestial objects are thought to originate in the
furthest parts of the asteroid belt, a couple of
times more distant from the Sun than Mars
itself. The same is true for Deimos.

___But there is a sticking point: the orbits these
moons follow are nothing like those expected

for captured asteroids. Both Phobos and
Deimos follow paths that lie close to the
equatorial plane of Mars. Had they been
captured, they would be orbiting on randomly
inclined paths.

___Equatorial orbits imply that the moons
formed in situ, from the same coalescing cloud
that became Mars. But, if this is the case, then
the moons' composition makes no sense;
Phobos and Deimos should resemble Martian
rock, not carbonaceous chondrites.

___The only clue may be that Phobos is not
a single chunk of solid rock. Its density is so
low that there are probably vast empty spaces
inside. This could mean that a giant impact on
Mars long ago threw big chunks of debris into
orbit that retain their ancient façade today,

even though the planet below them has
evolved. The chunks then settled against
one another at haphazard angles to form
the conglomeration we now call Phobos.

___More excitingly, it could be the staging
post humankind needs for exploring the Solar
System. Phobos is so small that it generates
only a weak gravitational field. Upon arrival
in Martian orbit, landing and launching from
Phobos would require only the smallest of
impulses. In those terms, it is cheaper and
easier to send a robotic spacecraft to distant
Phobos than it is to send one to the surface of
our own Moon, where landers have to fight
against the lunar gravity.

___On these terms alone, Phobos is an ideal
destination.

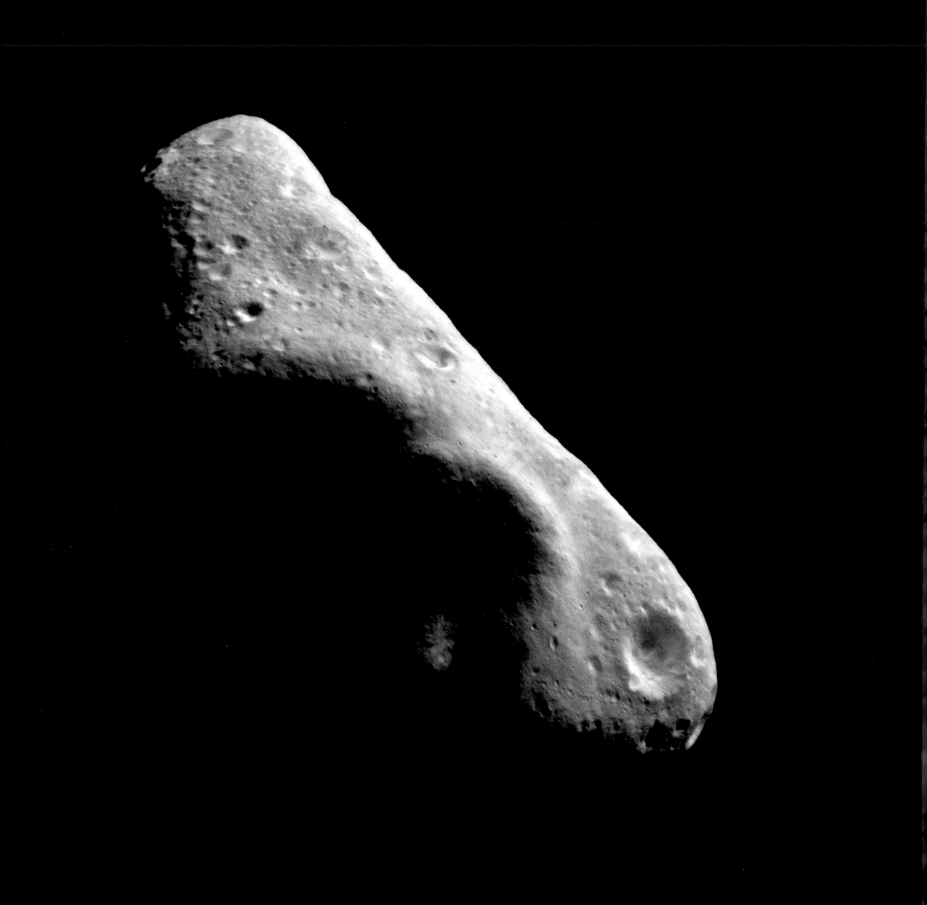

888.8 LIGHT SECONDS
       LIGHT MINUTES
       LIGHT YEARS
       KILO LIGHT YEARS
       MEGA LIGHT YEARS
       GIGA LIGHT YEARS

1   2   3

Stony messengers

The detritus of the Solar System's formation still surrounds us in the form of millions of asteroids. Most of them are safely tucked away in the asteroid belt between Mars and Jupiter – but not all. Some draw close to Earth, providing both tempting possibilities and a threat of global annihilation.

Sixty-five million years ago, life on Earth changed irrevocably. An asteroid or similar body smashed into the Earth, travelling in excess of 11 km/s. It hit just off the coast of Mexico, in the Yucatan peninsula, creating a flash of light brighter than a thousand suns. Giant tsunamis rolled across the seas, the blast wave circled the Earth several times and a fountain of shattered earth was thrown into the atmosphere. Immediately there was a climate disaster as the sunlight was blocked from the surface, and the temperature fell away. For the dinosaurs, it was the final straw, their death knell and exit from the tapestry of living creatures.

___Asteroids continue to swing by Earth to this day. This particular irregular lump of natural space junk is called Eros. It circles the Sun but loops around it, following a highly elliptical path. At 33 km long, Eros is 10 times larger than the asteroid that wiped out the dinosaurs.

___Despite spending most of its time much further away, Eros can sometimes approach our world to within just 75 light seconds. Yet it is not the most dangerous of the known asteroids. Even at its closest approach, in astronomical terms it is a safe distance away.

___Most asteroids are stony mountains such as Ida and its moon Dactyl [1]. Mathilde resembles Phobos in that it is partly hollow [2]. Gaspra [3] may once have been part of a larger body.

___The asteroid to really keep an eye on is Apophis. It will next go by Earth in 2013 but during 2029 it will approach within a cosmic hair's breadth of less than a tenth of a light second. This will be nearer than the geostationary satellites that handle our communications. Ironically, this close pass will take place on 13 April, which just happens to be a Friday.

___Like a shark preparing to launch an attack, an asteroid will tend to swing near to a planet before it strikes. Indeed, it is the unwitting planet's own gravity that blindly nudges the asteroid onto the final collision course, if the asteroid passes through a specific volume of space, known as a keyhole. Within the keyhole, gravitational forces conspire to set the asteroid on its fateful last orbit.

___Even when beyond these keyholes, the orbits of the asteroids and comets are not immutable. They can evolve with time, pushed and prodded by the faint gravity of the planets, changing their orbits and commanding constant vigilance.

LIGHT SECONDS
LIGHT MINUTES
LIGHT YEARS
KILO LIGHT YEARS
MEGA LIGHT YEARS
GIGA LIGHT YEARS

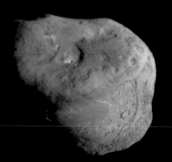

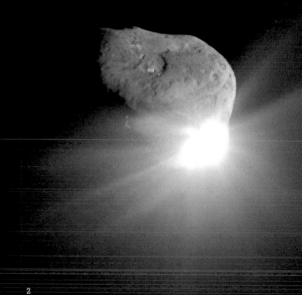

1

2

Ghost writers

Something really got under the skin of Comet Holmes.
During 2007, the usually shy comet made a true spectacle
of itself. It brightened 500,000 times more than usual and
expanded to almost three quarters the size of the Sun.
So where did all this ambition suddenly come from?

Comets are the icy heralds from a bygone
epoch. When the Solar System was forming
these icy leftovers brought water to the
inner planets. Now they are merely ghostly
messengers who write their stories in dust;
each statement costs the comet dearly.
___The Sun's heat works on the comet as
it draws closer to the sultry realms of the
inner Solar System. The comet's icy surface
evaporates away, diminishing it but producing
an arcing tail that can stretch through space.
Eventually the comet will fade into obscurity
when it has no ices left to give up, or it will
simply fall to pieces as the icy glue evaporates
from the rocky honeycomb.
___Comet Holmes, however, was determined
to go out in style. Between October 23–24 2007
it flared up. Comets have been seen to rally
before, but not like this. While the central
nucleus remained constant at around 3.4 km
across, the debris cloud grew to a diameter of a

million kilometres, which is about 70 percent
of the Sun's width. The mass distributed
throughout this vast volume remained
minuscule, only a little denser than the
vacuum a good laboratory could produce
using modern air pumps, but it caught the
sunlight and reflected it all across space.
___Either a meteorite struck the comet or
perhaps the Sun's warmth wheedled its
way inside where it blew open a cavity of
ice, ejecting the contents into space. Still to
this day, nobody knows what caused it.
___A comet's natural habitat is in the deepest,
darkest regions of the Solar System, way
beyond the planets, and part way to the
nearest stars. There could be a trillion of these
icy asteroids out there, all slung away by
Jupiter's mighty gravity early in the evolution
of the Solar System. Lofted to their great
distances, most comets are now only
occasional visitors to the inner regions.

By substantially reducing the threat of impacts
Jupiter has safeguarded our world and our
neighbours.
___This magnanimity comes at a price though;
from time to time Jupiter takes a hit itself.
In 1994, it snared a passing comet, crushed it
into pieces and then took blow after blow as
the fragment struck the planet's bloated body.
The resulting explosions created smoke palls
that drifted in the atmosphere for weeks and
smothered areas larger than Earth. Other
smaller impacts have been observed on
Jupiter since.
___But impacts are not always one-way.
In 2005, NASA's Deep Impact probe struck
comet Tempel 1 [1 & 2], excavating a crater
approximately 100 meters wide and 30 meters
deep. The probe's spectrometer revealed
the presence of silicates, carbonates, clays,
metal sulfides (like fool's gold) and polycyclic
aromatic hydrocarbons.

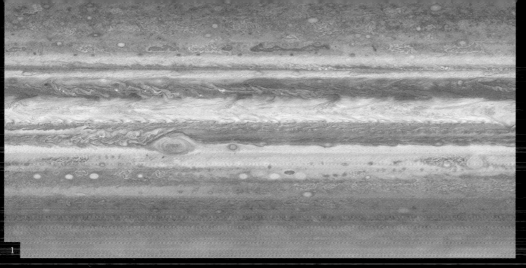

Stellar aspirations

Jupiter is the colossus of the Solar System. A giant stormy world that outweighs all other planets together by more than twice. Its pull of gravity diverts asteroids and comets from their paths and controls a retinue of moons. How then can Jupiter be thought of as a failure?

Condensed out of the same cloud that gave birth to the planets, giant Jupiter has more in common with the Sun than the rocky planets. This is because it is composed of the same gases as our central orb. Hydrogen and helium contribute 98 percent of its bulk. All the other elements that seem so familiar to us on Earth, the silicon in the rocks, the calcium in our bones, the iron in our blood, and all the other elements of the periodic table, comprise no more than a meagre two percent of Jupiter.

Though vast by planetary standards, 317 times more massive than the Earth, Jupiter remains slight in stellar terms. Less than one thousandth the mass of the Sun, for all its compositional aspirations Jupiter is still clearly

a planet – and this marks it as a failed star.

Only by adding some 80 times more mass to the planet, would the nuclear core be crushed to the point of igniting under its own weight. In that instant, the planet would transform itself into a star, but a lowly one. It would become a red dwarf, the smallest, dimmest stellar minnow possible.

Nevertheless, Jupiter does release some small measure of energy from its interior. It is generated because Jupiter is shrinking by about 2 cm per year. It is a habit left over from the planet's formation, when it was twice its current size. In the 4.5 billion years since, gravity has been pulling the planet ever denser and, as it does so, it squeezes energy out of the atoms.

As this escapes through the planet, it stirs the atmosphere into the perpetual storm belts that we see today [1]. The brightly banded layers of Jupiter stretch around the planet, sometimes deepening with a ginger flush, at other times fading away into the creamy background.

Jupiter is more than ten times wider than the Earth. Our entire planet could get lost in the storms that swirl across its face – and none are larger than the Great Red Spot [2]. This giant anti-cyclone rises about 8 km above the surrounding clouds and rotates once every six days. Most impressive of all, this storm system has been stable for centuries. No one knows how old it is, nor how long this 'perfect storm' will endure.

LIGHT SECONDS
LIGHT MINUTES
LIGHT YEARS
KILO LIGHT YEARS
MEGA LIGHT YEARS
GIGA LIGHT YEARS

Infernal Io

Forget the myriad volcanoes of Earth, the veiled vents of Venus, and the possibly extinct peaks of Mars. If there is a volcanic heart in the Solar System, this tiny moon of Jupiter is the place.

Io reinvents itself every thousand years or so. The catastrophically volcanic moon is constantly spewing lava onto its surface, painting itself a new face, and producing the youngest surface in the Solar System. Io has been driven into this volcanic frenzy by the tormenting pull of Jupiter, which gives rise to extreme tidal forces. On Earth, the tide from the Moon drives the oceans to lap the shoreline but, on Io, Jupiter's gravity forces the moon to turn itself inside out.

___The tidal force occurs because gravity weakens with distance, even across the width of a relatively small moon such as Io. With gravity pulling on one side of the moon harder than on the other, the moon is pulled into an elongated shape. This shape changes as Io follows its elliptical orbit around Jupiter, altering the strength of the gravitational force

it experiences. In this way, Io's innards are squeezed and stretched like a concertina and melted by the friction.

___Io does not produce molten rocks as Earth's volcanoes, but sulphur compounds that gush from plutonic depths. They rise to the surface through vents in the floor of paterae, flat-floored depressions bounded by steep walls. Some eruptions take place with such force that the lava is ejected high into the sky, reaching 200 km into space [1] before raining back to the surface in a hellish downpour.

___The lava results in the yellow stain that covers the moon. It gradually turns darker under the influence of the Sun's ultraviolet light. The eruptions surround Io in a thin fog of sulphur dioxide. While this is enough to constitute an atmosphere, it varies greatly both in temperature and density according to the

time of day and the ferocity of the volcanic eruptions.

___As well as the volcanoes there are extensive mountain peaks on Io, forced upwards by compression of the crustal rocks. Io eschews the long ranges favoured by Earth and prefers its mountains as isolated individuals. The tallest can be found at South Boösaule Montes. Reaching upwards for some 17.5 km, this extraordinary mountain is more than twice the height of Everest on Earth. Most of the mountaintops on Io are flat, each one stretching for kilometres to form rugged mesas. And all of the mountains are collapsing, mostly being dragged back down from the edges by the moon's gravity.

___The moon is constantly changing. So don't waste time mapping Io; it is a never-ending job just enjoy the spectacle.

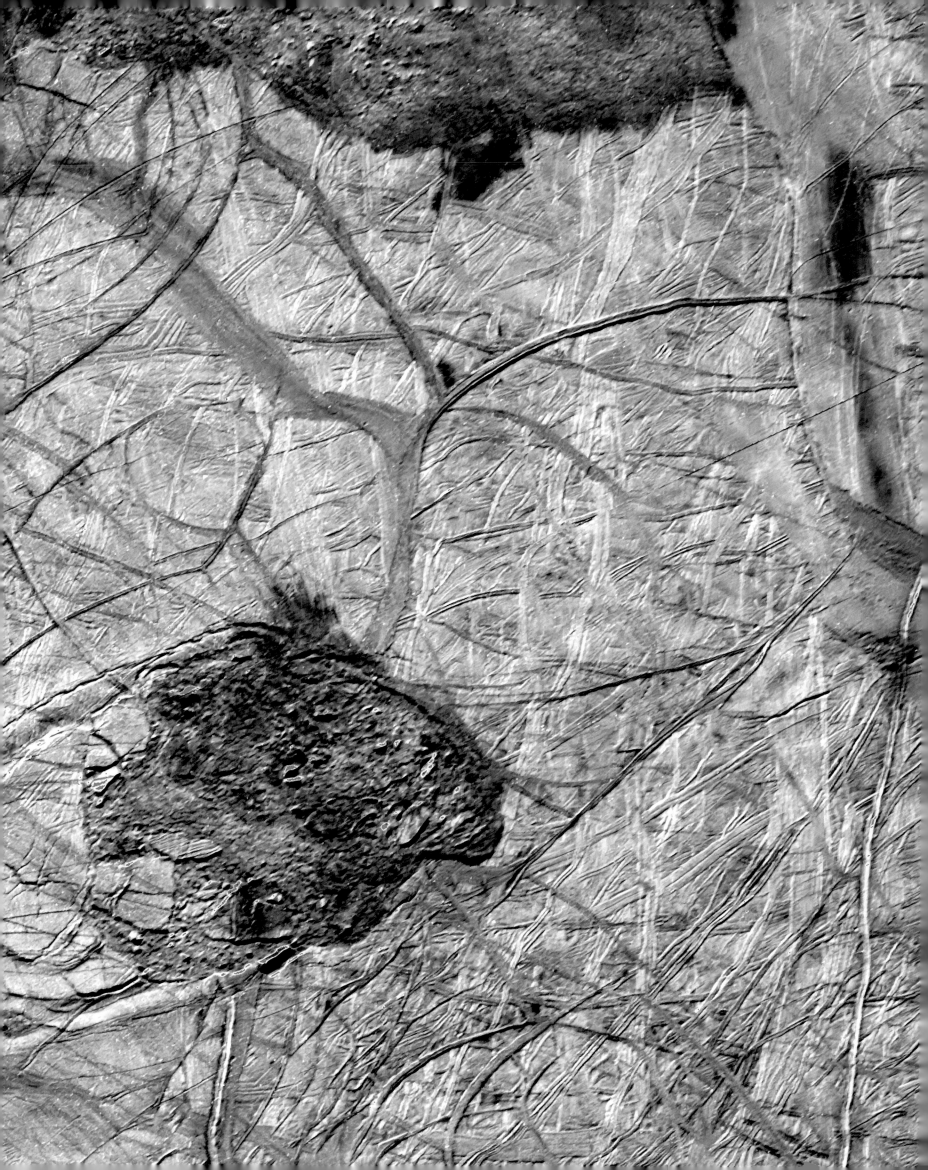

0000.0
LIGHT SECONDS
LIGHT MINUTES
LIGHT YEARS
KILO LIGHT YEARS
MEGA LIGHT YEARS
GIGA LIGHT YEARS

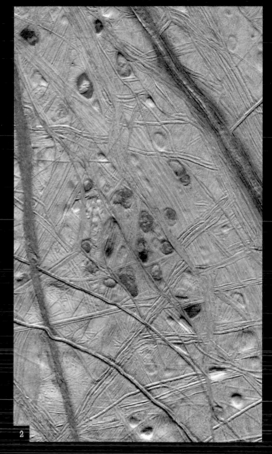

Dark eden

The same gravitational forces that have condemned Io to a state of constant flux, may just have endowed its sister moon with an unlikely oasis. If so, it is a dark oasis and we are going to have to burrow kilometres underground to find it.

Europa orbits Jupiter one and a half times further out than Io. Here, the vice-like grip of the planet has been loosened somewhat. The friction that its tidal forces engender may be enough to melt some of the moon's icy mantle, but not the rocks and chemicals themselves.

___Europa could possess an ocean tens or even hundreds of kilometres deep, trapped beneath an icy crust that is measured in thickness between 1 and 10 kilometres. If this is true, there could well be more liquid water on tiny Europa than on the entire Earth.

___Evidence for this ocean is found on the surface in the malleable formations there. Giant cracks riddle the surface [1], split by the tidal forces and tinted by the upwelling of mineral-bearing waters from below. In other

places, called chaos regions, the ice sheets appear to have broken up into giant bergs, briefly formed a floe and then re-frozen into a new position. Now they look like a giant's abandoned jigsaw puzzle. Ruddy freckles [2] mark regions where warm ice has risen from the ocean below.

___All these are signs that the ice crust is sitting on something mobile; a softly churning ocean would fit the bill. But this unknown ocean is pitch black, with no sunlight penetrating the icy layers. Nevertheless there is energy for life here.

___The energy absorbed from Jupiter may drive ocean vents, where hot water gushes up into the surrounding ocean. On Earth, such thermal vents may have been the birthplace of life, and today they maintain ecosystems that

owe nothing to the Sun for their survival. Could the same be true on this moon of Jupiter?

___To find life on Europa, or indeed elsewhere in the Solar System would have major ramifications for our understanding of biology. For example, would it be based on DNA? If so, could it be an offshoot of Earthly life carried from our world to there, or vice-versa? If it is not based on DNA, how does this alien life form pass on its genetic information?

___Life could have arisen once in our Solar System as the result of a random fluke, but twice would indicate there's something easier about the process than we think. If we were to find a second architecture of life, it would indicate that we should expect living things to be widespread throughout the cosmos.

1   2   3

Gravity's rainbow

Delicate grandeur greets the eye at Saturn. The pastel shades of its atmosphere and the graceful sweep of its rings speak of a place of serene beauty. Yet below the clouds, titanic forces are lurking, ready to break out and cause havoc.

No other planet can compete with Saturn. Its sublime rings, menagerie of moons and opalescent complexion [1] make it a world of staggering beauty. The rings themselves span 1,000,000 km but edge on they are just 1 km thick [2]. Despite their gossamer beauty, they are little more than rubble – icy rocks and pebbles that shine brightly in the sunlight. So brightly, in fact, that they must have been placed there relatively recently.

___Perhaps a moon was destroyed by a stray asteroid or comet, and the debris was corralled by gravity into the rings. That would explain why they are still so bright, as the icy material tends to discolour over time. Based on their reflectivity, Saturn's rings are estimated to have formed just a few hundred million years ago, at a time when dinosaurs were ruling the Earth.

___So it could be that mankind is simply lucky to share its existence with Saturn's rings, or it could be that the rings are a moon-recycling plant. Maybe they are constantly replenished as moons are destroyed, and perhaps they are even capable of forming new moons – if sufficient ring material were to fall together.

___However they were formed, the tapestry of rings is woven by the gravity of Saturn's many moons. Gaps both small and large divide the rings, and each gap can be attributed to the gravitational pull of a moon. Any ring particle that strays into a gap will be nudged back out by its lunar shepherd. Some gaps, such as the Encke Division and the Cassini Division span hundreds or thousands of kilometres, whereas others impart little more than textures that appear as ripples on the rings. The moon Pan

carves out the Encke Division, from its orbit inside the gap, whereas Mimas [3] controls the Cassini Division from afar.

___Below the rings lie the cloud tops, a subtle boundary of pastel beauty. Saturn guards its privacy and most of its weather takes place below those cloud tops, hidden from our view. But occasionally the planet shows its true temperament. Giant storms, usually pearl white and always larger than the entire planet Earth, can burst through the upper cloud decks. They bring with them violent bursts of radio waves and lightning. Peculiarly, these storms often appear at the same latitude in the planet's southern hemisphere, dubbed storm alley. They hint at the titanic forces at play within this beguiling gas giant.

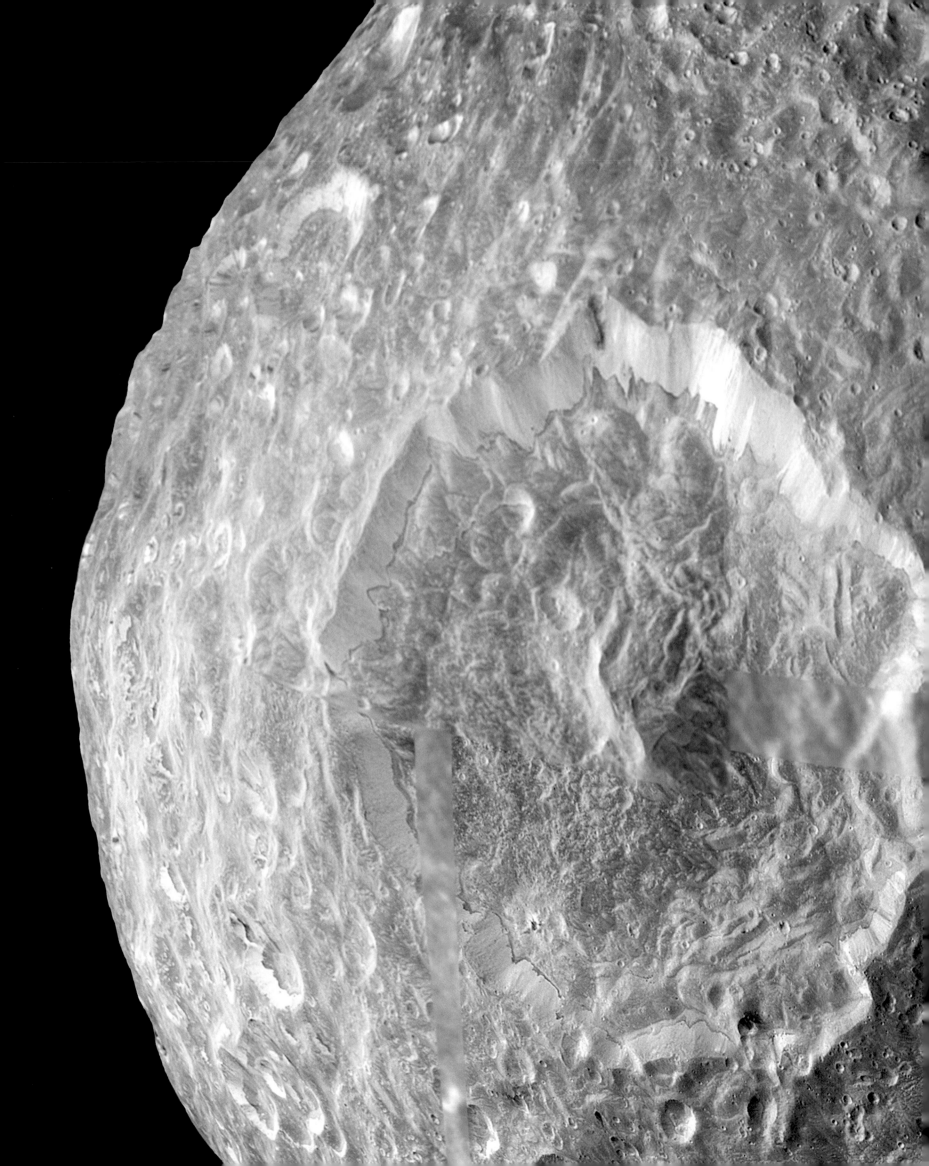

Mimas

MOON of SATURN

DIAMETER: 414 KM

LIGHT SECONDS
LIGHT MINUTES
LIGHT YEARS
KILO LIGHT YEARS
MEGA LIGHT YEARS
GIGA LIGHT YEARS

1

Breaking the ice

The icy surface of Mimas is representative of its interior.
There is hardly any rocky material in this moon, just ice
frozen solid by the frigid temperature of outer space:
Mimas is an iceberg in space.

At just three-hundredths of the diameter of Earth, Mimas is one of the smallest bodies in the Solar System to have pulled itself into a round shape. It has been battered over the course of its history by smaller asteroids and meteorites, and now displays the scars as craters [1].

___No crater can be more impressive than its Herschel Crater. At 130 km across it is almost one-third of the moon's total diameter. Its walls tower 5 km into the air and parts of the floor sink to 10 km below the rest of the surface. In the centre of the crater, like the solidified rebound by a giant water droplet, the central peak of the crater rises higher than 6 km.

___The impact that created the Herschel Crater may have come close to shattering the moon

because, in the opposite hemisphere, the surface is riddled with fractures. These are probably the result of seismic waves that rolled through the moon following the impact and ruptured the ice in their wake.

___The surface temperature of Mimas reveals a dilemma. As it is heated by the Sun, so its equator should be hotter than its poles. But if anything the reverse is happening. The equatorial temperatures plunge as soon as the Sun has passed by overhead but the higher latitudes continue to heat up well into the Mimantean afternoon. It is as weird as if you were to stand on Earth's equator and experience the afternoon temperature on a cloudless day suddenly plunge to its lowest night-time level.

This behaviour is probably the result of highly conductive impurities in the ice at the equator. As these absorb sunlight, they channel the heat down into the interior and so the surface temperature appears to drop quickly. Nearer the poles, these impurities are not in the ice and those areas retain their heat. But why there should be differences in the surface composition is unknown.

___And finally: yes, the similarity in appearance between Mimas and the Death Star from Star Wars has been noticed. It is entirely coincidental. Hershel Crater was discovered in 1979, two years after the first of the science fiction blockbusters was released.

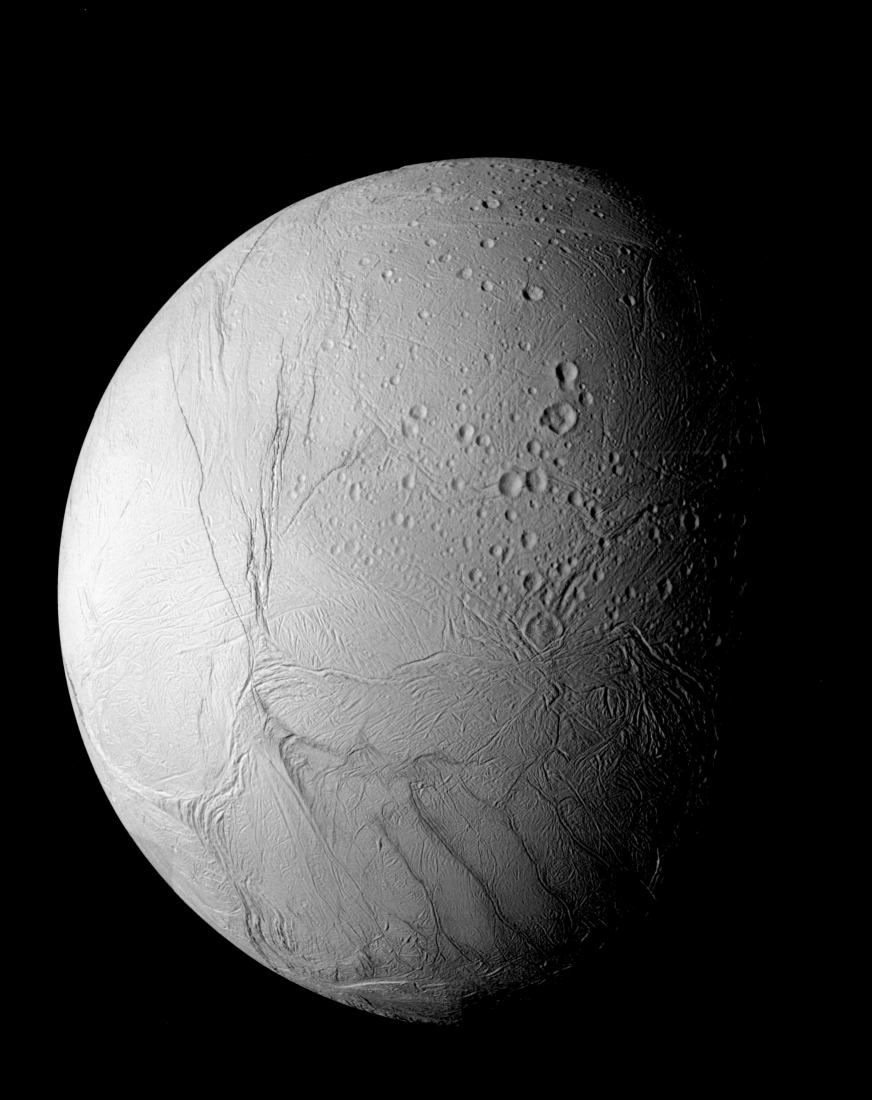

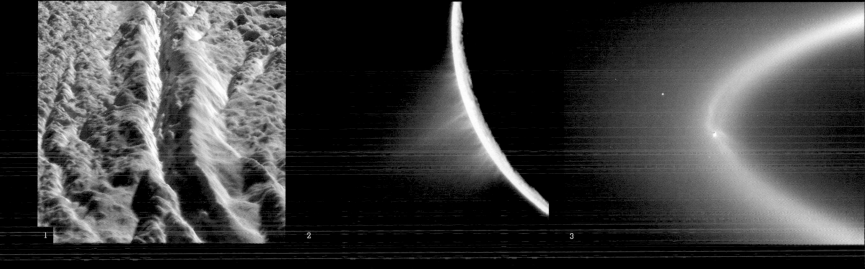

1

2

3

Tiger-stripes

Bright and shiny Enceladus is the most reflective body in the Solar System. It bounces 90 percent of the light that strikes its icy surface right back out into space. And that's not the only thing the moon spurns: jets of water burst from the south pole, never to return.

Containing almost the same surface area as the countries of France and Germany combined, Enceladus is a special place. It is one of only three moons in the Solar System wracked by volcanic activity.

___Geologically, it is a place of variety. There are at least five different types of terrain on the moon including smooth plains, cratered regions, cracks and ridges. Warmth from within may be melting the plains smooth, erasing millions of years of history from the surface.

___The most intriguing of the features are the 'tiger stripes', sinuous coloured markings that snake across the moon's southern pole. They are cracks leading to Enceladus's restless depths [1] and the origin of strange fountains of water that reach high into the black sky [2]

but never fall back to the ground. The plumes are stunning examples of cryo-volcanism, so called because they take place only in frigid realms where molten lava is replaced by liquid water.

___To feed the geysers on Enceladus, it is imagined there must be misty caverns partly filled with water existing beneath the thick icy surface. These natural reservoirs hold water seeping up from below through the cracks, and then explode it into space because, in the airless environment, the water turns straight to vapour. It jets out of Enceladus like steam from a kettle. The moon's gravitational pull is just a hundredth of that on Earth so the water does not fall back down. Instead, it launches into space where Saturn's gravity catches the

microscopic particles and confines them to Enceladus' orbit, creating the tenuous E ring that girdles the giant planet [3]. Although spanning a million kilometres in width, the ring would decay to nothing in between 10,000–1,000,000 years, if it were not for the constant replenishment from Enceladus's alien geysers.

___The water rushing from the moon is unlikely to be freshly melted ice because it contains sodium salts, leached from the rocks where it had prolonged contact. A similar mechanism makes Earth's oceans salty.

___The conclusion is inescapable: far down in Enceladus a deep ocean must rest unseen, as one does at Europa around Jupiter, halfway back towards the Sun.

LIGHT SECONDS
LIGHT MINUTES
LIGHT YEARS
KILO LIGHT YEARS
MEGA LIGHT YEARS
GIGA LIGHT YEARS

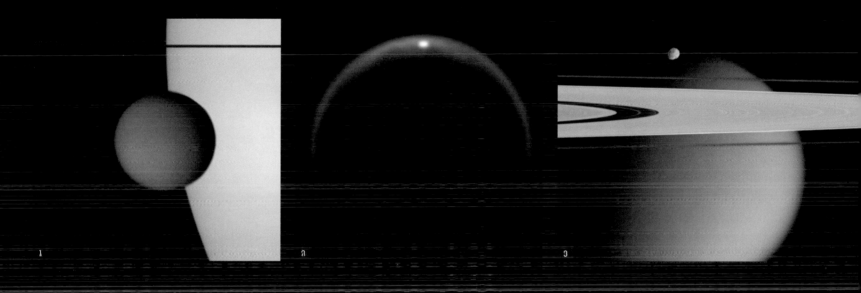

1　　　　　　　2　　　　　　　3

The twilight zone

Out around Saturn, 10 times further from the Sun than the Earth, Titan receives just one hundredth of the warmth that permits widespread life on our world. But don't write off Titan; it could be humankind's lifeboat in aeons to come.

Of all the moons in the Solar System, Titan stands out because it is the only one with a thick, hazy atmosphere [1&3]. Despite being just one-third the size of Earth, Titan has more atmosphere than our planet. The gases press down on its surface 1.5 times harder than on ours, and are mostly nitrogen, with a noxious mixture of methane and hydrogen adding some chemical piquancy.

___The valleys and hills of Titan's surface present a familiar landscape, but it is all built from an alien chemistry. Water ice takes the place of rocks, frozen to granitic strength by the −180 °C daytime temperature. When it rains on Titan, liquid methane and ethane torrent through the ravines that twist down the moon's hillsides into lakes where it glints

___Methane and ethane are not the only things to fall from the sky. A gentle snow of tarry particles also drifts down. They are produced in the upper atmosphere where ultraviolet light breaks up methane molecules, which then grab any chemical they can get their molecular hands upon. The resultant particles rain out, coating the surface with a grimy hydrocarbon layer.

___With all that said, Titan might actually be giving us a glimpse into our own past, an inkling of what the Earth was like before life began. Stuck out in the celestial deep freeze, Titan has preserved its primordial atmosphere whereas ours has been changed irrevocably with the passage of time. Perhaps all Titan needs to develop into a pleasant, though

In a few billion years, that might be exactly what it receives.

___In that distant future, the Sun will begin to exhaust its stock of hydrogen. This will trigger a sequence of events inside our star that bloats it into a red giant. At that point it will grow so large that it will engulf the inner planets, including Earth. But Titan stands to gain.

___The red giant Sun will be much brighter than our present day luminary, and could supply Titan with enough energy to shrug off its frigid complexion. If it develops a clement aspect, it could become a safe haven for any humans still around.

___So Titan is a fixer-upper, a place full of potential but in need of time and energy.

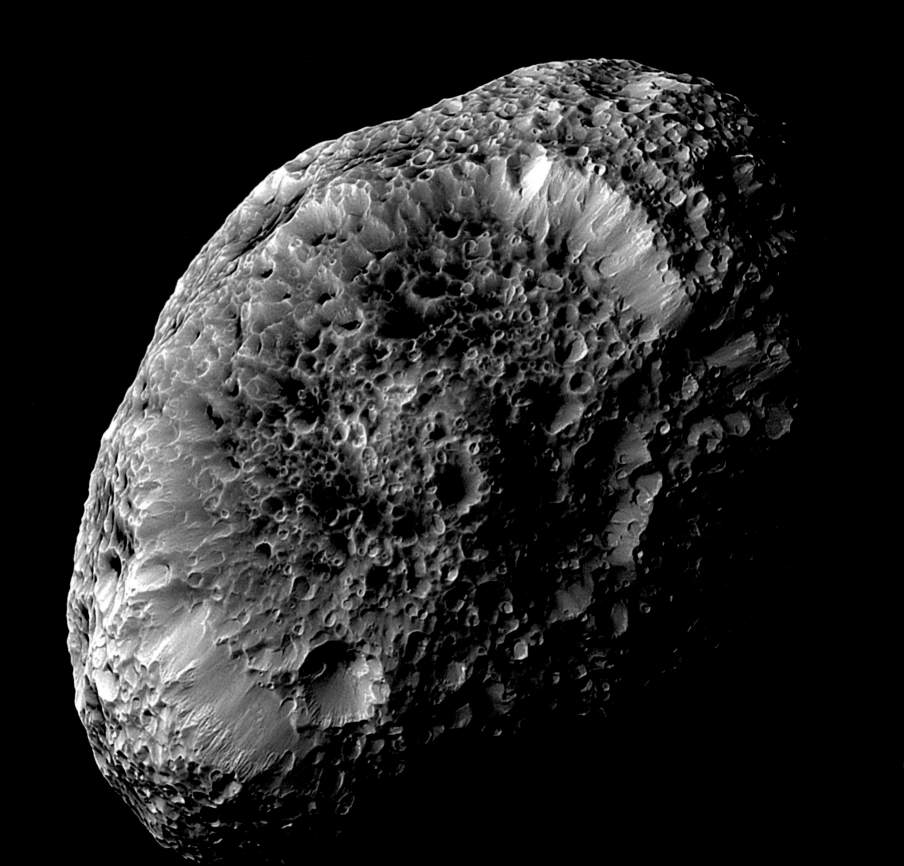

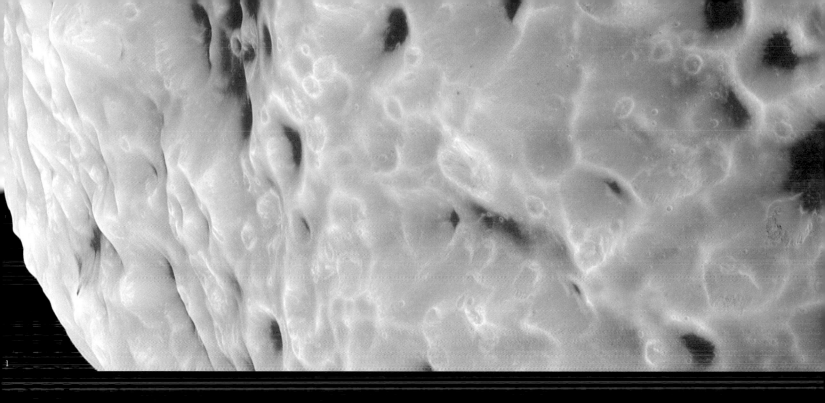

Caverns of Hyperion

Imagine being on a world and not being able to predict the time of sunrise or the length of the coming day. Nothing you can measure will let you be certain of these fundamental quantities; they change chaotically every day. Welcome to Hyperion.

Looking like a giant sea sponge in space, Hyperion spins unpredictably as it follows an eccentric orbit around Saturn. It is not just the period of rotation that changes but the imaginary spindle around which the moon rotates as well. One day, the Sun – visible only as an intensely bright star from Hyperion's distance – will simply bob its head over the horizon, another day it will rise and stay overhead for hours. On yet another day, it will begin to set and then rise again before dipping below the horizon.

___This moon's out-of-control rotation is the result of a conspiracy of factors. The first is its irregular shape, the second is its elongated orbit and the third is its occasional proximity

to the large moon Titan. All of them unsettle Hyperion, which tries to respond to the myriad gravitational fields acting on it, and their ever-changing strengths based on its distance from Saturn and Titan.

___The cratering is dense on Hyperion [1], perhaps a product of its chaotic rotation as every surface is repeatedly laid open for assault. Even so, one impact stands out. It is a behemoth measuring 120 km across, while the average radius of the moon is only 135 km. Gouged to a depth of more than 10 km deep, how could such a giant impact not shatter Hyperion into a billion fragments?

___Perhaps the secret lies in Hyperion's interior. In common with many of Saturn's moons, it is

more ice than rock but the secret is that, rather than being a solid lump, Hyperion is a honeycomb. Up to 40 percent of the moon could be empty, with vast caverns stretching through the interior. It may not even be a single object, just a pile of celestial rubble that has been pulled together by gravity. But the gravity is insufficient to crush the rock and ice together into a single, solid body.

___This porosity acts as a crumple zone, allowing Hyperion to absorb the energy of an otherwise fatal impact. So, when Hyperion suffered the mighty strike, it collapsed inwards producing not so much a crater as a dent, but otherwise remained intact – or as intact as a celestial rubble pile can ever be.

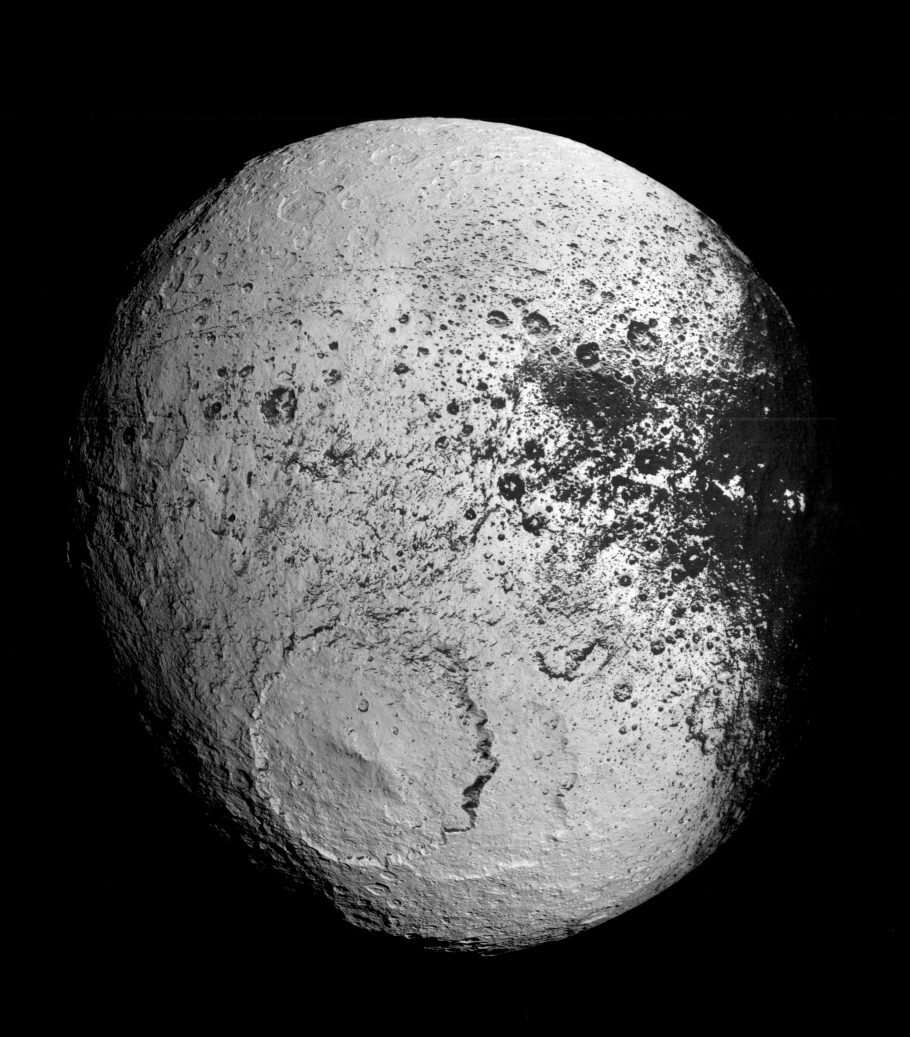

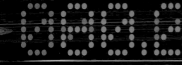

LIGHT SECONDS
LIGHT MINUTES
LIGHT YEARS
KILO LIGHT YEARS
MEGA LIGHT YEARS
GIGA LIGHT YEARS

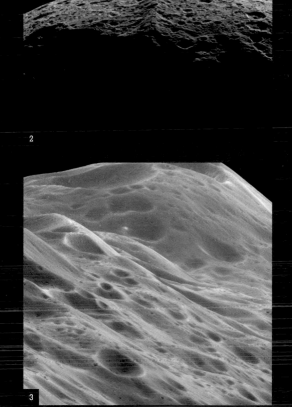

Cosmic graffiti

Something has painted Iapetus but not finished the job.
While one hemisphere of this Saturnian moon shines
with gleaming ice, the other is distinctly saturnine.
Stenciled with grime, it begs the question: who is the
cosmic graffiti artist?

By all rights, Iapetus should be just another icy moon. All indications are that it is composed mostly of ice with just a fifth of its interior made from rock. On its surface there are the usual mix of craters and other markings but one feature stands out. It is unique amongst the many worlds of the Solar System.

One hemisphere of Iapetus is stained with a dark material [1], which absorbs more than 95 percent of the light that falls on it. The other face is bright ice with a sharp boundary between the two colours.

The black powder itself is a mix of carbon-bearing molecules that resemble the organic material found in comets and some meteorites. These molecules represent the chemical building blocks that made life possible on Earth. In the frigid, airless wastes of Iapetus, however, they are preserved for all to see.

As they built up, so they absorbed more sunlight, warming that hemisphere of the moon and driving the bright surface ice to escape. This loss further darkened the hemisphere, leading to its current midnight complexion. But why did it accumulate on just one hemisphere?

The first clue is that the gleaming hemisphere is the trailing one. Saturn has trapped Iapetus into always turning the same face to the planet, exactly the same as the Earth has done to the Moon. This means that one half of Iapetus always faces forwards while the other looks behind, and it is the forward-facing hemisphere that is caked in the dark deposits. So the stuff is in Iapetus' orbit. Now, how did it get there?

The culprit is Phoebe, another of Saturn's moons and 9.5 million kilometres further out. This chunk of a moon is just 100 km across, little

more than a glorified comet, and it is coming apart at the seams. Spewing dust into space, Phoebe has surrounded Saturn and the visible ring system with an almost invisible girdle of sooty particles. Reaching from the orbit of Phoebe across millions of kilometres of space, the dusty particles litter Iapetus's orbit, which are then splattered onto the moon as Iapetus ploughs through the grimy cloud.

It is not just Iapetus that suffers; Hyperion also receives a share of Phoebe's grime. Though because of its chaotic rotation, the particles have accumulated more evenly across Hyperion's tumbling surface.

But Iapetus is more that a painted face, an equatorial spine of mountains runs 1,300 km around the moon [2]. More than 10 km tall, these peaks are the Himalaya of Iapetus [3], but their origin remains mysterious.

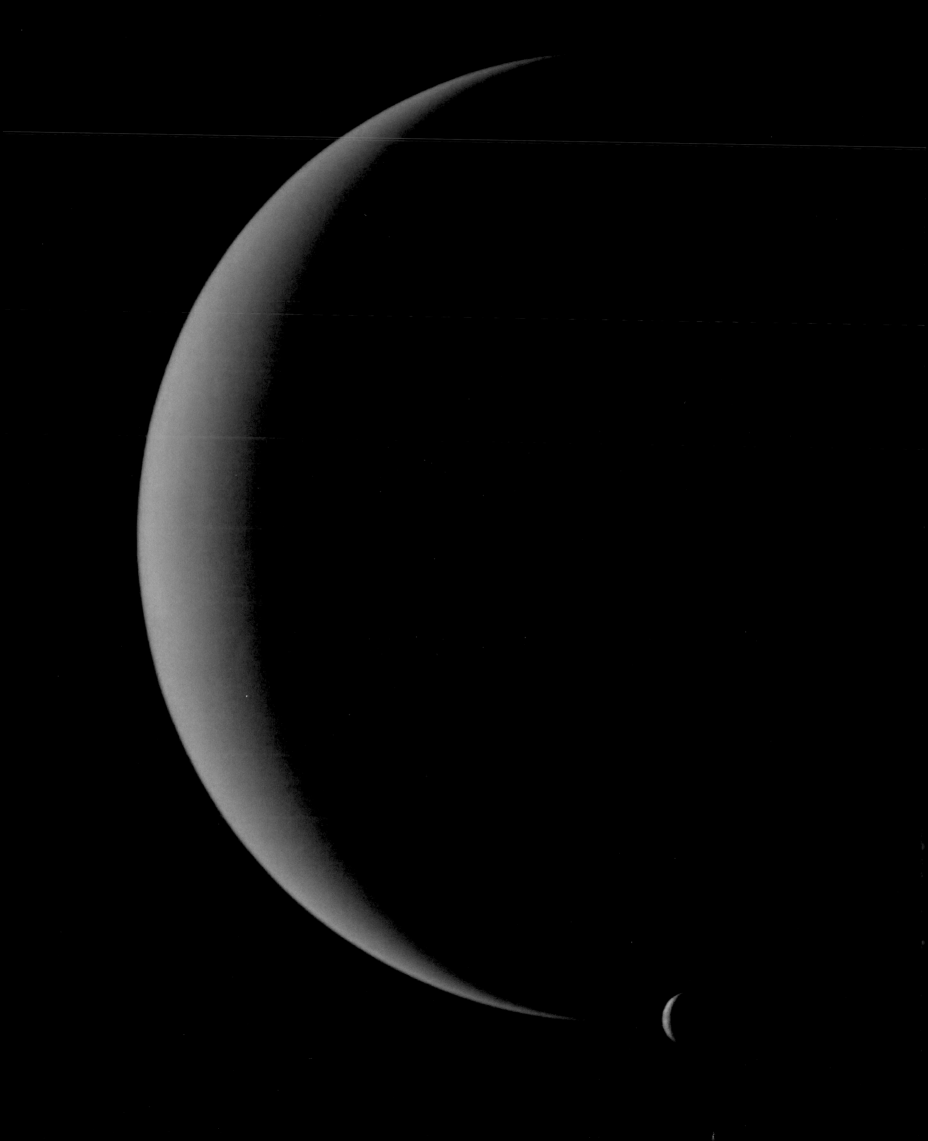

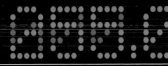

LIGHT SECONDS
LIGHT MINUTES
LIGHT YEARS
KILO LIGHT YEARS
MEGA LIGHT YEARS
GIGA LIGHT YEARS

1

2

The ice giants

Something is stirring the clouds of Neptune. Whereas
its planetary brother, Uranus, presents a glassy
appearance, devoid of activity or markings, Neptune
is a dynamic world of storms – possibly the result of
an indigestible dinner.

Uranus and Neptune are strikingly similar
in terms of composition. Mostly composed
of light gases such as hydrogen and helium
they both possess a noticeable component of
methane, ammonia and water vapour in their
atmospheres. This reflects the fact that these
planets formed in the further expanses of the
Solar System, where the strength of sunlight
was so low that ices found it easier to condense
into planetary material.

___But these planets probably did not form
as far out as we see them today. Uranus sits
15 times further from the Sun than the Earth,
and Neptune doubles that to 30 times. That's
a puzzle because, at those distances, and
certainly that of Neptune, there simply should
not have been enough material to build
a planet 17 times the mass of the Earth.

___Instead, Neptune most probably formed

significantly closer and then migrated to its
current orbit as gravitational forces exerted
themselves between the planets, and moved
them into some state of equilibrium.

___Neptune is a dynamic world of storms
and cloud systems. The Great Dark Spot
on Neptune was discovered in 1989 and
measured to be large enough to swallow the
Earth [1]. Unlike the Great Red Spot on Jupiter,
however, it proved to be a transitory feature,
disappearing by 1994. In its place other storms
have occasionally appeared, providing a
continual reminder that all has not settled
inside the planet.

___Uranus on the other hand, does not
show any signs of atmospheric shenanigans;
even spotting clouds on the planet is almost
impossible [2]. This is strange because Uranus
receives four times the amount of sunlight that

Neptune does, yet seems to do nothing with it.
Something must be driving Neptune's weather
from the inside.

___The solution may be the early safari that
the planet took to reach its current orbit. This
would have swept Neptune through a swarm
of dwarf planets, similar to Pluto, also jockeying
for position. If Neptune drew sufficiently close
to one of these, it could conceivably have
swallowed it whole, as a snake devours its
prey. Maybe the subsequent release of energy,
as it digests this planetary mouthful, continues
to this day, stirring the atmosphere.

___Yet it is peaceful Uranus that displays the
most peculiar attribute of this pair of giants:
it has fallen onto its side, spinning over and
over rather than round and round, and
receives more solar heat at its polar regions
than at its equator.

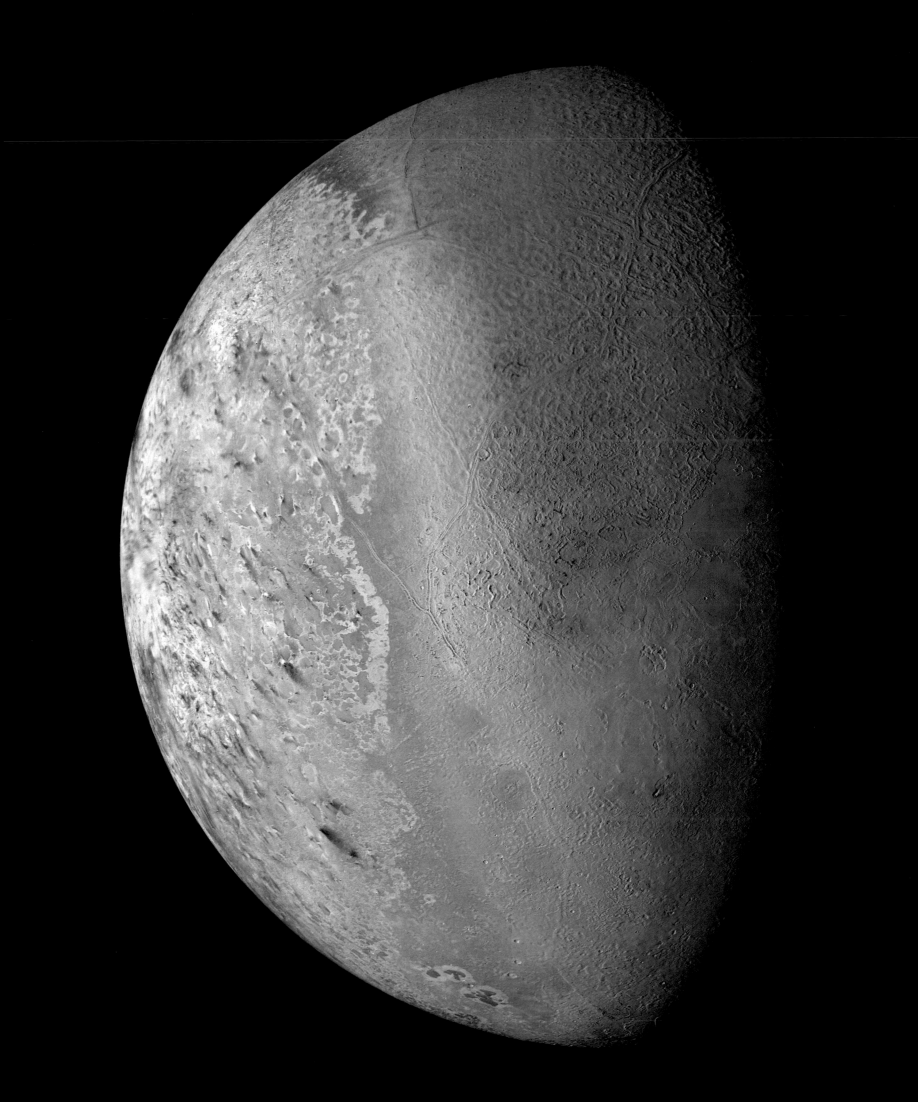

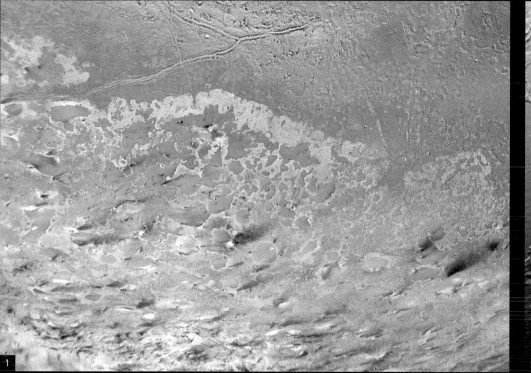

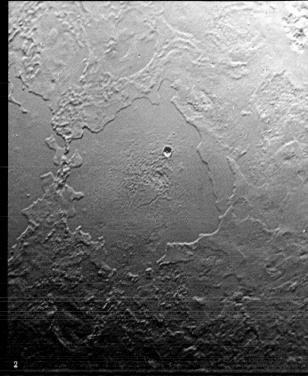

Kidnapped moon

Neptune's largest moon Triton defies easy description.
Its pink south pole receives a constant stream of sunlight
from the Sun. Although weak because of distance, this
illumination is somehow enough to spark volcanic
activity in this icy outpost of the Solar System.

Neptune's largest moon must somehow have been kidnapped by the large planet, snagged by its gravity and hoisted into orbit. A naturally occurring moon would follow an orbit more-or-less around the parent planet's equator, travelling in the same direction as the planet spins. Triton, however, opts for the difficult life: a backward path around the planet, and so inclined it sweeps within easy sight of Neptune's polar regions.

___Triton's seasons are dominated by the slow march of Neptune around the Sun, which takes 165 years to complete an orbit. This means that a season on the moon lasts some four decades. Triton is currently holding its southern hemisphere sunward, and this is driving a bizarre form of volcanic activity on it.

___The average surface temperature on Triton is a chilly –235 °C. Nonetheless, black streaks mark out a volcanic region [1]. This is where the icy surface is being heated by the distant Sun, forcing geysers of invisible nitrogen gas to erupt upwards to an altitude of 8 km. As the gas blasts skyward, it carries with it dark dust blown by a faint breeze. Falling downwind, the dusty particles daub the surface.

___Once an eruption starts it can last for up to a year, spraying debris across 150 km downwind of the geyser. This behaviour may be similar to that happening in Mars's polar regions during the spring months.

___The atmosphere itself amounts to nothing more than a tenuous collection of gases, 20,000 times lower in pressure than the Earth's, and during the long winter it will freeze to the surface creating a bright layer of frost.

___Craters are gradually healed on Triton as the internal warmth of the moon allows the ice to flow and slowly fill its wounds, erasing them over millions of years [2].

___Were Triton to be magically released from Neptune's clutches, it would resume an orbit around the Sun, and be sufficiently large to be proclaimed a dwarf planet in its own right. The dwarf planets are a newly classified group that includes Pluto. There are a handful of examples known so far. These include Ceres, the largest asteroid, the distant worldlet of Eris and the fancifully named Haumea and Makemake. There could be many more, perhaps hundreds or even thousands that lie, yet to be observed, in the distant reaches of the Solar System.

INTER
STELLAR

Leaving the planets behind, we see them swiftly shrink
to pinpoints and disappear into the glare of the Sun.
Now we are truly in deep space. There is nothing but
blackness, and the misty light of the Milky Way
beckoning to us, urging us on.

Somewhere around us are a trillion comets, all but invisible because their dirty icy surfaces are reflecting nothing but the feeble starlight. This tenuous shell of leftovers from the planets' formation was scattered into these exiled realms by the gravity of the giant planets. They are a lost resource: the mountains of Iapetus that never were, the plateau of Titan that missed its mark, and the inland sea that never found its way to Earth.

___They no longer concern us, we have more luminous targets in sight but to reach them we will have to lengthen our stride. The stars in our part of space are separated by light years, and to visit the marvels that adorn our Galaxy we will have to cover tens of thousands of them.

___On the puny time scale of a single human lifetime, the stars are immutable, fixed and constant. But taken across the entire sweep of the Milky Way, they are a varied population covering all stellar races and ages.

___At the smallest end of the scale are red dwarf stars. These celestial minnows are the misers of the Galaxy. They have little fuel and what they do have they are determined not to fritter, so they produce a weak glow of red light that burns for 100 billion years. At the opposite end of the scale are the spendthrift blue supergiants. These furious dynamos burn themselves away in just a few million or a few tens of millions of years.

___The lifespan of each star is governed by the interplay of gravity against pressure. Gravity tries to squeeze the star into an ever more compact configuration, while radiation pressure tries to blow it apart. The harder gravity squeezes, the faster the nuclear reactions in a star's core occur and the more energy they produce. This is why we experience the seemingly paradoxical situation that the smallest stars, with the lowest fuel stocks, live the longest, while the profligate massive stars live fast and die young.

___At the heart of each star is an alchemist's furnace capable of turning plentiful hydrogen and helium into rare heavier chemical elements. With each transmutation, so energy is produced to keep the star shining and alive. When the star eventually dies, either in a graceful flowering of its outer layers or

in the calamity of a supernova, it bequeaths the newly created elements back into space, enriching the interstellar medium with the seeds of future stars and planets.

___Mature stars often come in pairs or more. These groupings are for life. Once joined at birth, nothing can part them. Fully half the stars in the Galaxy are partnered in one way or another; they pull each other into pirouettes that can take decades to complete or just mere hours.

___But as brilliant as the stars are, it is the beautiful nebulae that attract the most attention; they blossom from the great bulk of the giant molecular clouds that drift through the Galaxy. Each colossal nimbus has stitched itself together out of the disparate wisps of dust and gas found in interstellar space, gradually sealing off its interior from view. In these secret realms, the process of stellar gestation can take place.

___Shrouded in utter darkness, it is only when these stellar embryos are close to being born that they begin to burst with light. And not only light, for magnetic windows can open in their atmospheres out of which a wind of particles blows. These streaming stellar winds begin to carve a way out of the nebula for the star. In the case of the largest stars they are assisted in their task by the welter of ultraviolet radiation they exude.

___All of this combines to open a cavity around the star, pushing ever-greater quantities of dust and gas away until ultimately the leading edge of the bubble reaches the outer surface of the cloud. Now, the cavity opens up to view, and a magnificent luminous cavern is revealed in which dwell young stars, ready to take their place on the galactic stage.

___There is an embarrassment of these celestial jewel boxes close to the Solar System. From the radiant beauty of Orion to the towering pillars of the Eagle Nebula, by way of the hydrogen waves of the Lagoon Nebula and the misty mountains of creation in Carina, each one is riddled with embryonic stars.

___We quickly encounter more of these regions than we might otherwise expect because the Sun sits in the middle of a mysterious ring of star formation called Gould's Belt. It is inclined

from the stars of the Milky Way by 20 degrees and the Sun is misplaced from its centre by 325 light years. This sparkling necklace was formed some 60 million years ago and is now responsible for some of the most recognizable constellations in the sky. Gould's Belt supplies bright stars for Orion, Scorpius and the Southern Cross amongst others.

___What set this giant ripple in motion is not well known. It could have been a giant molecular cloud dive-bombing the Galaxy, or a similar collision with a clump of the hypothetical particles known as dark matter.

___Theories of galaxy formation postulate that this, as yet undetected, stuff must surround every galaxy in a giant sphere, termed a halo. Each one is more than ten times wider than the visible portion of the galaxy, contains at least ten times more mass than the stars and is clumpy rather than smooth. These clumps are the last vestiges of all the smaller halos that the galaxy has swallowed in order to grow to its present size.

___Regardless of its origin, Gould's Belt is now 3,000 light years in diameter, and contains a few thousand high-mass stars as well as hundreds of thousands of low-mass stars.

___Pressing onward, no journey through space would be complete without a visit to the dark heart of our Galaxy. Situated 26,000 light years from Earth, the centre of the Milky Way is the dwelling place of a supermassive black hole. It is the kernel around which the Galaxy originally formed; the black hole itself may even be the original seed. Now cloaked in the blinding fog of X-rays from a spiralling whirlpool of doomed matter, it sits feeding on anything that passes.

___Finally as we turn our sights upwards to soar out of the Galaxy, we pass the spherical bulks of the globular clusters. With populations in the millions, these ancient stellar metropoli have seen it all; they are the silent witnesses to the Galaxy, having been present for its formation and its subsequent 10 billion years of evolution.

Right: M27, aka the Pleiades or the Seven Sisters, a cluster of hot blue stars some 440 light years away

LIGHT SECONDS
LIGHT MINUTES
LIGHT YEARS
KILO LIGHT YEARS
MEGA LIGHT YEARS
GIGA LIGHT YEARS

First impressions

Sitting towards the centre of the Galaxy is a cornucopia
of stars, big and small, young and old. Wrapped in
vibrant dust clouds, the combined starscape resembles
a canvas from an impressionist master.

This particular canvas is huge, 10 light years
across. Although it appears to hang on display
just above the crowded galactic core [1], it is
actually much nearer to us.

___The medium used to create this masterpiece
is dust and gas – amounting to 3,000 solar
masses of the stuff – and fortuitous alignment.
The giant star of Antares sits towards the
bottom of the image, just to the left of M4,
a mass of stars known as a globular cluster.
M4 is seen through a rare window in the cloud.
It is much further away and takes no part in
the business of the cloud.

___Antares is another interloper, more than a
hundred light years behind the dust cloud.
Outshining our Sun by 10,000 to 1 at visible
wavelengths, and by 65,000 times at infrared,

its light punches through the dusty realms.
Were Antares to magically replace our
Sun, it would engulf the inner Solar System,
reaching to the asteroid belt. Its extremities
are thousands of times less dense than water
and it exhibits a lazy pulsation that follows
no particular pattern in brightness or period.

___But the centrepiece is Rho Ophiuchi, a
pair of blistering stars, embedded in the white
orchid just above the centre of the image. Each
one is a giant, eight and nine times the mass of
the Sun and blazing with surface temperatures
of around 20,000 °C. The stars keep their
distance, circling each other at 400 times the
distance between Earth and the Sun, shifting
their bulks through their conjoined orbits only
once every 2,000 years.

___All the stars in this complex are between
100,000 and 1,000,000 years old. They include
nearly 200 almost formed T Tauri stars and
more than 400 condensations that are on their
way to becoming stars. In the infrared [2], the
youngest stellar objects reveal themselves as
bright points, mimicking the stars they will
one day become.

___Radiating away from the whole complex
are black fingers of unilluminated dust. They
stretch off for hundreds of light years into space,
perhaps connecting this region to other hotbeds
of star formation throughout the Milky Way.

___In the epoch to come, the cloud will be
utterly consumed by these burgeoning stellar
fires, and replaced by a gloaming star cluster.

LIGHT SECONDS
LIGHT MINUTES
LIGHT YEARS
KILO LIGHT YEARS
MEGA LIGHT YEARS
GIGA LIGHT YEARS

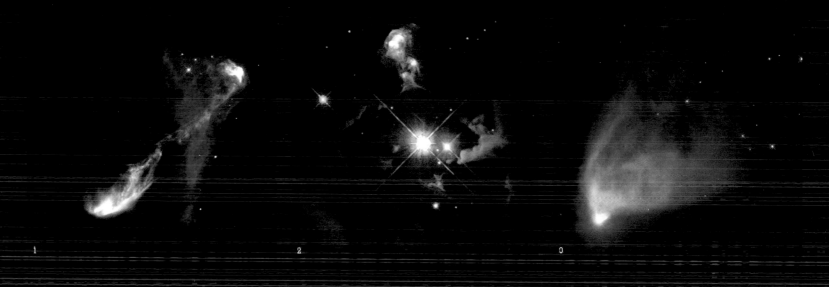

1   2   3

Stellar dawn

Stars are born in darkness, richly swaddled inside
cocoons of dust and gas. Just as in the insect kingdom
on Earth, the first task of the stellar newborn is to break
free of its protective swathes. It does it with an early
act of rebellion.

By strict definition, the shining object at the
centre of this view, surrounded by veils of
dust, is not even a star. T Tauri, as it is known,
has yet to achieve the core temperature and
pressure necessary to ignite its nuclear furnace
and thus generate its own energy. But it is
already shining brightly.

___Its secret power source is that it is still
contracting: pulling itself together by dint of
the gravity its mass creates. As it shrinks, so
it squeezes out energy from the movement of
the atoms and this allows it to shine, giving it
the outward appearance of maturity, like a
child dressing up and pretending to be adult.
All of this play-acting should take place behind
the veils of dust but somehow the star has
managed to emerge.

___Before the discovery of nuclear fusion,

contraction was thought to be the means by
which all stars shone. But if that were true, stars
would live truncated lives, burning themselves
out in a million years or less. The only force that
can keep so many stars shining in the Universe
is nuclear.

___How T Tauri and other stellar newborns
emerge from their cocoons is still mysterious.
The first stirrings of nuclear fusion are thought
to pour radiation into the surrounding clouds,
pushing them away and rending holes to
peer through.

___Nuclear ignition does not start smoothly.
The hallmark of a nuclear engine stuttering
into life are million km/h jets of gas launched
trillions of kilometres into space [1]. They
inflame the surrounding cloud, causing knots
of gas to fluoresce brightly [2]. Such distinctive

stellar blowtorches are known as Herbig-Haro
Objects.

___These tantrums excavate increasingly large
conical cavities [3] and starve the protostar
of matter, stunting any further growth. In
T Tauri's particular case, it is destined to
become a star similar to the Sun, although
orbited by two other stars. These two siblings
are still too young to be readily visible, having
failed to emerge yet from their cocoons. No one
knows whether there are planets around any
of these stars.

___T Tauri has become so influential in the
study and the understanding of young stars
that it now gives its name to a whole class of
stellar show-offs: the T Tauri stars. Each one is
about a million years old and readying itself
for the big wide cosmos.

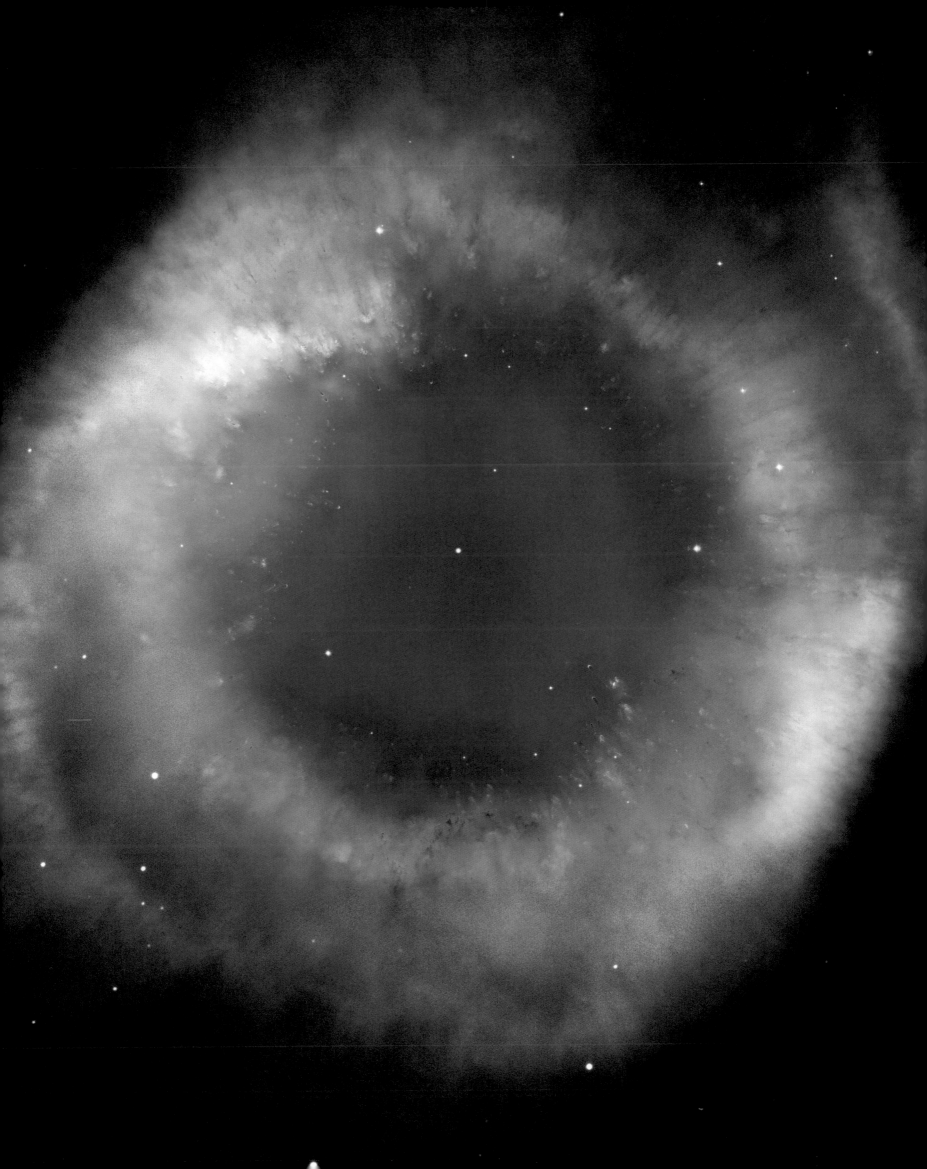

LIGHT SECONDS
LIGHT MINUTES
LIGHT YEARS
KILO LIGHT YEARS
MEGA LIGHT YEARS
GIGA LIGHT YEARS

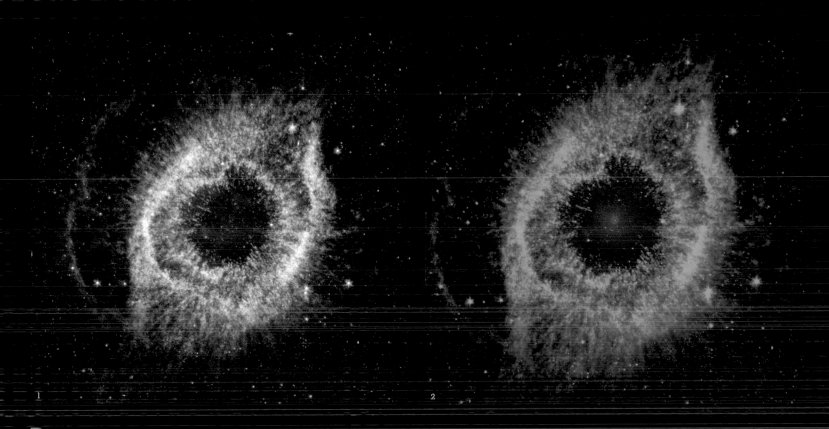

1

2

Death spiral

While the double helix of DNA is one of the secrets of life on Earth, this single celestial helix shows us the secrets of stellar death – and offers some clues about the next generation of stars.

This is how stars die, not in faded senescence but rather at their most beautiful. Around 12,000 years ago, there would have been nothing to distinguish this star. It would have been a bulging red giant, shining with ruby lustre. Now, it is a fluorescent bloom. As the nuclear fusion in its core faltered, so the star blossomed, discharging its outer layers to the mercy of space.

___Contrary to appearances, the Helix is not a spiral but a tunnel of glowing gas that we happen to be looking into. And we catch it early in its formation. Stellar flowers such as these bloom for just 50,000 years before they disperse into the more tenuous interstellar dust and gas all around them.

___The death throes are governed by the fusion of helium inside the star. It is a highly temperature-dependent affair, with small changes in a star's core temperature leading to large variations in the rate of energy output. These palpitations cause dramatic changes, blasting the outer layers away into space and creating a planetary nebula.

___The term 'planetary nebula' is a misnomer from the 18th century when William Herschel thought that these celestial blooms bore a faint resemblance to his recent discovery, the planet Uranus. He guessed they signified the construction of solar systems, rather than their destruction. Despite their true nature becoming apparent as knowledge increased, the name has stuck.

___In the Helix Nebula, thousands of tentacles appear to be reaching back towards the central, dying star. This is an illusion. At the head of each tendril is a knot of dust and gas, previously ejected from the Helix Nebula's central star. Now the knots are getting in the way of the other streaming gases, deflecting them and giving rise to these filaments. In the infrared [1] the tentacular nature of the nebula is emphasized. At even longer wavelengths the Helix fixes the cosmos with a baleful red eye made from the dust of immolated comets [2].

___Planetary nebulae are instrumental in changing the composition of the Galaxy. Inside red giant stars, turbulent currents of roiling gas dredge up the heavier elements synthesized in the nuclear core during the star's lifetime, including life-giving carbon and oxygen. As the outer layers lift off into space, so these elements are transported along with them. They enrich the gas and dust in interstellar space forming the building blocks of the next generation of stars.

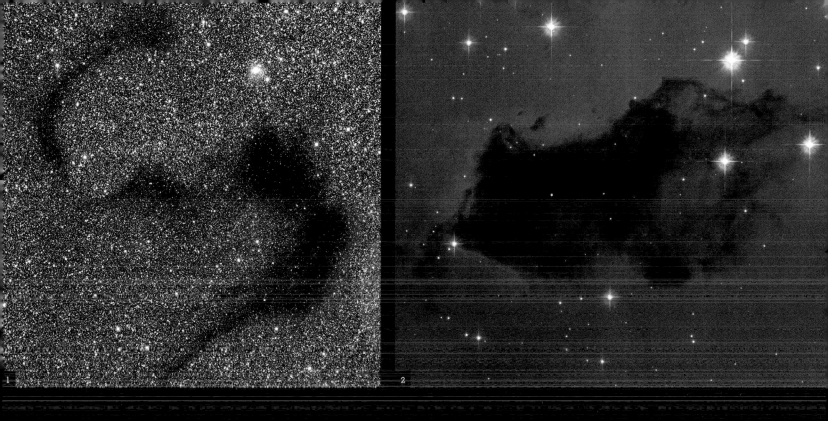

In the snake's belly

A snake of dust slithers across this star field, jealously protecting its innards from the ravages of starlight. In this dusty incubator the stage is set for new stars and planets to grow, one molecule at a time.

Once the Snake Nebula was thought to be a hole in space, a window into the deep void beyond the kingdom of the stars [1]. Now, however, we know differently. The Snake is anything but empty. Think of it as the cosmic equivalent of a cloud in the azure sky.

__It is dark because it is dense, filled with dust and gas that is impenetrable to ordinary starlight [2]. This offers the fragile, gaseous molecules within a measure of protection. If they were at large, the ultraviolet starlight that bathes space would ravage them, breaking them into a simpler combination or even down to their constituent atoms.

__But here inside the dusty incubator, they can grow ever longer and ever more complex. Amino acids, organic molecules vital for the construction of proteins, have even been found sheltering in the Galaxy's dark clouds.

__But the growth of these molecules is not simple. Inside the cloud, the gas is still so tenuous that collisions between individual atoms and molecules are rare. Instead, they rely on dust grains to catalyze the procedure.

__The dust grains themselves are a mélange of compositions. Some are simple silicate grains and are the smallest possible building blocks of planetary rocks. Other grains are sub-microscopic slivers of iron, sent tumbling by the impact of starlight and they line up in the interstellar magnetic fields like fence posts. Still others are amorphous blobs of carbonaceous material.

__All can capture molecules if they happen to collide and hang on to them. Sticking to the surface of the dust grain, the molecule waits until another happens to bump by. Nature is patient in this respect; the dust grain can hold its molecular cargo for thousands of years, picking up molecule after molecule until it finds two that can bond. The minuscule energy released in this combination kicks the newly formed molecule off the dust grain, allowing it to fly freely again, back in the cloud where it could encounter another dust grain and start a new session of bonding.

__The dark clouds themselves are set on their path to grow denser and denser until they fragment into clumps that will go on to form stars and planets, incorporating the newly formed molecules.

660.0
LIGHT SECONDS
LIGHT MINUTES
LIGHT YEARS
KILO LIGHT YEARS
MEGA LIGHT YEARS
GIGA LIGHT YEARS

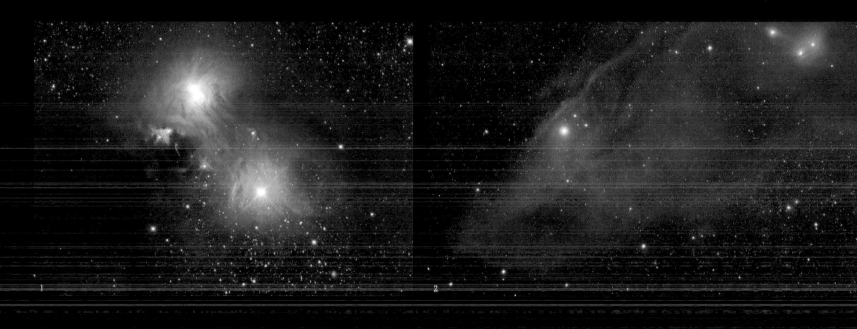

1

2

The blue witch

Look closely at this tumble of interstellar dust and gas.
With a touch of imagination it resembles a witch's head
in profile, with pointy nose and chin. As strange as it
may seem, this ethereal blue glow is conjured up for
the same reason Earth's daytime sky is blue.

Light does not always travel in straight lines through space. Occasionally it can be diverted from its path by collisions with dust particles. This is exactly what is happening here, light is streaming into this cloud of dust and gas from the nearby bright star Rigel, which denotes the right shoulder of Orion, the Hunter. The star itself is not visible on this image, resting just beyond the top right-hand edge.

___While the majority of Rigel's light passes straight through cloud, a small percentage collides head-on with myriad dust grains and is scattered in all directions. Some of that light happens to bounce towards Earth, allowing us to make out the cloud where otherwise we would see nothing.

___But why does this cloud show only blue light when Rigel releases all the colours of the rainbow? It is because not all colours respond to the dust in the same way. The shorter wavelengths of light, which we perceive as blue colours, are far more susceptible to bouncing off the dust grains. Whereas the longer, redder wavelengths find it easier to bypass the grains of dust.

___We exploit this property of light on Earth, by using orange streetlights that penetrate fog more successfully than white lights. It also gives rise to our blue skies and red sunsets.

___At noon, about fifty percent of the sunlight is scattered around the sky, mostly at blue wavelengths. The remaining light from the

Sun appears with a yellowish tinge. In space, the Sun appears to give out more of a white light; hence there was no yellow tint on the airless lunar landscape photographed by the Apollo astronauts.

___On Earth, as the evening approaches and the Sun sinks to the horizon, it takes on a roseate hue. This is because its light is shining through more layers of atmosphere, as it runs parallel to the ground and so more of its blue light is being bounced out of its beams.

___In space, blue is the characteristic colour of reflection nebulae, as shown by the Corona Australis Complex [1], and IC 4592 surrounding the star Nu Scorpii [2].

Vela Supernova Remnant
NGC 2736
SUPERNOVA REMNANT
DIAMETER: 113 LY

LIGHT SECONDS
LIGHT MINUTES
LIGHT YEARS
KILO LIGHT YEARS
MEGA LIGHT YEARS
GIGA LIGHT YEARS

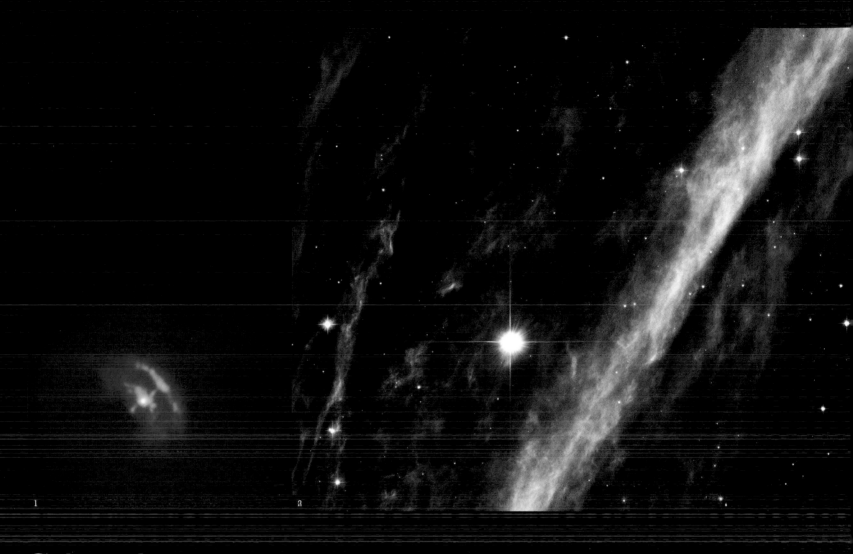

Celestial tsunami

The fury of the heavens is never more obvious than during a supernova. Each of these catastrophic stellar detonations unleashes celestial tsunamis that plough through space, ripping apart atoms in their wake. In the constellation of Vela, the havoc began 11,000 years ago; it's still going on – and it's heading our way.

It took little more than a single day for this star to die and then 11,000 years for it to sculpt these extraordinary filaments of gas. For millions of years of life before its demise, the star's nuclear heart had been furiously generating energy, smashing atomic nuclei together to feed its rapacious appetite for energy.

___Energy is all that stands between any star and death. Without the constant outrush of power to provide support, gravity would crush it utterly. As long as the nuclear furnace can be maintained, the star can live. But inevitably the fuel runs out.

___When a massive star begins to build iron in its heart, its fate is sealed. Its remaining lifetime can be measured in hours.

___Iron cannot fuse easily and so builds up like

the ash at the bottom of a fire, robbing the centre of the star of the energy it needs for support. It take just a day for a star to build an iron core roughly the size of Earth and containing almost one and a half times the mass of the Sun. At such proportions, the core can no longer fight gravity and spontaneously implodes.

___In microseconds, it is crushed together by its own weight to become a tiny, ultra-dense neutron star no bigger than an asteroid [1]. This robs the star of its foundations, and the overlying layers come crashing down, triggering the supernova: an explosion that cannons gas in all directions throughout space.

___In Vela, this cataclysm took place 11,000 years ago. The leading edge of the shock wave

has now reached 200 light years into space [2], and although it has slowed a little from its original velocity of 35 million km/h, still the violence of its passage is enough to shred atoms as it passes, leaving them to light up space as they recombine in its wake. And it's heading our way.

___It has already covered 200 light years and has some 600 left to go. However, by the time it arrives, in around 24,000 AD, its power will have diminished so much that it will pack no further punch. Nevertheless, such waves contribute to the general turbulence of the interstellar gas, helping to determine how easy it is for new stars to form.

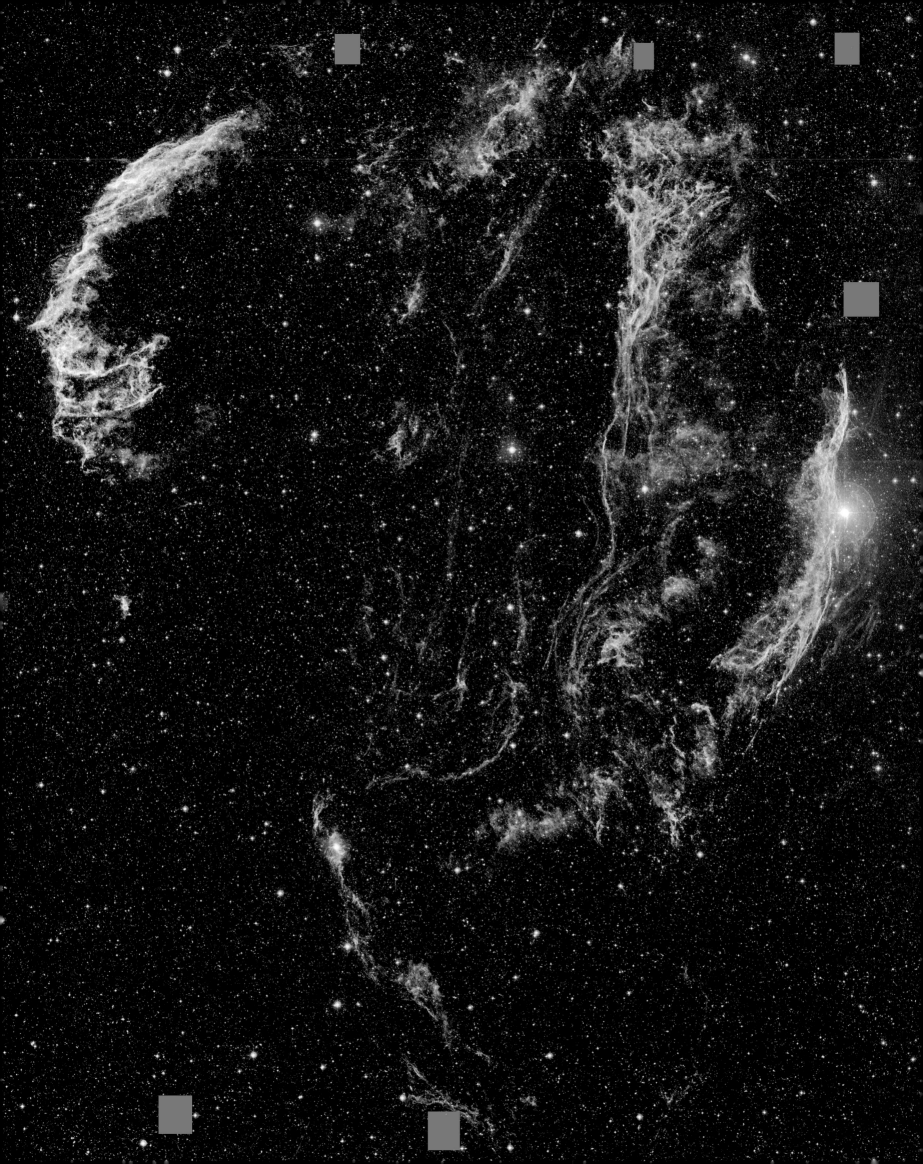

Cygnus Loop
NGC 6960, 6992, 6995, 6997
SUPERVOVA REMNANT
DIAMETER: 20 LY

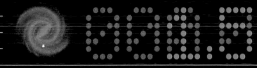

LIGHT SECONDS
LIGHT MINUTES
LIGHT YEARS
KILO LIGHT YEARS
MEGA LIGHT YEARS
GIGA LIGHT YEARS

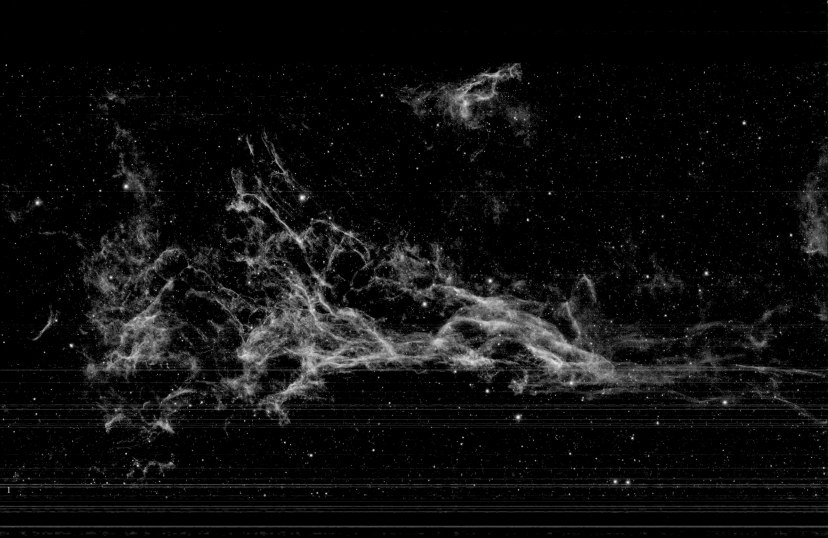

1

Dusty demise

Supernovae are fleeting but dramatic. Our Galaxy should produce one such celestial suicide every 50–100 years. But something is wrong. These spectacular explosions seem to have stalled in our Galaxy because no one has seen one here since 1604.

The Cygnus Loop is not the celestial conflagration it once was. Now 10,000 years old, it is beginning to lose its power. It can no longer be traced as a continuous loop in the sky and in another 10,000 years it will have faded into obscurity. Before it fades, the filaments of Fleming's Triangular Wisp [1] reveal the presence of oxygen and hydrogen ready to seed the next generation of stars.

___As one remnant disperses, so another should be ready to take its place. With an estimated Galactic population of stars that number several hundred billion, there should be one or two cataclysmic explosions every century. There is the remnant from Tycho's supernova that exploded in 1572 and there is Kepler's from 1604 but, since then, no one

has seen another new star in the sky. Just as certainly, however, supernovae must be occurring because the aftermaths are scattered throughout space.

___There is a cloud of gas known as G1.9+0.3, a young supernova remnant that is expanding so fast it must have exploded within the last 140 years. Yet, no records from the nineteenth century speak of such a convulsion of light in the sky. Another supernova remnant, known as Cassiopeia A, must be 330 years old, but there are no sightings of this supernova going off either. What is going on – invisible supernovae? Impossible, they regularly burn with the light of a few hundred billion stars – often outshining all the rest of the stars in their host galaxies put together.

___The answer is covered in dust. The microscopic shards of solid matter that constitute interstellar dust account for about one percent of the mass floating through free space. This is enough to block out most of the stars from our view. And if we can't see the stars, the chances are that we will not see all the supernovae either. So it is the copious dust in the Milky Way that is foxing us here, blotting our view of the drama, even though we have ringside seats.

___The supernovae are happening and leaving their searing signatures in the form of super-heated bubbles of gas. We just have to get better at peering through the dusty shrouds of the Milky Way to spy on them.

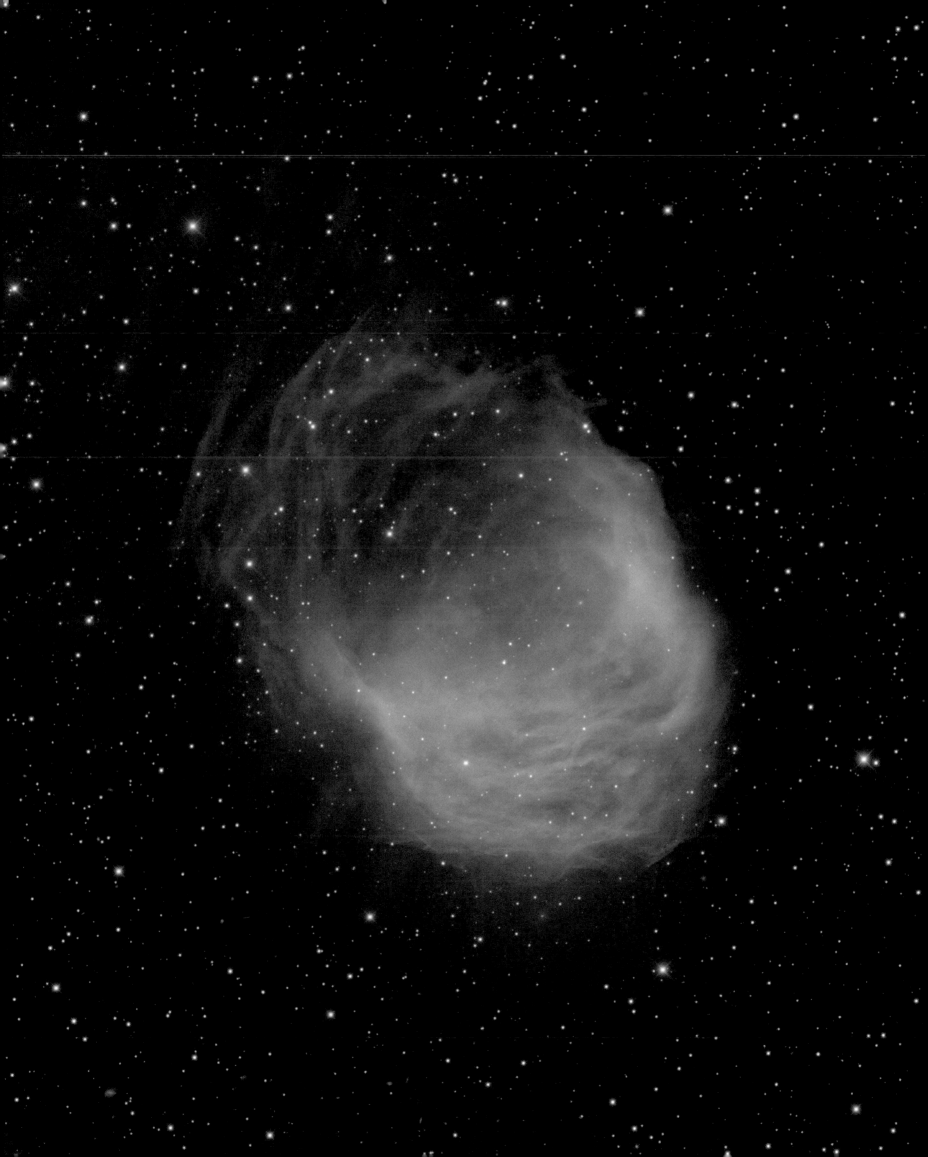

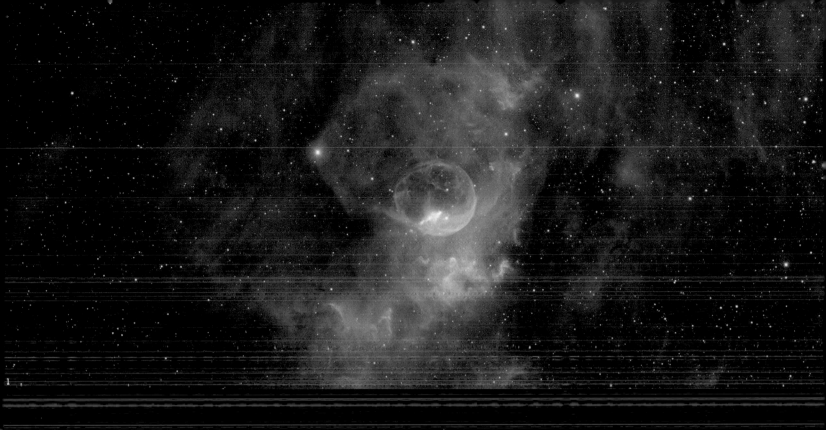

Petrifying prospect

Serpentine braids of gas wreath the star at the heart of the the Medusa Nebula. According to mythology, the snake-headed Gorgon was capable of turning flesh into stone. In its own way, this star is also turning things to stone, but one dust grain at a time.

The Medusa Nebula is an old planetary nebula, formed from the dying remnants of a once-proud red giant star. Now billions of years old, back in its heyday the star would have been 200 times larger than the Sun, though it probably contained a similar amount of mass. In such a hugely distended object, the outer layers are so far away from the central core that they are only loosely bound by gravity. The pressure of the dying star's lurching radiation can loft them into space, the first step in the creation of a planetary nebula.

___As these gaseous outflows cool, dust collects like soot in an industrial chimney. The chemicals needed for the dust were

created in the star's heart and brought to the surface by mammoth upheavals during which the star exchanged its outer layers for those originally near the nuclear core.

___The dust released by such red giant stars restricts our view of the Milky Way to within a mere 6,000 light years of Earth. Only by looking out of the plane of the Galaxy, or by switching to longer wavelengths of radiation, can we see the rest of the Universe. Without the dust, our view would be unrestricted across the entire Galaxy.

___However, there is an upside to this stellar dust storm. Dust plays an important role in the Galaxy's ecology. It acts as seed for molecules to coalesce around, slowly building

the raw ingredients of new stars, planets, moons and, just perhaps, life.

___The more massive a star, the shorter its life span and the earlier it begins to shed its outer layers. In the case of the celestial bubble known as NGC 7635 [1], the giant star at its heart is up to 40 times the Sun's mass, 400,000 times more luminous and just a few tens of millions of years old. Yet it has already begun to shrug off its outer layers.

___In this case, the discarded material is too hot for dust to form; instead it serves to enrich the interstellar realms with new flavours of gas. These too will find their way into the next generation of stars and planets. And so the cycle begins again.

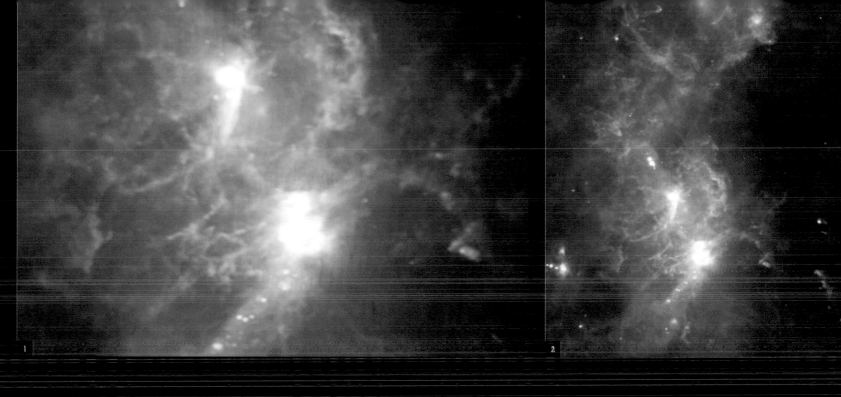

Star factory

Lying just a celestial stone's throw away from Earth is the Orion Molecular Cloud Complex, a vast, freezing production line that exists with only one purpose: to churn out stars.

The constellation of Orion is one of the largest in the night sky. Its distinctive shape dominates the northern skies in winter. In mythology, Orion is a hunter; in space, he is a giant. His body is 240 light years long and is composed of hundreds of thousands of solar masses of dust and gas [1]. It stretches across the entire constellation [2] and is made of the coldest gas in space, naturally chilled to temperatures as low as –263 °C.

___It is a giant molecular cloud, one of a thousand such conglomerations spread throughout the Milky Way. These clouds are found close to the Galaxy's equator and roughly trace spiral patterns from the galactic centre outwards. They naturally sink towards the equatorial belt of the Galaxy because they are cold, sluggish regions that have little power to resist gravity.

___Such clouds are the sites of star formation and in Orion the process has well and truly started. The entire region is covered with faint traces of glowing hydrogen, a sure sign of active stellar construction. In addition, like icebergs peeping above the polar ocean's surface, brilliant nebulae betray the most vigorous hotbeds of activity.

___Surrounding the Orion cloud complex is an even larger structure known as the Orion-Eridanus bubble. The bubble spans 400 light years of space and is testament to a previous generation of stars that formed from the molecular cloud. Sitting at the epicentre of this bubble is a group of several dozen stars. The most prominent of these mark out Orion's belt and sword.

___Whether it is simply the powerful starlight given out by these stars that has crafted the bubble, or whether it is the last remnants of an old supernova is currently unknown. What is certain is that the eastern extremity of this bubble is marked by a curving arc of glowing hydrogen called Barnard's Loop.

___Whatever created the bubble it is having a profound effect. In contrast to the molecular cloud, the bubble is highly rarefied. What gas there is exists in the form of individual atoms zipping around at relatively high temperatures. In this part of the complex, star formation is impossible.

___But in the denser gas, down in the heart of the molecular cloud, star production is at full throttle. In millions of years' time, all Orion will be alight, glittering like a treasure chest of newborn stellar jewels.

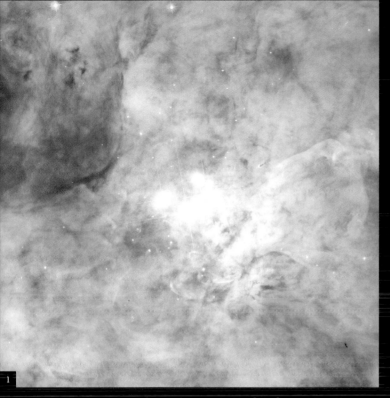

Orion's monsters

A glowing cave of gas, the Orion Nebula is the lair of the fearsome giant stars that comprise the Trapezium cluster. These four titans swamp space with radiation but may actually be decoys: the real monsters lie hidden behind them.

On their own, the stars in the Trapezium would be terrifying [1]. Even the smallest of the four large stars shines thousands of times more brightly than the Sun. The leader is a star of 40 solar masses, pumping out more energy than 400,000 Suns combined. It is almost solely responsible for carving the opening that is the Orion Nebula.

___The nebula is like a burst blister on the side of the Orion Molecular Cloud facing Earth. As it has ruptured, so it has allowed us to peer into this incandescent hideout and glimpse the giant stars' swarming minions.

___There are thousands of smaller stars, all struggling to survive the ultraviolet onslaught. Some of the smaller stars are surrounded by dusty discs that, left to their own devices,

would have grown into planetary systems. But under the welter of radiation from the Trapezium, the condensing planets are electro-magnetically sandblasted back to their constituent atoms. A bow-shaped shockwave engulfs the star LL Ori as it melts in the face of this unstoppable assault [2]. Chillingly, this sustained violence in nothing compared to that taking place behind the Trapezium.

___Still embedded in the surrounding molecular cloud is a trio of giants, which easily rival the Trapezium stars. Originating from these stars are about 40 iron-tipped cosmic bullets that have been blasted outwards by some sort of savage stellar event. Each bullet is a cloud of iron vapour ten times wider than our Solar System, ploughing through the

surrounding molecular cloud at a speed of 200 km/s and trailing a wake of hydrogen gas. The bullets are hot, blazing at a temperature of 5,000 °C, which is hotter than the surfaces of most stars in the Galaxy. Whatever shot these outward expended tremendous power.

___The event had to be a stellar detonation of some type, and probably in the last few thousand years. The fact that there is iron in the bullet tips betrays that a giant star must be somehow involved because only in such an extreme nuclear furnace can this element be synthesized. But what exactly caused this supreme act of stellar ruination, no one knows for sure.

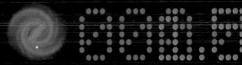

LIGHT SECONDS
LIGHT MINUTES
LIGHT YEARS
KILO LIGHT YEARS
MEGA LIGHT YEARS
GIGA LIGHT YEARS

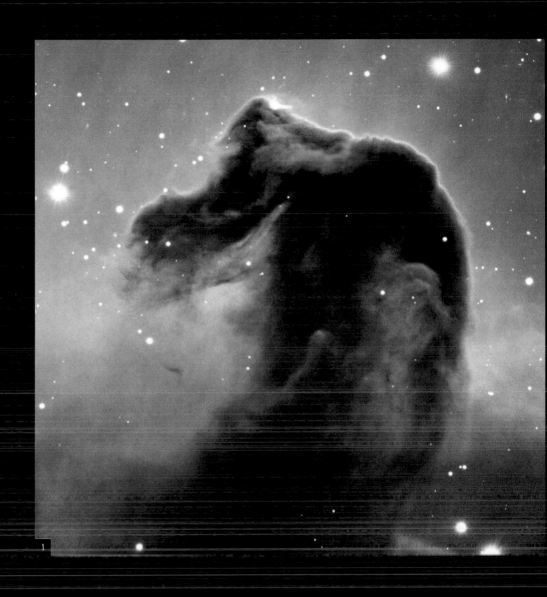

1

Dark knight

It is the equivalent of a stellar shoreline; a cliff-face of hydrogen gas and dust being pounded by an ocean of light. As wave upon wave of ultraviolet energy strikes the interstellar promontory, so it is being eroded away.

The Horsehead itself is a large dusty peninsula, [1] rising out of the expansive gas cloud that covers the lower portion of this image. The equine silhouette is pure chance, blindly sculpted by the forces of nature as the surrounding gases have been eroded away.

___The shadow play would be completely invisible were it not for the bright stars of Sigma Orionis that sit offstage but provide the energy to carve away the gas. The star system is a quintet, five brilliant orbs united by their mutual gravity. Two of them orbit each other every 170 years, with a separation about as wide as our Solar System. They are the hottest stars in the group with surface temperatures of over 30,000 °C.

___Three smaller stars orbit the central pair, and pose a stellar riddle. The furthest of the quintet displays an over-abundance of helium in its makeup. Sigma Orionis E, as it is known, contains seven times the mass of the Sun but once upon a time it was much larger. In its formative days, this celestial glutton sucked in more star forming material than it could digest, so in a gush of stellar wind the excess material was ejected, driven by the intense radiation generated in the star's core.

___This sudden hiccup reduced its mass but acted predominantly on the lighter hydrogen atoms, flinging them back into space to rejoin the molecular cloud and leaving Sigma Orionis E endowed with more helium than is normal.

___The entire five-star system may also be coming apart at the seams. The gravitational forces acting on each star change constantly as the stellar family swings through a near infinite number of orbital configurations. Almost certainly, this will ultimately result in a falling out, and one or more stars will be ejected from the system to wander space as orphans.

___But for now, the five stars continue to work in uneasy partnership, supplying the power needed to sculpt the Horsehead. As the energized hydrogen rises from the cloud's surface, it is shepherded on its way by the ephemeral magnetic fields that permeate space.

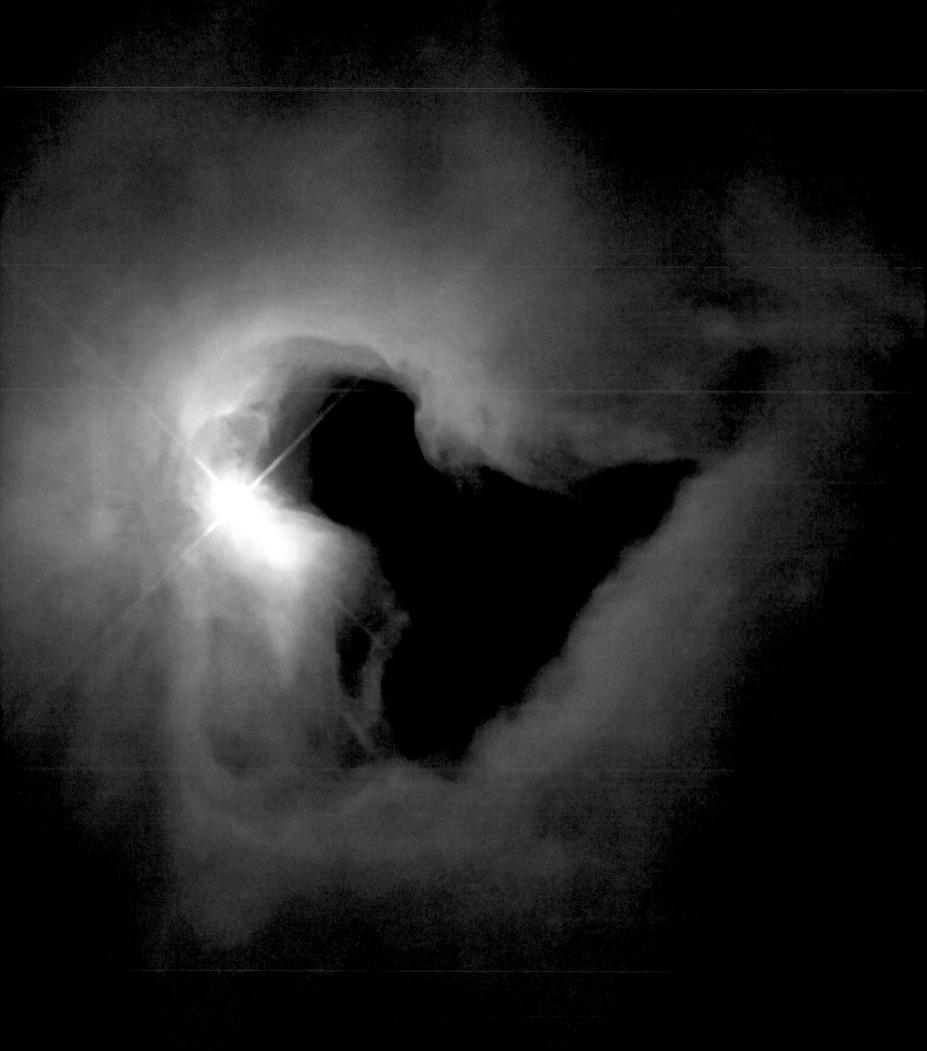

The hole in space

Once thought to be a dense cloud of obscuring dust, this black patch amid the pearly swathes is now known to be a keyhole, peering into a stellar birth cloud. It is providing a window onto the way young stars burst out of their cradles.

Stars don't so much grow out of their cradles as smash their way to freedom. As the nuclear processes inside them gain a foothold, so the stars become belligerent. They begin to shed particles in great tempests that sweep across space. And sometimes these winds can be confined to relatively narrow jets.

It is unclear exactly how this happens but, almost certainly, it has something to do both with the planet-forming disc of matter that can surround a stellar newborn, and with the magnetic fields that a nascent star generates. In the former mechanism, the dusty, doughnut-shaped disc acts as a dam, confining the star's radiation to the polar axis. Meanwhile, the magnetic field could also help to focus the

huricane of particles into a jet, because each particle carries an electrical charge, which allows it to be corralled.

However the jets are formed, they surge into space, spraying particles outward at speeds higher than 100 km/s. They erupt from the top and the bottom of the forming star, boring their way in opposite directions light years into the adjacent clouds of dust and gas. Some parts of the jets can be invisible; at other times they glow brightly. Whenever they hit denser pockets of gas, they create colourful shockwaves that light up their surroundings.

In the case of the keyhole in NGC 1999, they have carved a recognizable shape out of the cloud's forward face. This act of interstellar

vandalism would have gone unnoticed were it not for the bright star V380 Orionis that sits just outside the cloud. A triple star – three individual stars in close orbits around each other – V380 shines onto the cloud, which reacts like a milky mirror, scattering the light back into space.

Where the cloud has been blasted away by the jets, there is no dust to perform this reflection and so the hole appears black. But the culprit is not owning up. There is a gang of adolescent stars holed up deep inside this cloud and the jets responsible could be coming from any of them.

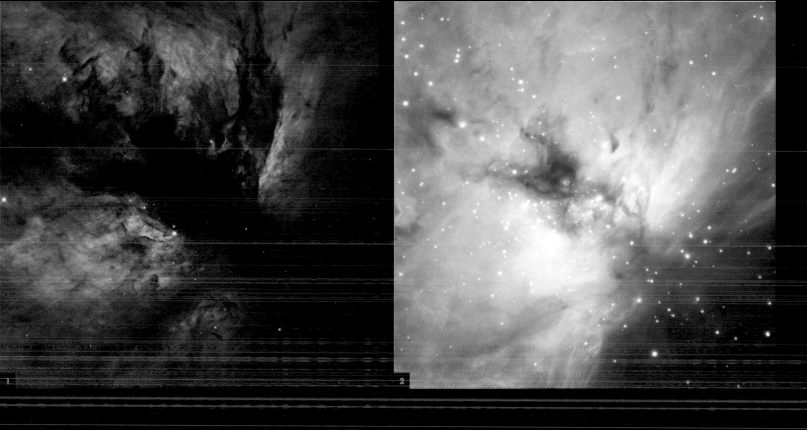

1

2

Hidden fires

They may look like sinister clouds coming to menace these young stars but in reality they are the curtains being pulled back so that the Universe can fully appreciate the newcomers. Already, the stage is radiant with the pure light of stellar youth.

Once again an interstellar cloud is lit up by the stellar debutantes it presents. Ready for the new season, these youngsters are emerging to take their place on the Universal stage.

___M78 occupies a small part of the colossal Orion Molecular Cloud system that stretches for hundreds of light years across space. It is a visible 'iceberg' in the largely unseen cloud and contains around 200 new stars of all sizes. They appear to be forming in families, each a tightly knit cluster that will nevertheless grow further apart as time goes by and the individual stars find their own way through the Galaxy.

___But for now they are united. Some are giants, tens of times more massive than the Sun

and tens of thousands of times brighter, others are destined to be almost identical to our parent star.

___Elsewhere, the cloud is still threaded by rich lanes of dust, the interstellar equivalent of untapped veins of precious ore. They contain the raw material from which yet more stars may form. Dotted about are red beams of gas signifying jets from young stars, fighting their way out of the cloud, queuing for the next season.

___Nearby is the Flame Nebula [1], a star birth conflagration and perhaps a glimpse of what M78 will become once its stars mature a little. The Flame Nebula burns in the brilliant light of Alnitak, the easternmost star in Orion's belt.

A blue supergiant twenty times larger than the Sun, Alnitak holds two other stars captive in orbit around its great bulk.

___Together the three stars muster more than 50 times the mass of the Sun, and pummel the Flame Nebula with a relentless flood of light. The dense core of the nebula is completely hidden to our eyes, but at infrared wavelengths [2] it reveals a smouldering treasure chest of stellar newborns.

___In the nurturing darkness of the cloud, these condensing stars have so far been spared from Alnitak's assault, but their defences won't last. Blue supergiants are the Universe's brightest and hottest stellar spheres, and their scouring radiation can't be denied.

LIGHT SECONDS
LIGHT MINUTES
LIGHT YEARS
KILO LIGHT YEARS
MEGA LIGHT YEARS
GIGA LIGHT YEARS

The race for life

As soon as the first stars have been born inside an interstellar cloud, an almighty struggle begins. On one side gravity maintains its attempt to pull things together; on the other, radiation pressure tries to blow things apart. At stake are the lives of the as yet unborn stars.

In the confines of a stellar nursery, all is darkness and quiet until the first stars light up. If the newborns are heavyweights, then the effect is dramatic. Their first adult act is to flood their dusty cradles with ultraviolet light blowing away their surroundings of dust and gas.

___But like a giant who doesn't know his own strength, the largest stars do not stop at just blasting away their own surroundings. Their emanations are so powerful that they can reach deep into the rest of the cloud and begin to gnaw away at regions that were nothing to do with them.

___Here, in the Pelican Nebula, is a classic example of this behaviour. The ruddy colours mark a cloud of dust and gas that is well on the path to producing stars. Thousands of them could lie inside this celestial incubator. Yet now their peaceful gestation is threatened – they are in a life or death race against time.

___The leading edge of their dusty incubator is glowing fiercely, being boiled away by the glare from a slightly earlier crop of stellar newborns (1). Their radiation will carve through the cloud, eroding back into gas any protostars that have yet to start radiating their own energy.

___Towards the top of the cloud some stars do look destined to survive. They cannot be seen directly yet but in the very tip of some tendrils, short jets of gas are appearing – like devils' horns. These are evidence that inside the tip is another young star ready to burst out. They are the lucky ones, but they too will show no mercy to their slower siblings. As soon as they are revealed, their radiation will also contribute to eroding away the rest of the cloud – and any nascent star that gets in the way.

___It is a story that is being repeated throughout the Galaxy.

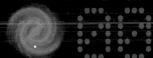

LIGHT SECONDS
LIGHT MINUTES
LIGHT YEARS
KILO LIGHT YEARS
MEGA LIGHT YEARS
GIGA LIGHT YEARS

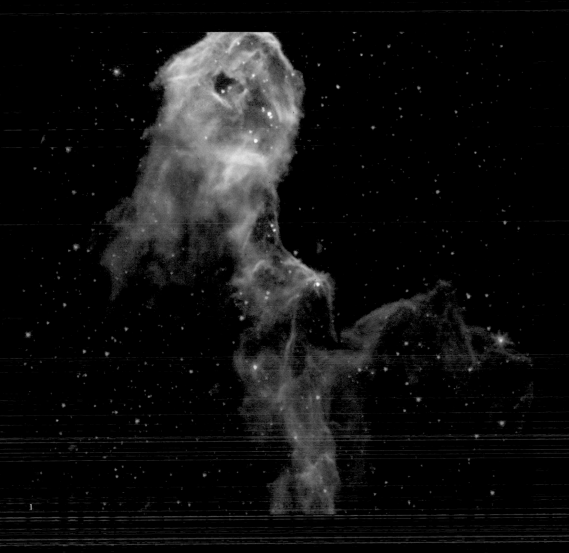

Elephant gun

Like a reef in space, the Elephant's Trunk Nebula forms
a natural barrier to the sea of starlight around it. But it
is fighting a losing battle; not only is it steadily dissolving
in the light of nearby stars, but deep within its clouds
something unusual is stirring.

Hanging in space, the Elephant's Trunk Nebula is an enormous dusty column that stretches out across 130 light years of space. The sanguine glow of hydrogen gas is all around, testament to the nearby presence of powerful stars.

___Inside its length, new forces are already stirring. It is studded with the dusty fruits of star formation. A pair of slightly older stars has already appeared near the top of the nebula. These are the precocious elder children of the Elephant's Trunk, flexing their luminous muscles and exerting their influence over their surroundings. They have already blown a bubble in the top of the trunk and the compression this is causing is helping to trigger star formation in the rest of the region.

___Hundreds of protostars are forming in this interstellar hatchery. Although impossible to see them at visible wavelengths, some are given away by the infrared light they emit [1], others by a bizarre form of natural laser that so far defies explanation.

___On Earth a laser produces amplified light rays by stimulating their emission from a gas or a crystal. It requires the utmost exactitude in manufacturing because the wavelength of visible light is so small. Microwaves, however, have a much longer wavelength, sitting right at the beginning of the radio frequencies. A laser that produces microwaves instead of light is known as a maser.

___As amazing as it might seem, clouds of molecules around some of the young stars in the Elephant's Trunk appear to be producing maser emission. The molecule responsible is water and, somehow, a large cloud of it can release invisible beams of microwave energy.

___Such natural masers are known elsewhere in the Universe. Saturn's moon Enceladus has produced masers from the clouds of water that it jets into space, as have comets. Some old red giant stars also have tenuous outer envelopes of gas that become natural masers.

___Inside the Elephant's Trunk, although not every new star generates a maser, they do all emit an increasing quantity of radiation as they climb to maturity. As these waves of starlight, infrared, X-rays and microwaves continue to pound the inside of the nebula, so it will be dislodged into space. Eventually this dark dusty reef will be replaced by a shining archipelago of stars.

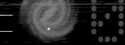

NGC 2264
EMISSION NEBULA
DIAMETER: 30 LY

LIGHT SECONDS
LIGHT MINUTES
LIGHT YEARS
KILO LIGHT YEARS
MEGA LIGHT YEARS
GIGA LIGHT YEARS

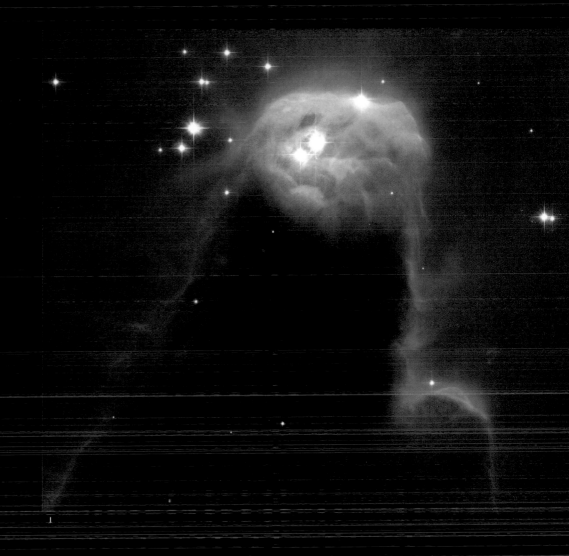

Interstellar cloudspotting

Another widespread area of star formation drapes itself
across the surface of a giant molecular cloud. As when
cloudspotting on Earth, we look for familiar shapes. This
one gives the illusion of a fox fur stole, a simple cone
and an upside down Christmas tree.

It is tempting to think of star formation as a relatively gentle process in which the dense pockets within giant molecular clouds become unstable. As each pocket passes a certain threshold, so it begins to collapse in on itself. In the process, it will fragment into a number of dense cores, each of which eventually becomes a star. If only it were that simple.

___The fact that stars form in collectives suggests that the process must be more complicated than this orderly ideal. Individual stars are capable of interacting with one another, pinching from each other's food stores, and scrumping extra gas from passing cloudlets. Most of this mischief takes place under the cover of darkness, imposed on the youngsters by the shells of dust that incubate

them, but occasionally we can catch a glimpse.
___The youngest stars in NGC 2264 are not yet visible at optical wavelengths, but can be seen in the infrared. They are arranged in spokes. Each one of these stars is a mere 100,000 years old. If they were humans they would not yet have learnt to crawl, let alone walk. So each is still placed exactly where it formed, following the pattern of dense filaments in the surrounding cloud. As time goes by and these stars do move apart, so the radial pattern will disperse and they will begin to vie for supremacy.

___This cluster inhabits just one part of the surrounding cloud. At 30 light years across, the entire region is so large that different parts of the nebula find themselves at different points

in the evolutionary cycle. A seemingly luxuriant region of hydrogen at the top right is known as the Fox Fur Nebula. Taken together, the entire central region is reminiscent of a Christmas tree, but upside down.

___One of the most developed centres is the Cone Nebula towards the bottom of the region [1]. This is a dusty tower, 2.5 light years long, upon which sits a newly born star. Large by the standards of the Sun, this star is slowly eroding away its seat. The dust is blown downwards, forced away by the pressure of the starlight but the gas is driven off by a different process. Once it absorbs enough energy it lifts itself from the dust column, and begins to fluoresce in the ultraviolet glare. Eventually only the densest parts of this dust column will remain.

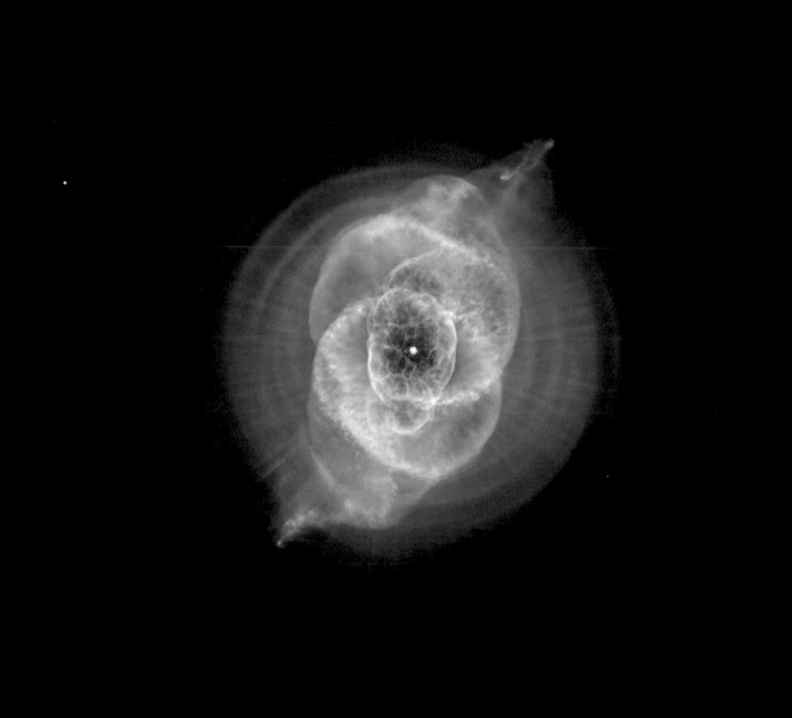

0000.0

LIGHT SECONDS
LIGHT MINUTES
LIGHT YEARS
KILO LIGHT YEARS
MEGA LIGHT YEARS
GIGA LIGHT YEARS

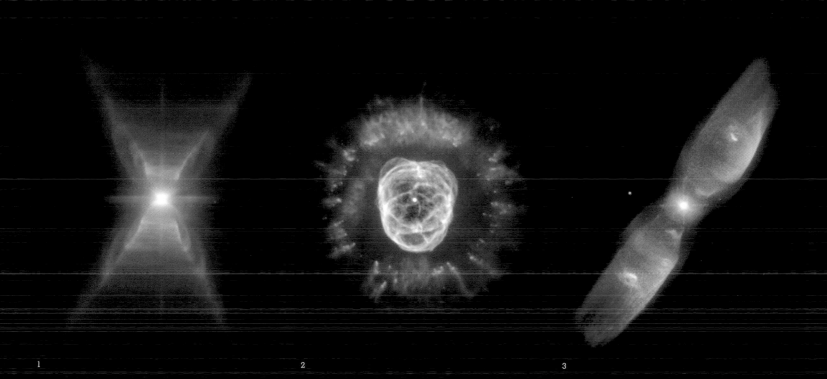

1 2 3

Blaze of glory

<u>The hypnotic spirals of the Cat's Eye Nebula betray a complicated story of protracted stellar death. But as yet, the plot is not completely clear. It seems to involve a sequence of stellar pulsations, tremendous outbursts, and the shadowy influence of a covert companion.</u>

Casting off its outer layers begins the final stellar obsequies. It is thought to be a rather regal process, with the gentle removal of gas and the final revelation of the star's white hot core. Not so in the Cat's Eye Nebula, however.

___The diverse swirls reveal high-speed jets of material cutting through the gossamer sheets, as knots of shocked gas gleam into the darkness. Surrounding the filigree are eleven shells of gas, like a sliced onion, with the Cat's Eye at the centre.

___The onion rings are the oldest components of this complicated structure, having been puffed off by the central star in a series of gentle pulsations. Each one of these slow-motion upheavals lasted 1,500 years, and on every occasion billions of tonnes of gas were lofted into space.

___Initially, the star would have dimmed

cocooned behind concentric layers of cooling gas and dust. Then, about 1,000 years ago, its behaviour abruptly changed. The pulsations ceased and, inside the cocoon, the Cat's Eye began to form. Instead of a uniform release of matter, things became messy. Jets of gas began to squirt like an out-of-control garden hose, and intense ultraviolet light came hurtling forth from the star's exposed inner layers. The effect on the nebula was overpowering: the gaseous shells were driven into frenzy, lighting up in a glorious blaze of florescence.

___The snowflakes of the stellar realm, no two planetary nebulae are the same [1, 2 & 3]. Their colours are determined by the chemical composition and physical condition of the gases but the mechanism behind their intricate patterns is not always clear.

___The Cat's Eye may owe its form to the action of a companion star, orbiting the dying luminary and disturbing the outpouring gases. But if so, why did it only start stirring things up 1,000 years ago when the star had already been out-gassing? Confounding this idea is that there is no observational evidence to support a companion star. If it is there, it remains hidden.

___Could it therefore be smaller, perhaps a planet? If a gas giant planet were to spiral in towards its central star, it might be able to shape the outflow as it fell.

___Interstellar blooms such as the Cat's Eye were famously misnamed planetary nebulae two centuries ago, and the name has stuck despite their clear relation to stars. Perhaps the Cat's Eye has revealed this label wasn't such a misnomer after all.

LIGHT SECONDS
LIGHT MINUTES
LIGHT YEARS
KILO LIGHT YEARS
MEGA LIGHT YEARS
GIGA LIGHT YEARS

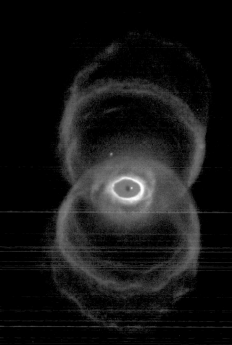

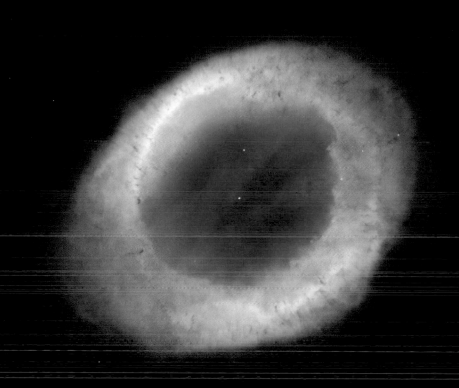

Blowing bubbles

So faint it evaded detection for years, this cosmic 'soap' bubble is the picture-perfect end to the life of a Sun-like star.

Most dying stars like to make a final statement. They transform themselves from points of stellar light into giant gaseous sculptures resembling ants, hour-glasses [1], butterflies, jelly fish... or anything, so long as it contains a semblance of symmetry – like a colourful cosmic inkblot test.

___It is thought these wild variations are dictated somehow by the amount of matter lying in orbit around the star and the faltering way nuclear fusion comes to an end inside the stellar core. It may also have something to do with the way the star generates magnetism.

___A star's magnetic field provides highways and ring roads through its atmosphere for the gases escaping from its surface. The ring roads divert the gas back down toward the surface,

whereas the highways are the magnetic fields that flow out into space. Once any gas is caught in one of these, it is funnelled off the star. If the Sun is anything to go by, these magnetic highways are more prevalent at the rotation poles that at the equator. So dying stars may already have a propensity to expel matter off at the poles.

___However, a small number of nebulae are ring-like. These could be optical illusions created by looking down the breach of an hourglass or elliptically shaped nebula. Such an alignment would be rare but not impossible. The so-called Ring Nebula, M57, is the embodiment of such an alignment [2].

___M57 shines in space with a beautiful concentric ring structure but it is actually a

lozenge-shaped envelope of gas viewed from one of the pointed ends. Only in a handful of cases are these ring nebulae genuine bubbles of gas expanding equally in all directions.

___The Soap Bubble Nebula appears to be the real deal. This apparently perfect bubble of gas hangs in front of an emission nebula where new stars are presently being created. So, in the midst of all this new stellar life, this particular star is dying. The bubble has been expanding into space for thousands of years and will eventually fade away into nothing. It has lived its life, probably standing witness to the Universe for 10 billion years or so. Now its time has come and with poise and dignity, it is exiting the stage before the young celestial turks burst out of their birth clouds

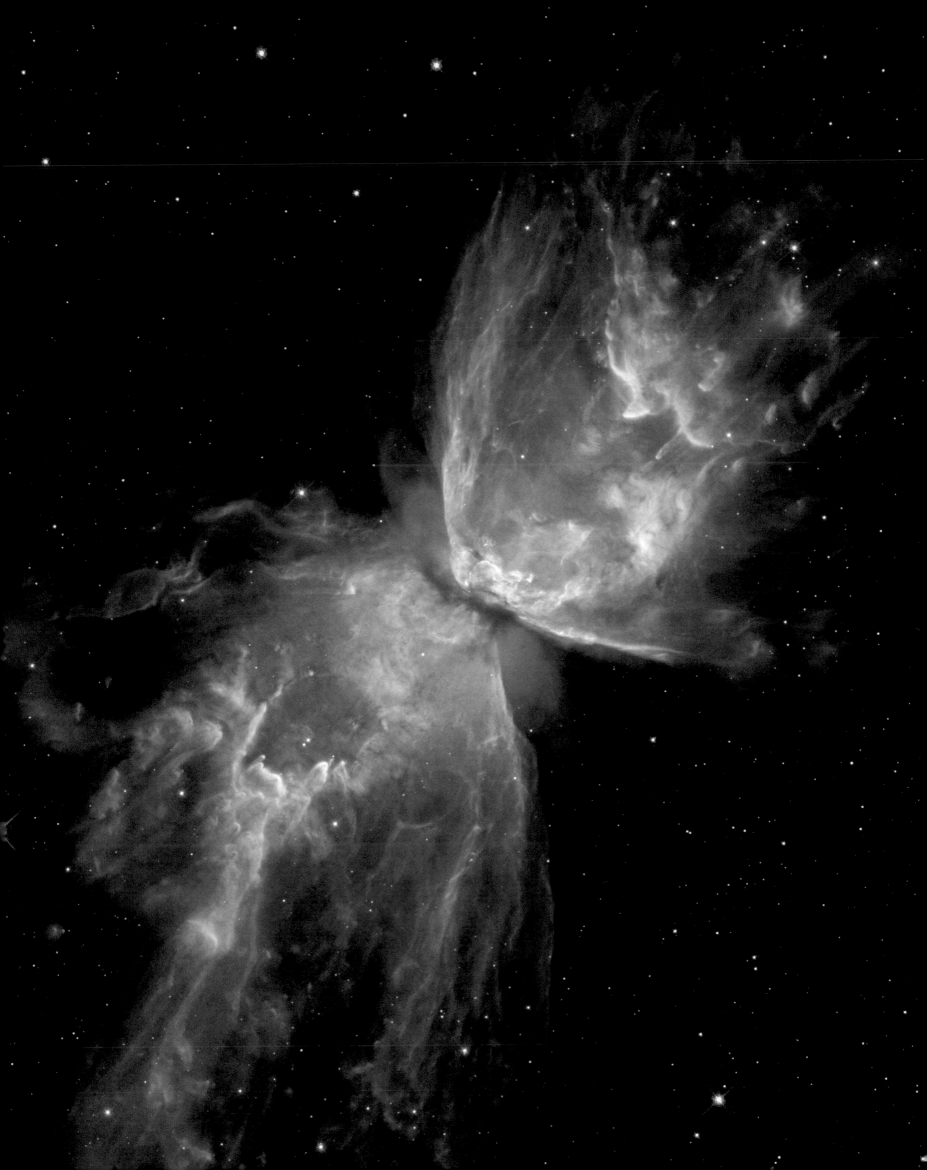

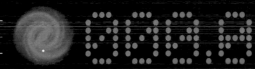

LIGHT SECONDS
LIGHT MINUTES
LIGHT YEARS
KILO LIGHT YEARS
MEGA LIGHT YEARS
GIGA LIGHT YEARS

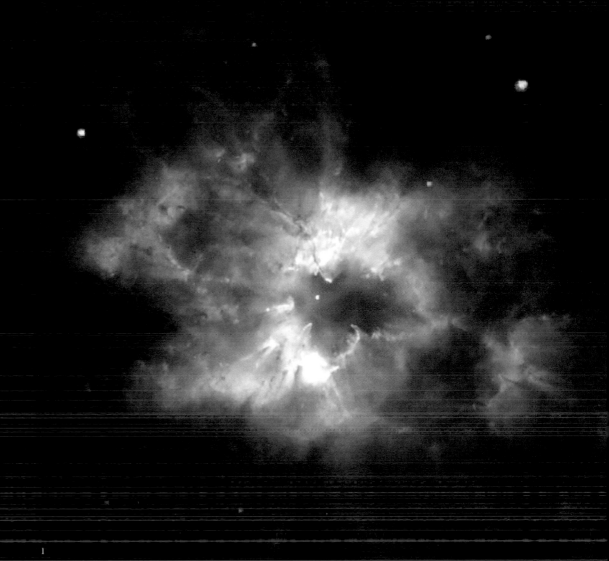

1

Raging butterfly

These dainty butterfly wings are best appreciated from a distance. The gas is tearing through space at more than 270 km/s, having been given a hiding by one of the hottest stars in the galaxy.

Up close, the apparent delicacy of the Butterfly Nebula's wings proves to be an illusion. They are a raging torrent of radiation and atoms, blazing like a moth in a flame. For over 2,000 years, this dying star has been unfurling its wings across space. They are now so large that, were one tip placed by the Sun, the other would reach over halfway to the nearest star.

___The nebula is cinched at the waist, indicating that the star driving this furore must be surrounded by a disc of dust, perhaps even a solar system full of planets. Whatever is there, it is taking the full brunt of this assault, containing the outflow in those directions and giving rise to the butterfly shape.

___The central star is a dense stellar oddment called a white dwarf; although the size of the Earth, it contains the mass of the Sun. It is one of the hottest stars in the galaxy. Measuring a blistering 200,000 °C, it is 35 times hotter than the surface of the Sun.

___Despite this impressive temperature, it is a dull ember compared to what it used to be. Once the forbidding heart of a star, its prodigious nuclear engine, it enjoyed temperatures of 15,000,000 °C.

___It was this fire that the surrounding layers were there to stoke, pressing down on it to keep the nuclear conflagration burning. The outer layers provided a tempering presence on that

searing energy, moulding it into visible light that wouldn't have such a damaging effect on its surroundings. Now those layers have gone, the fires have gone out and the star's slowly cooling heart is laid bare for all to see [1].

___Eventually, the butterfly's wings will fade as the gas drifts off into space and the white dwarf loses its potency. Left on its own, the white dwarf is destined to wander space for the rest of eternity. It will play no further part in the cosmic ecosystem. All the life-giving carbon and the oxygen that could play a role in making habitable planets has been withdrawn, locked firmly by gravity inside the white dwarf.

LIGHT SECONDS
LIGHT MINUTES
LIGHT YEARS
KILO LIGHT YEARS
MEGA LIGHT YEARS
GIGA LIGHT YEARS

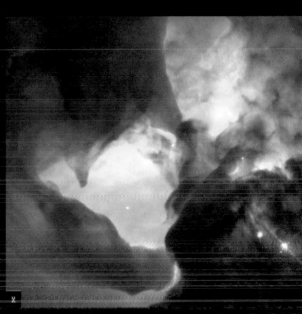

Celestial twisters

Not a blue lagoon, but certainly a vast one. On the scale of the Milky Way Galaxy, a lagoon can be a cloud of glowing gas a hundred light years from shore to shore – where the pebbles are whole stars.

In the depths of the Lagoon Nebula lies a cluster of young stars just 2 million years old, numbering about 100 individuals. These stellar pebbles shine brightly enough to keep the whole cloud in a state of blushing brilliance.

___Contrasting with the bright stars, are dark globules. These are the cocoons of the next generation of stars, patiently incubating before they too are born into the cosmos and radiate their contribution of starlight onto the nebula.

___Inside each globule most of the mass will be in the form of gas composed of individual atoms and molecules set spinning in space. They will be heading for a gravitational rendezvous in its centre that will eventually become a star or two. Only one percent of the

matter exists in the form of dust grains, yet each sub-microscopic speck contains several trillions of atoms. Most importantly, these dust grains will go on to form planets, moons and asteroids around these newly forged stars.

___As yet no one knows whether the pattern of planets in our Solar System, with rocky planets innermost and gaseous planets in the outer regions, is unique or the norm. The extrasolar evidence so far suggests that gas giant planets are often found much closer to their central stars.

___At the very heart of the Lagoon is a particularly large conglomeration of dust and gas where the finishing touches are being applied to another cluster of new stars [1].

Of these stars, Herschel 36 is the patriarch. It shines its intense light on an eerie structure known as the Hourglass Nebula [2]. This is made up of a set of twisted funnels of dusty gas that may be swirling, like whirlpools or tornadoes on Earth. But here they are vastly larger: each celestial twister is around half a light year long.

___Herschel 36 pummels the outer surfaces of the funnels in the Hourglass, heating them while their interiors remain cold. When columns of air in Earth's atmosphere are heated from the outside, developing a large temperature difference from the interior, they begin twisting and turn into tornadoes. The same could be happening here.

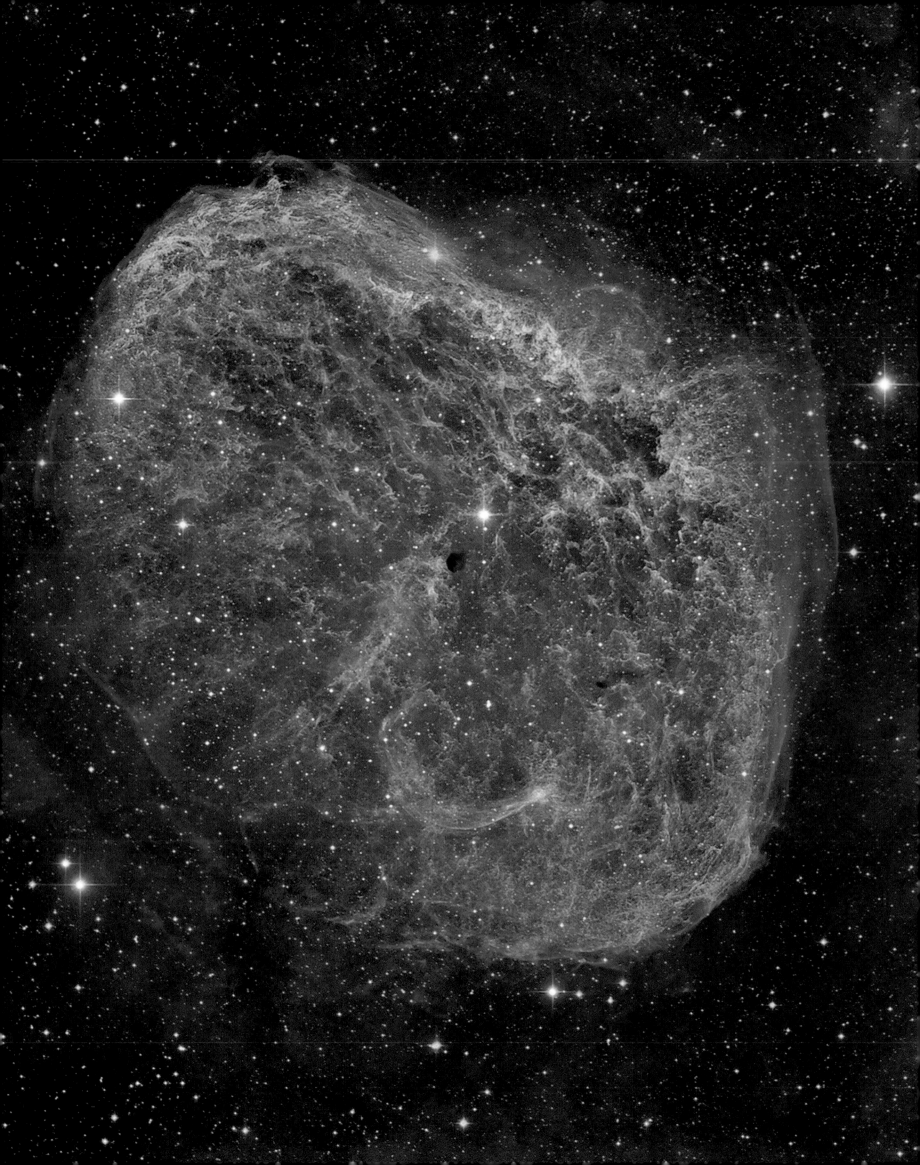

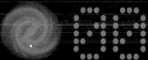

LIGHT SECONDS
LIGHT MINUTES
LIGHT YEARS
KILO LIGHT YEARS
MEGA LIGHT YEARS
GIGA LIGHT YEARS

Wolf at the door

This star is disintegrating before our eyes. Rare and massive, it is burning too brightly and has created the Crescent Nebula from its own lifeblood of hydrogen gas. It can only lead to stellar catastrophe in the form of a supernova.

Live fast, die young. That has to be the motto of this star. At the heart of the Crescent Nebula burns a transitory object called a Wolf-Rayet star. It contains at least 20 times the mass of the Sun and glares into space with a surface temperature not far short of 50,000 °C.

___Unlike most stars, which possess only a tenuous atmosphere of gases, Wolf-Rayet stars have a thick atmosphere, sometimes doubling the extent of the star. This particular example has gone one step further, actually expelling a huge quantity of gas. At its current rate of loss, it is shedding the mass of the Sun every 10,000 years. This is about a billion times faster than the mass loss from a typical star.

___The process began around 250,000 years ago, meaning that there is now as much gas in the nebula as remains in the star: each containing around 25 times the mass of the Sun.

___This extraordinary behaviour comes about because chemical elements such as carbon and oxygen are formed in the centre of the star and then gradually pushed outwards by the irresistible pressure of the escaping radiation. As these heavier chemical elements reach the surface layers they mingle with the transparent hydrogen up there, helping it to catch the light percolating up from below. Just like a kite catching the wind and soaring

upwards, so this lifts the star's outer layers.

___First the process creates an atmosphere and then, if the action is robust enough, it starts to make the star disintegrate. To have enough carbon and oxygen to undertake this act of self-immolation indicates that the nuclear factory at the star's heart is well into production, and that the star is nearing the end of its life.

___This star will become a supernova, blowing itself to smithereens as a result of the nuclear reactions triggered by the core's collapse. When this happens, perhaps sometime in the next few million years, the Crescent Nebula will be swept away, carelessly erased in the most violent fate that can befall a star.

102

LIGHT SECONDS
LIGHT MINUTES
LIGHT YEARS
KILO LIGHT YEARS
MEGA LIGHT YEARS
GIGA LIGHT YEARS

1

Best in show

A shining halo of gas celebrates the birth of a new cluster of stars. The Rosette Nebula is a prominent cloud of star-forming gases, driven into luminescence by the action of its newborn stars, just another battle in the never-ending war between gravity and radiation.

Sitting in a cavity of its own making, the star cluster NGC 2244 floodlights the surrounding gases of its birth nebula. Ten thousand times the mass of the Sun remains in this interstellar swaddling, waiting either to become stars or to be dispersed to obscurity. As ever in the Universe, it is the never-ending fight between gravity and radiation pressure that will determine the outcome.

__Away from the cluster itself, there are patches where gravity appears to be gaining the upper hand. The surrounding Rosette is fringed with towering banks of cloud that glow favorishly in the infrared [1] as new stars make their bid for genesis.

__Hanging above the centre of the main image, at least one of these foetal objects has been revealed prematurely by the retreat of the cloud. It now finds itself in no man's land

hopelessly exposed to the onslaught of ultraviolet radiation and having to make its stand early. It is brandishing a single jet of gas as if it were a sword.

__Harsh rays are tearing at its dusty armour, stripping it away and ensuring that whatever destiny once awaited this star, it will now be born greatly diminished in both mass and intensity. If it loses enough mass it could be stillborn, robbed of its ability to generate its own energy and doomed to spend eternity as a brown dwarf.

__It could even be born as a planetary-sized object, and left to make its way around the galaxy with the much larger, bona-fide stars. Such objects, which resemble planets but travel in orbits like stars are called planetars.

__This particular confrontation will be played out time and time again as the nebula evolves

But the harsh truth is that when individual stars ignite so they turncoat and begin working for the opposition. They contribute their own radiation into the nebula, working against the gravity that has given them life.

__And it is not just radiation, the more massive stars in the nebula produce winds of particles that slam into each other, creating violent shocks that catapult the temperature of the gas to a blistering 6,000,000 °C, helping it escape into space.

__Even if the radiation pressure from the central stars wins this time, and the surrounding gases are flung back into the diffuse interstellar medium, patient gravity will simply begin its work all over again, pulling together the atoms and molecules piece by piece until a new area of star formation takes shape.

LIGHT SECONDS
LIGHT MINUTES
LIGHT YEARS
KILO LIGHT YEARS
MEGA LIGHT YEARS
GIGA LIGHT YEARS

1

2

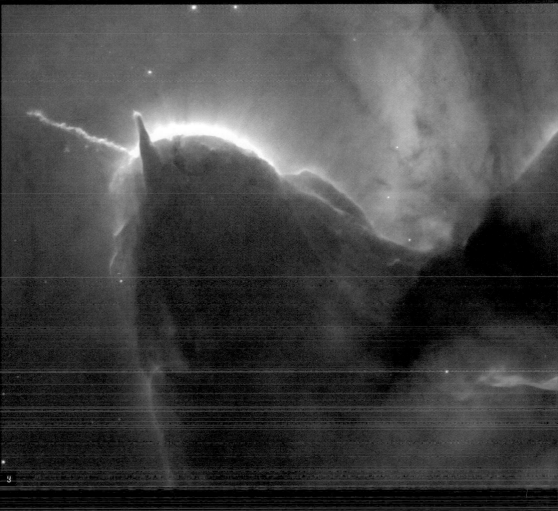

3

Nebulous trinity

Split into three by obscuring dust lanes, the Trifid Nebula is a flashpoint for star formation. Hundreds of newly built stars linger in its interior, creating the differently coloured clouds in this part of space. And there may be more stars on their way.

Smouldering away in the deeper recesses of the Milky Way, the Trifid Nebula combines three different types of nebula into one breathtaking object. There is the pink glow of hydrogen gas that is so characteristic of a stellar nursery where larger stars are being nurtured. Hydrogen is just one of the gases that has been driven into florescence here, sulphur and oxygen have been, too.

Above this emission nebula is a patch of contrasting blue. This is a reflection nebula created not by gas but by the dust in this part of space. It scatters the blue light from the large stars into all directions through space.

Dust shows up in the emission nebula as well, but as the dark lanes of obscuring material that cut the nebula into three. Giving the impression of the lead filigree holding a

stained glass window together, these dark channels are likely to be harbouring more individual pockets of gas that are destined to become stars. Only when the rising density, pressure and temperature inside these gaseous blobs passes the critical threshold, will they start generating energy and metamorphose into stars.

At least three new stars are revealed at the apex of the dust lanes. These are the bright giant stars that are mostly responsible for lighting up the nebulae.

Infrared views of the emission nebula mimic photographic negatives. At longer wavelengths [1], the darkest regions suddenly show up as bright, because the lower temperature of the dust in these areas stimulates them to release infrared rather than optical light. Shorter

wavelengths [2] have allowed the identification of thirty previously unknown stellar embryos in four knots of dusts, and 120 newborn stars – none of which are yet otherwise visible. The biggest of the stellar embryos are always found in the centre of their respective dusty knot, suggesting that the other stars forming around it feed from its leftovers.

In the lower part of the emission nebula, a translucent mountain range appears against the background. A close-up of this region [3] reveals spikes of matter reaching upwards. The longest of these measures three-quarters of a light year. The ends of the spikes have been termed EGGs, for evaporating gaseous globules, and they are the dusty incubators of yet more new stars.

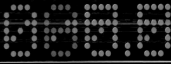

LIGHT SECONDS
LIGHT MINUTES
LIGHT YEARS
KILO LIGHT YEARS
MEGA LIGHT YEARS
GIGA LIGHT YEARS

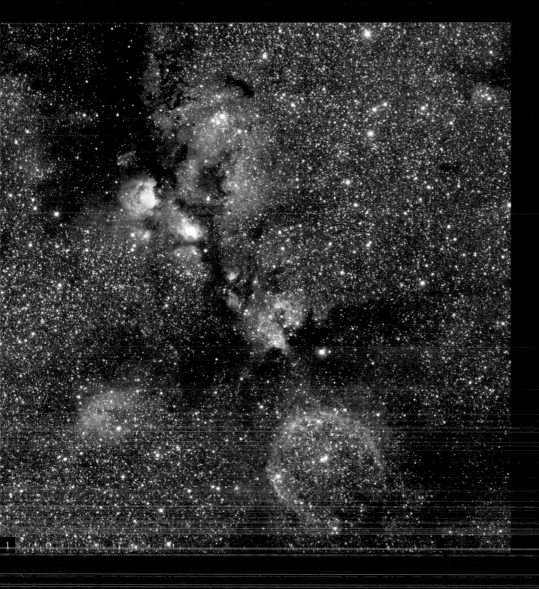

1

Tyger, tyger burning bright

It would have been a large cat indeed that left this paw print. The Cat's Paw Nebula is 60 light years wide and segregated into islands of star formation that give the illusion of the pads on a feline foot. It is the home of tens of thousands of restless stars.

Stars nearly ten times the mass of the Sun have been born in this interstellar cloud during the last few million years. While it is these stellar grandees that snatch the limelight, the region is home to perhaps tens of thousands of smaller stars making it one of the most active nurseries of massive stars in our galaxy.

___The Cat's Paw is buried in the star clouds of the Milky Way, a fact that can be most easily appreciated at infrared wavelengths. Countless stars crowd the view, and rivers of galactic dust seem to flow through this part of space, reaching their confluence at the centre of the Cat's Paw.

___Here the amount of dust is sufficient even to block these wavelengths of infrared light [1], and it is a sure bet that more would-be stars are congregating in this darkness, edging towards their own births.

___The nebula's deep red colour comes not just from the tormented hydrogen in the gas clouds. Lying close to the plane of the Galaxy, the nebula's light must negotiate banks of dust that lie in the 5,500 light years of intervening space between it and Earth. The price of its passage is to lose some of its blue light, hijacked by the dust grains and flung into random directions. Hence, the Cat's Paw's blush becomes deeper.

___One of the most interesting objects in the nebula is the quilted bubble of gases in the bottom right of the image. This is not a signpost of new stellar life, but a warning of impending stellar death. It is the outer layer of a massive star, set free into space by some enormous nuclear upheaval in its central engine. In time, the rest of the star will follow, blasted into space by runaway fusion reactions or the sudden cessation of nuclear activity that triggers the implosion of the star.

___In this avalanche a supernova explosion is generated, and the shockwaves it sends, pummelling into this cloud, will unleash a sudden burst of star formation that completes the process of stellar genesis that gravity had begun.

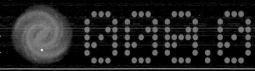

LIGHT SECONDS
LIGHT MINUTES
LIGHT YEARS
KILO LIGHT YEARS
MEGA LIGHT YEARS
GIGA LIGHT YEARS

1

Smoky origins of life

Although not obvious from the appearance of these magnificent looping arches, there is a dreadful form of dirty pollution suffused in this beautiful cloud. The irony is that these noxious substances could be the very stuff that jump-started life on Earth.

Residing in the Sagittarius arm of the Milky Way [1], NGC 3582 is a jumble of stars, some of them young, others nearing the ends of their lives. The giant loops of gas that rise from the nebula are the result of older stars beginning to shed their outer layers into space. The stars responsible will soon be lost to the Universe, collapsed into dense white dwarfs.

___Meanwhile, there is a new generation preparing to take their place. Catalogued as RCW 57, this tight cluster in the centre of the nebula contains more than 30 massive stars. Inevitably there will be hundreds of much smaller stars in here as well, unobservable in the glare of the bigger ones.

___But it's some of the very smallest objects in this cloud that make it most interesting. The

objects are molecules, polycyclic aromatic hydrocarbons to be exact. Such PAHs are families of molecules, each of which is made of rings of carbon atoms. They are the most abundant complex molecules yet discovered in space. We find them on Earth in the exhausts given out by cars, the smoke from forest fires and the charred bits of barbecued meat.

___They can be seen in the tails of comets and have been found in meteorites. They are thought to be a key ingredient in the primordial oceans of Earth. Being composed of carbon atoms, which make up the backbone in life-giving molecules of DNA, they may provide one of the first steps from simply chemistry to life.

___Although not usually soluble in water, the PAHs can be made so with the help of

ultraviolet light. Light wounds the molecule, which then bandages itself up with whatever nearby molecule it can find. Often this will be made of oxygen and hydrogen and, magically, the molecule becomes more soluble.

___But not all the parts of the molecule are comfortable in water. Once submersed, the PAHs form rings to protect their hydrophobic parts, like a wagon train making a circle to protect the interior from attack. As these rings jostle, the transition to long carbon chains could be promoted. If so, a step towards DNA will have been taken.

___While this scenario remains speculative and untested, should it prove to be true, then life may be widespread throughout the Galaxy, because PAHs are everywhere.

110

111

LIGHT SECONDS
LIGHT MINUTES
LIGHT YEARS
KILO LIGHT YEARS
MEGA LIGHT YEARS
GIGA LIGHT YEARS

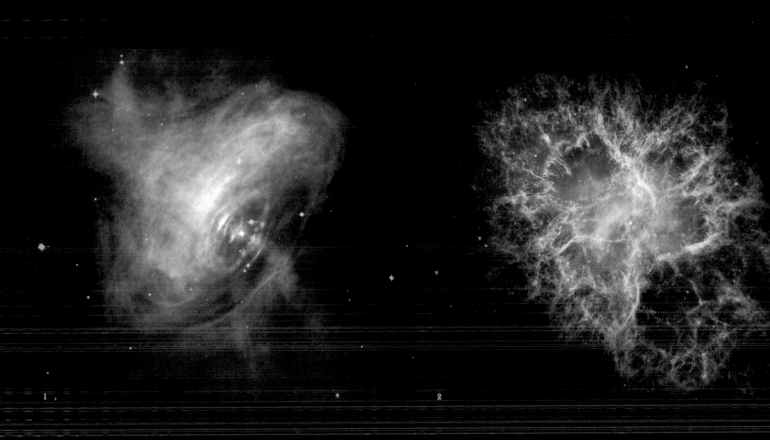

1

2

Back from the dead?

The striking filaments of the Crab Nebula glow as
brightly as they did a thousand years ago, when they
were the freshly detonated remains of a giant star.
What keeps them powered now? A member of the
celestial undead...

This was once a star; all this gas was packed
into a dense spherical volume and generating
energy. Then in AD 1054 the end came. The
core collapsed and the star extinguished
itself in a final blaze of glory. Except that not
everything was blown to pieces: a stellar
cinder of tremendous power remained, and
now it energizes the whole remnant, driving it
to glow as brightly as it did a millennium ago.

___The early life of this supernova remnant
was powered by radioactive decay. The
nuclear conflagration that engulfed the star
provided the maelstrom in which nature's
heaviest elements were forged, including
radioactive isotopes.

___As these isotopes such as nickel-56 and
cobalt-56 decayed, their energy fed the
remnant's appetite and kept it glowing.

The puzzle is that, a thousand years later,
the Crab remains as energetic as ever – it is
75,000 times as luminous as the Sun – long
after it should have begun to fade. Its secret
lies where the star once did, deep inside the
Crab, where a new engine is at work.

___It seems barely credible that anything
could survive a supernova – several hundred
billion stars' worth of energy discharged in
one fell swoop. Yet the star's core rode the
storm, although not without terrific cost: it
lives on as a stellar zombie, or a neutron star.

___Most of the matter from the star's former
heart remains – some three times the mass
of our Sun – but it is now compressed into a
sphere just 20 km across, and it more closely
resembles a single, large-scale atomic nucleus
than a collection of atoms. It is so dense that a

single teaspoon of neutron star weighs more
than 5 billion tonnes and its surface gravity is
200 billion times stronger that Earth's – an object
dropped from a height of one metre above a
neutron star would hit its surface moving at
7.2 million km/h.

___This particular example is a species of
neutron star known as a pulsar, a highly
magnetized body spinning in a breathtaking
pirouette that it completes 30.2 times a second.
As it turns, it acts as a dynamo, accelerating
particles to near light speed before spitting
them out into the nebula to reinvigorate the
remnant's debris clouds. X-ray wavelengths
reveal [1] the swirling disc that surrounds the
furiously rotating neutron star, while a multi-
wavelength [2] image puts it into context with
what we can see with our own eyes.

LIGHT SECONDS
LIGHT MINUTES
LIGHT YEARS
KILO LIGHT YEARS
MEGA LIGHT YEARS
GIGA LIGHT YEARS

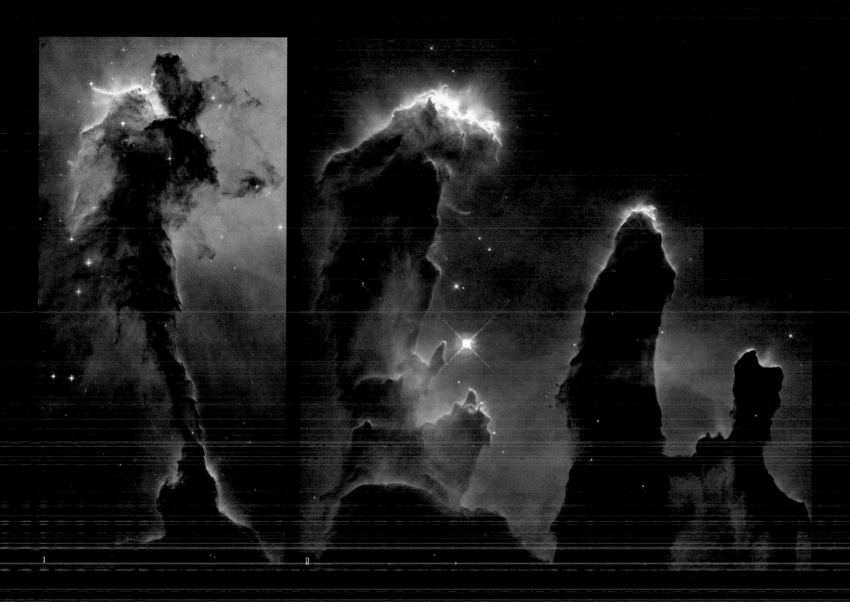

1   0

Soaring though space

The Eagle Nebula soars through the Milky Way, its gaseous wings outstretched and its colourful plumage on proud display. Its magical eggs will hatch one day not into birds but fully fledged stars.

This particular Eagle is a fearsome beast. Four iconic pillars of dust [1 & 2] nearly 10 light years tall pierce the nebula's clear heart like outstretched talons. All point towards the burning heart of a star cluster, NGC 6611 – the Eagle hatched these stars 1 million years ago.

   Recently, the dark pillars have been found to contain a number of would-be stars. These are the latecomers who have largely missed the party because star formation in the Eagle Nebula is winding down.

   To reinforce this, there are numerous sources of X-rays that dot this nebula. It is most likely that these powerful invisible rays are coming from young stars but they do not appear to be embedded within the dusty pillars. Instead, they are the product of an intermediate round of star formation. When they were just hatching this clutch of stellar eggs would have released so much radiation that the Eagle would likely have spread its wings even further across space.

   From that peak of star formation, 1 million years ago, the trend has been downwards. These days the nebula is on its last legs, with disaster approaching.

   The pillars themselves were carved from a larger, denser portion of the nebula and even now they continue to be visibly eroded. The onslaught is from the ultraviolet light of the nearby star cluster and produces a fringe of yellow light at the top of each pillar. Yet this is nothing compared to the assault racing up from behind.

   The oncoming catastrophe takes the shape of an enormous bubble of super-heated gas. The blast has come from a supernova and it will slam into the pillars in about a thousand years from now. When this barrage hits them, they will topple as they do not contain enough matter to withstand the attack. The pillars will be washed away as if they were sandcastles defending a beach against the incoming tide.

   The Eagle's days are numbered, there is no way for it to fly out of harm's way.

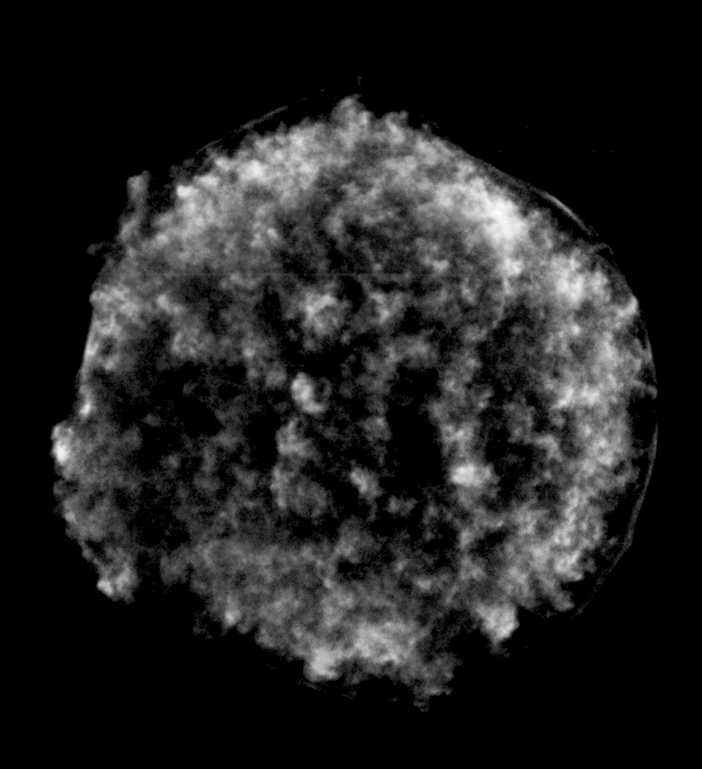

LIGHT SECONDS
LIGHT MINUTES
LIGHT YEARS
KILO LIGHT YEARS
MEGA LIGHT YEARS
GIGA LIGHT YEARS

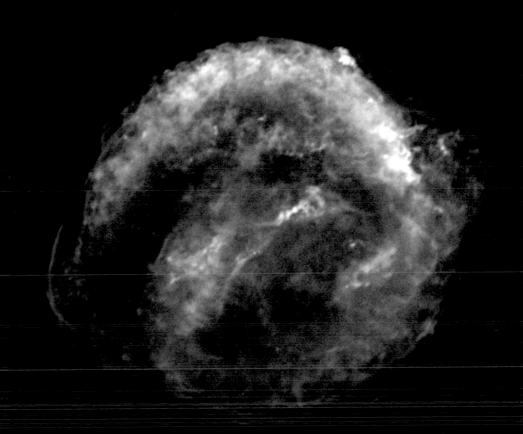

1

The collapse of certainty

This celestial object changed our view of the Universe forever. It was 1572; its unexpected birth – and one man's observation of it – triggered the collapse of 2,000 years of received astronomical wisdom, leading to astronomy as we know it today.

Danish nobleman Tycho Brahe was kidnapped at birth by a jealous uncle, lost the bridge of his nose in a teenage duel, and became the despotic ruler of Hveen Island. He was also the greatest naked-eye astronomer the world has ever known.

___His revelation took place in November 1572, almost four decades before telescopes were invented. Waxed moustache drooping from beneath his disfigured nose, Tycho glanced skyward and saw a new star shining through the chill winter air. Burning more brightly than any other star, not even daylight could drive this stellar herald from the sky. It produced consternation across Europe.

___According to the astrological thinking of the time, an additional celestial influence could only foretell swingeing change and new political landscapes. In England, Elizabeth I

summoned her astrologers. Brahe, himself, said it presaged fatal times ahead. Yet it was not kingdoms that fell, but Aristotle's dogmatic view of the Universe.

___According to the ancient Greek, change could only take place below the orbit of the Moon. This view was absorbed into Christian belief as an indication that the Universe was God's perfect creation and therefore incapable of changing, because any alteration would drive it away from perfection. Only on the Earth, then thought to be the centre of the Universe, was corrupting change possible.

___Tycho shattered this belief by measuring the position of the new star night after night, week after week, month after month and finding that it stayed resolutely fixed in the pattern of distant stars, proving that it was at the same distance they were. Any closer to

Earth and it would have drifted across the background of fixed stars as the planets do.

___The revelation that the Universe could change emboldened astronomers. Until then everything had seemed so certain. Now they saw that the Universe was in a state of flux. German mathematician Johannes Kepler embodied the new astronomy, questioning 2,000 years of received astronomical wisdom, including the position of the Earth in space. Ironically, Tycho himself never believed that Earth moved.

___In 1604 Kepler spotted his own supernova [1]. Looking in the direction of these stars, we see their superheated remains even today. Although the loss of a star or two is nothing to the Universe, thanks to Tycho's observations and Kepler's mathematics, human perception of the cosmos was changed forever.

LIGHT SECONDS
LIGHT MINUTES
LIGHT YEARS
KILO LIGHT YEARS
MEGA LIGHT YEARS
GIGA LIGHT YEARS

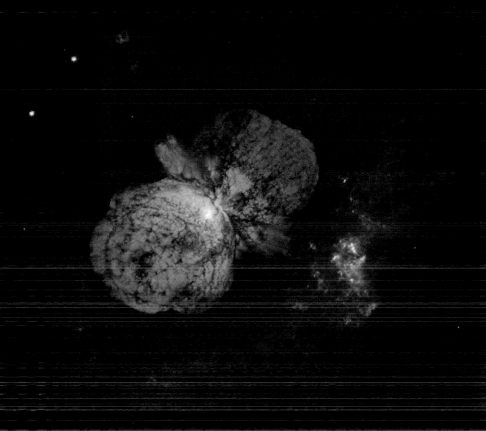

1

2

Hyperstar

Eta Carinae is no ordinary star. Called a blue hypergiant, it is one of the rarest in the Universe. Bulging with between 120–150 times the mass of the Sun, it rages with a luminosity almost 2 million times greater.

Eta Carinae is encased within a dumbbell-shaped nebula [1] that makes up little more than a spot on low centre of the large-scale image opposite. Nevertheless, the star has carved out an expanding bubble and daubed the walls with the opulent colours of energized interstellar gas. The nebula is immense [2] – the inner region alone covers 53 light years – yet it is all that remains of a once even larger giant molecular cloud.

___There are only a few dozen stars like Eta Carinae known to exist in the Galaxy today but 13 billion years ago, they may have been the only kind of stars that could form.

___Back in those ancient days, the chemical composition of the Universe was almost entirely

hydrogen and helium. Without any heavier elements, the clouds of gas in space would find it difficult to cool down and collapse into stars, so they just got bigger and bigger. Eventually, they contained so much mass that gravity became overwhelming and forced the giant cloud together, producing extremely massive stars. Some of these stellar mammoths could have swollen to hundreds or even a thousand times the mass of the Sun.

___Almost totally unstable, they would have blown themselves to pieces in just a million years or so, but not before their rapacious nuclear engines had converted about half a percent of the bulk into heavier chemical elements. These were blasted across space

in the resulting detonation and created a seasoning of heavier chemicals that stabilized the whole process of star formation.

___They helped the gas clouds radiate energy more easily, making them collapse into the next generation of stars before they reached such gargantuan proportions. So these days, the megastars have largely vanished, replaced by long-lived stars that use their time and energy rather more judiciously than their forebears.

___Nevertheless, Eta Carinae reminds us what these flamboyant individuals must have been like. The cosmos would have been a more dangerous place, but with each one blasting a million times the light of the Sun into space, it would certainly not have been dull.

1   2

Accident of birth

This moustachioed promontory hides a star approaching
adulthood. It will probably be similar to the Sun and,
if so, would have a life expectancy of around 9 billion
years. But it won't live that long. Through no fault of its
own, it is doomed to die in a tiny fraction of that time:
less than 10 million years.

This star along with dozens of hidden siblings
revealed only in infrared [1] is forming within
the last vestiges of the Carina Nebula. The
hurricane blast of nearby Eta Carinae's stellar
wind and its blistering ultraviolet radiation has
compressed the surrounding walls of hydrogen
[2] and other gases so much that it has forced
a second round of star formation. Within this
three-light-year-long mountain of dust lies a
young star, almost ready to be born.

___The first sign of its impending arrival is
the moustache of light that the promontory
is wearing. The two halves are jets created by
the star's magnetic field, and they are fuelled
by matter from its surroundings that has been
busily making planets. They will drill away
at this dusty outcrop from within, gradually

whittling it away until the star can shine its
light freely across space for the first time.

___On one side the jet has entered a zone of
denser gas and this has resulted in a curved
bow shock, a kind of sonic boom that rolls
through the interstellar gas. On the other side
there is no such structure, indicating that this
region is largely empty.

___When the jets complete their work, and the
star comes into view, it is likely to be a yellow,
sun-like star that may shepherd a solar system
of planets. There could even be an Earth-like
world complete with breathable atmosphere
and life.

___But all of it is doomed; not because of any
flaw in its make-up but because of the accident
of its birth so close to Eta Carinae. When

the nearby giant star rips itself to shreds as a
supernova the current stellar wind will appear
sweet by comparison.

___Gross energy will tear through space,
abrading all the stars and planets that it
sweeps across. Even if the atmosphere of the
planets is not completely sandblasted away,
any protective ozone layer will be disintegrated
by the hellish radiation from the supernova.

___Giant supernovae, called gamma ray
bursts, may be capable of emitting enough
radiation to sterilize a whole galaxy. Thankfully
for the rest of the stars and planets in the Milky
Way, not even Eta Carinae is big enough to
create a gamma ray burst.

LIGHT SECONDS
LIGHT MINUTES
LIGHT YEARS
KILO LIGHT YEARS
MEGA LIGHT YEARS
GIGA LIGHT YEARS

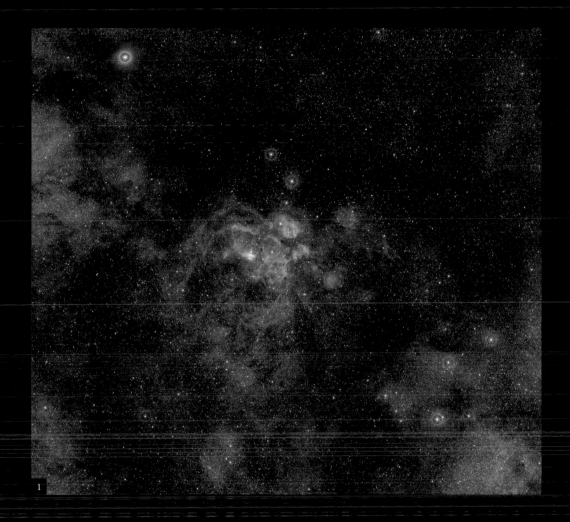

1

Double trouble

A young star cluster hurls its abrasive light into the nebula that gave it life. It has hewn out great pillars of dust that soar upwards, while pushing the rest of the cloud into full retreat. The leader of the attack is the giant star Pismis 24-1, a star whose mass apparently defies reason.

Almost a third of the way towards the Galactic centre, NGC 6357 [1] gave birth to the Pismis 24 star cluster no more than a million or two years ago. The stars immediately turned on their natal cloud, shredding it with radiation. The leader of the attack is Pismis 24-1, the brightest of the stars in the cluster. This titan has all the characteristics of a star containing 200–300 times the mass of the Sun. But if it were truly this big, not only would it be the most massive star in the Galaxy, it would also create a giant scientific headache because such stars are thought to be impossible in the present-day Milky Way Galaxy.

___With the smattering of heavy chemical elements that now exists in the Milky Way, a collapsing gas cloud finds itself less able to resist gravity and so falls together more quickly.

stellar behemoths that do manage to emerge lead fitful lives, producing such powerful bursts of energy that they end up coughing and spluttering their outer layers into space. Yet this apparently monstrous star is not surrounded by bubbles of gas and looks entirely stable.

___The mystery is explained because Pismis 24-1 is actually two stars, locked together by gravity, but otherwise separate entities. They are still giants, each containing at least 100 solar masses. Individually, that makes them rare; together the pair could be unique in the Galaxy.

___For every one star created containing 65 solar masses or more, an estimated 18,000 stars similar to the Sun will form. Since giant stars live for only 3 million years or so, while their Sun-like counterparts survive for around 10 billion, there are millions of solar mass stars for each massive

___In fact, there is another 100-solar mass star elsewhere in this small cluster, making it a true oddity in the Galaxy. Regardless of how three such massive stars were born in such close proximity, the trio are destined to end their lives in spectacular explosions that will destroy the remains of the nebula. As each star goes supernova, so they will leave behind collapsed cores in the form of either neutron stars or black holes.

___The two black holes or neutron stars locked together in Pismis 24-1 could then go on to spiral into one another creating another almighty explosion, greater than their original supernovae.

___Despite the apparently peaceful scene, stellar heavyweights such as Pismis 24-1 are the Galaxy's real troublemakers.

122

LIGHT SECONDS
LIGHT MINUTES
LIGHT YEARS
KILO LIGHT YEARS
MEGA LIGHT YEARS
GIGA LIGHT YEARS

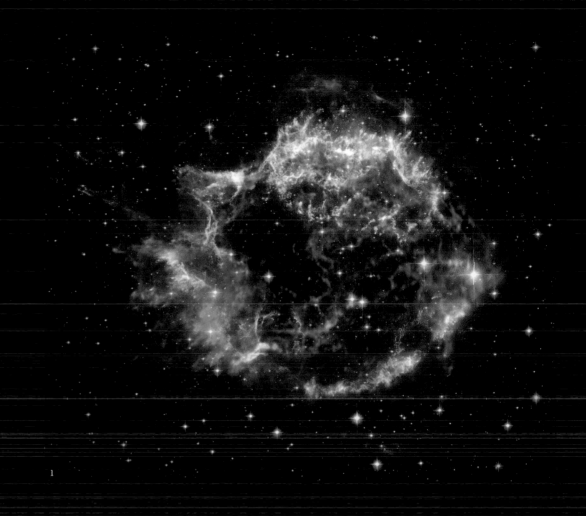

1

Ghost supernova

Although no one saw this star's colossal flare up,
it is more than making up for it today. Visible as a
tracery of shockwaves, it screams into the void at
radio frequencies. Although more than 300 years
old, it is still pelting Earth with smashed atoms.

By all rights, when this star exploded during the mid 17th century, it should have lit up the night sky and probably been visible through daylight, too. Yet there are no records that tell of it gracing the heavens.

____This could be because the star had a false start, coyly surrounding itself with a thick shell of gases after a failed supernova ignition. Later, the star mustered the energy to try again and this time, it succeeded. Its self-destructive ambition tore it to pieces but, to the outside Universe, the intense burst of light was blocked from view by the surrounding shroud of matter.

____Then later still, the blast slammed into the surrounding shell, heating its gases to temperatures of 10,000,000 °C and driving them into a frenzy of emission. Colour coded images taken at a variety of wavelengths [1] reveal the entire blast zone is roiling with clouds of oxygen, sulphur, hydrogen, nitrogen,

neon and aluminium. But this elemental bounty is not the only thing speeding outward from a supernova.

____As the shockwave tumbles outwards, brutally compressing the gas in its path, ambient magnetic fields are squeezed and amplified. Its impact shatters atoms, revealing their electrical charges and making them susceptible to the amplified magnetic fields. As a result, particles stripped by the shockwave can suddenly find themselves accelerated to enormous speeds, transformed into cosmic rays.

____They shoot across the Galaxy, immediately outpacing the shockwave. With no friction in space to slow them down, the cosmic rays speed on, constituting an interstellar radiation field of enormous power.

____Those that happen to be heading in our direction can hit Earth's atmosphere with a

billion times the energy of a particle produced in even the most powerful of man-made particle accelerators. When they strike the molecules in Earth's blanket of gases, they produce a sudden flash of light and burst into a shower of secondary particles, summoned into existence by the sudden release of the cosmic ray's energy.

____As these cascade downwards, they may even trigger discharges of atmospheric electricity that give rise to the forks of lightning seen in thunderstorms.

____High-flying humans are directly affected too. When astronauts close their eyes, they often see faint flashes of light. Each tiny flare is the result of a cosmic ray colliding with a molecule in their eyeball — the pale ghost of a supernova hundreds, or even thousands, of light years away.

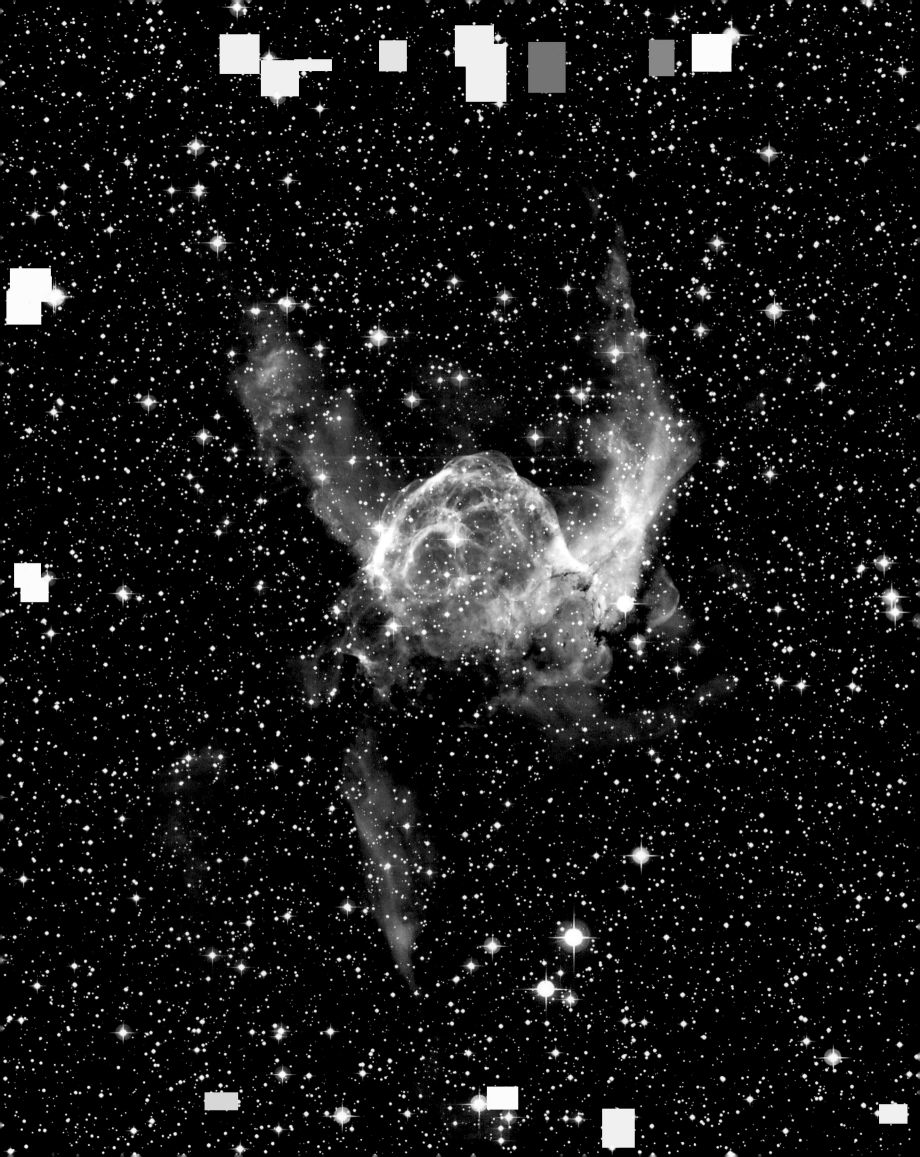

Final performance

Donning a suitably Wagnerian helmet, this stellar actor is embarking on the role it has always been destined to play. This star will soon become a supernova: a once-in-a-lifetime performance.

It may look as if this blue giant star has already exploded, but in fact this is just the first act in a play with an altogether more violent climax. The star has been preparing for this role since it was born. The moment it garnered more than eight times the mass of the Sun, its fate was sealed. And this one went even further, accumulating more than 20 times the Sun's bulk. and now, it is using this great bulk to light up the heavens.

  Flayed by a stellar wind billions of times of stronger than our Sun's, this star is laying itself bare to its audience of stellar spectators. The first act requires that it casts off the layer of nitrogen and oxygen-rich gases that kept it powered during its youth. this is the material responsible

for most of the 30-light-year dome that bubbles and boils around the star here.

  In the next act it will expel layers of carbon-rich gas, remnants of its helium-fusing days. This excruciating striptease is a reminder that age is cruel to massive stars. They are forced to consume heavier and heavier fuels just to keep going. They start on hydrogen, move to helium, then carbon, oxygen and silicon, each transition coming quicker and quicker as they move up the periodic table. The end of the road is iron. No star can fuse iron nuclei. With nothing to burn its nuclear furnaces go out and the star abandons itself to gravity.

  Given free reign, gravity crushes the star's core into the exotic stuff of neutron stars. Such

an instant metamorphosis unleashes a prodigious shockwave and a multi-billion degree blaze of radiation that will rip the star open in a matter of hours and flood the heavens with light. This is the big one, the role this stellar heavyweight was always destined to play: that of the leading star in the Galaxy.

  For a few weeks it will shine with the light of hundreds of billions of stars, a final incandescent soliloquy. When the epilogue is over, and its brilliance has faded from the celestial stage, rest assured there will be another star waiting in the wings, preparing for its own once-in-a-lifetime starring performance.

LIGHT SECONDS
LIGHT MINUTES
LIGHT YEARS
KILO LIGHT YEARS
MEGA LIGHT YEARS
GIGA LIGHT YEARS

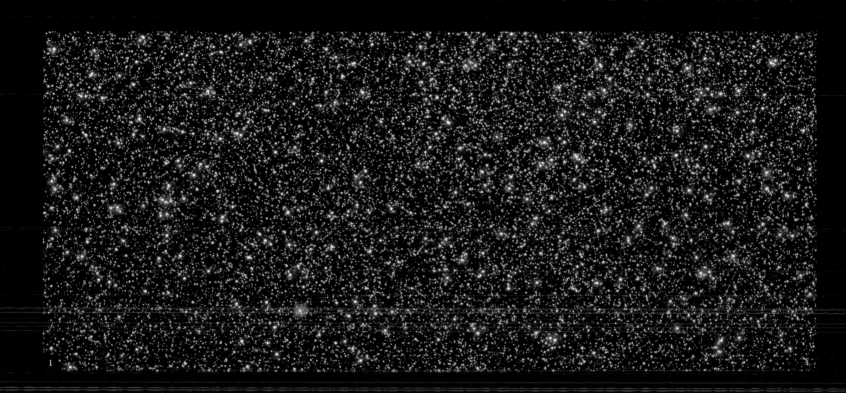

1

Methuselah's metropolis

This gleaming swarm rests in silent witness to the Milky Way. In its core 10 million stars are united by gravity and huddled together into a sphere just 160 light years across. It's a relic from a time gone by and hides a dark secret in its core.

Located beyond the main sweep of stars in our Galaxy, Omega Centauri is the largest of 150 such swarms that circle the Galaxy. Each formed in antiquity, the globular clusters have seen the Milky Way grow and evolve, as they themselves have aged.

The stars in Omega Centauri are all billions of years old, glowing with the distinctive golden hue of maturity. Some are more advanced, swollen to enormous size and turned red in a final blush of glory before the inevitable collapse into obscurity.

All traces of star formation are long gone from this cluster: no inky black cocoons to harbour stellar embryos, no rippling nebulae of light to draw attention to the nascent star clusters. Instead, it suffers the inexorable slide into oblivion, the cluster growing ever older, its stellar population diminishing one by one.

But look more closely and there is a paradox.

Lurking within this astral Methuselah are blue stars – their colour a clear sign of stellar youth [1]. Yet with no star forming regions to have given birth to them, what power lies within to rejuvenate the stars?

The fountain of stellar youth turns out to be the density of the cluster. This tightly knit community is crowded together, each star roughly 13 times closer to the next than our Sun is to its nearest neighbour. Standing on a planet in this stellar metropolis would be a never forgotten experience, with the night sky full of stars – and as bright as day.

Jostled together, stellar collisions are commonplace. Each titanic impact results not in the destruction of the stars but in their merger, stoking the now combined nuclear furnace with new fuel and giving the illusion

of stellar youth, as the celestial fire rages.

But, is Omega Centauri hiding yet another secret? A much larger secret? The stars in its very heart are racing round their orbits, tormented by the gravitational grip of a large black hole, tens of thousands of times the mass of our Sun. This betrays Omega Centauri as a chimera, because true globular clusters don't have black holes, they are not large enough.

The resolution to the mystery is that Omega Centauri is probably a dwarf galaxy that strayed too close to the Milky Way. Like a bird that has had its flight feathers clipped, so this galaxy has had most of its outer stars ripped away, leaving just the core and a superficial resemblance to a globular cluster. Robbed of its stars and orbital energy, Omega Centauri is now trapped in a gravitational cage of the Milky Way's making.

LIGHT SECONDS
LIGHT MINUTES
LIGHT YEARS
KILO LIGHT YEARS
MEGA LIGHT YEARS
GIGA LIGHT YEARS

Family fortunes

Two whole clusters of stars are popping into view from this molecular cloud, provoking the surrounding hydrogen and oxygen gas into a brilliant display of colour. The newly smelted families of stars are so powerful that they now control the cloud's fate, helping to disperse its remains back into space.

Stars never form in isolation. As huge clouds of dust and gas reach a critical density the process of gravitational collapse is initiated. As the cloud contracts, particular knots collapse faster that their surroundings and these kernels become the hotbeds of star formation. Typically, stars are born in families of a few tens to several thousand individuals.

About half of these stars will be locked into a gravitational dance with one or more of their neighbours. These binary and multiple stars are destined to spend their entire lives together, endlessly circling each other. In systems of three or more stars, a pair tends to form in the centre and then the other stars revolve around them. Sometimes the dance is more complex: in quadruple star systems, two orbiting couples also pirouette around each other.

Those siblings not locked into the gravitational dance will slowly drift away into their own separate orbits around the centre of the Galaxy. Eventually it becomes impossible to tell which stars were born together.

So many stars speckle this image that it is difficult to pick out the two newest-born star clusters. One sits directly in the centre, the other resides in a patch of pink gas to its right. Together with the brightest star near the bottom left of the image, they are sculpting the rest of this nebula.

The dark dust lanes that criss-cross the nebula are places of future star formation but the glowing gas is probably destined to miss out this time. Typically, only around 10 percent of the matter in a cloud of gas is transformed into stars. The rest is set glowing by the newborns and dissipated by their copious radiation. This unwanted gas returns to the diffuse reaches of interstellar space where, in time, it will be press-ganged into a new molecular cloud; ready to take its chances in another round of star formation.

LIGHT SECONDS
LIGHT MINUTES
LIGHT YEARS
KILO LIGHT YEARS
MEGA LIGHT YEARS
GIGA LIGHT YEARS

1

Band of brothers

A collection of stellar jewels peeps out of its hydrogen
birth cloud. Just another in a long line of such young star
clusters? Not so, this one is special; its stars are packed
so tightly that this could be one of the rarest sights in the
whole Universe.

The young stars of NGC 3603 are crammed
together, more than 10,000 in a central volume
with a diameter of just 3.5 light years. Back at
the start of our journey, near the Sun, such a
volume of space contains just one star – the
Sun – with its nearest neighbour sited 4.3 light
years away.

___At this density, the stars of NGC 3603
conjure up so much mutual gravity that it
is unlikely that they will ever let go of one
another. Most young star clusters float apart,
with each individual star eager to make its
own way in the Universe. Once free from
their siblings, the stars merge into the general
stellar population of the Milky Way, eventually
making it impossible to recognize other
members from the same family.

___This is not the future that awaits NGC 3603;
they will always be bound together. And that's
a puzzle because the only star clusters that
behave in this way are the globular clusters,
stellar brotherhoods that orbit the centre of the
Milky Way, but in tilted orbits usually far from
the plane of the Galaxy.

___So could this star cluster be a newly minted
globular cluster? Maybe, and if so it is one
of the rarest sights in the Universe because,
of the 150 globulars that orbit the Milky Way,
all appear uniformly ancient, having formed
around 12 billion years ago at the same time
as the Milky Way. In short, there are no recent
globular clusters around the Milky Way,
certainly none with a birthday measured
just a few million years ago as is this case.

___NGC 3603 is small compared to a true
globular cluster, nevertheless it represents
an exceptional event: a giant gas cloud,
supremely dense [1], that collapsed together
in a sudden fit of star formation, and has now
produced a modern simulacrum of a globular
cluster. Only in the case of massive collisions
between galaxies can we sometimes see newly
formed globulars, recognizable from a great
distance because of their bright blue colours.
Now, we appear to have one on our cosmic
doorstep.

___Whatever triggered this star cluster to form,
it is a glimpse of a process mainly long gone
from the cosmos. As such, this peculiarly dense
star cluster may be showing us what happened
before our Galaxy was even born.

LIGHT SECONDS
LIGHT MINUTES
LIGHT YEARS
KILO LIGHT YEARS
MEGA LIGHT YEARS
GIGA LIGHT YEARS

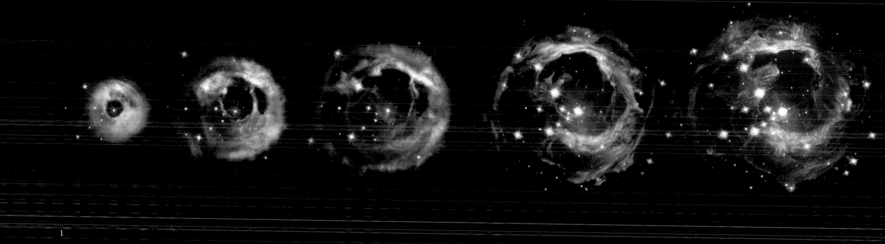

1

Cannibal star

The unexpected bloom of this stellar rose is a celestial
mystery staring us in the face. No ordinary stellar
explosion, instead of fading away as normal, it
became weirder and weirder. Now the conclusion is
inescapable, this is a cannibal star – but what did it eat?

V838 Monocerotis, as this star was hurriedly
named, came from nowhere. In spite of all
the telescopes and the surveys that now scan
the heavens, it had evaded detection until its
flare-up on 6 January 2002. In March, just as it
was fading back into obscurity, it erupted again,
then once more in April. From total obscurity it
transformed itself into one of the most luminous
stars in the whole Galaxy, pumping out a million
times the power of the Sun.

___When finally it disappeared from view, it
reinvented itself and began emitting most of
its energy in the infrared region of the spectrum.
If our eyes could have seen in the infrared
the star would have pierced the glare of our
daylight skies.

___The star swelled up as the mysterious
eruption continued until, by October 2002,
it was so bloated that if it were to replace the
Sun, its outer layers would reach the orbit
of Jupiter. Not only that but the light from the
eruption began to reflect off giant mantles of
gas that had been shrouding the star, giving
it the appearance of an enormous celestial
rose blooming in space [1].

___Clearly this was no ordinary stellar
explosion. Only one explanation fitted such
bizarre behaviour: a collision in which the
star ate a smaller companion. And a planet
wasn't big enough to unleash such havoc;
only another star would do.

___In this apocalyptic scenario, the first

outburst took place when a large star, perhaps
eight times the mass of the Sun, was clipped by
a smaller companion, about one-third the Sun's
mass. The smaller star survived only to return
a month later, resulting in the second outburst.
This robbed the smaller star of so much orbital
energy that it limped around once more before
plunging to its doom. The third encounter
ripped it to shreds and surrounded the main
star with its debris, creating the cool, bloated
object of October 2002.

___How many stars in our Galaxy collide like
this? Very few it would seem. Erupting stars
that share similarities with this one come along
rarely: perhaps one in 1994 and another in
the 1670s.

MILKY WAY CORE
DIAMETER: 10,000 LY

LIGHT SECONDS
LIGHT MINUTES
LIGHT YEARS
KILO LIGHT YEARS
MEGA LIGHT YEARS
GIGA LIGHT YEARS

1

Galactic hubbub

We finally arrive at the hub of the Milky Way, a seething
maelstrom of ancient stars surrounded by towering arcs
of dust and gas sculpted by stellar winds, magnetic fields,
tidal forces and shockwaves.

Forever barred from view at visible wavelengths
because of the swathes of dust that lie between
us [1], the centre of the Galaxy nevertheless
blazes with light in the more exotic parts of
the spectrum. It is the kernel around which
everything has been built during the last
12 billion years. It is the original seed that
condensed out of the primordial ocean of gas
that filled the Universe. Like the fledglings
of Earth's spring season, it is largely down to
luck that it has survived long enough to grow
to full adulthood.

___In the beginning there were no large
galaxies. Just like all babies, galaxies began
small and grew bigger. They did it in one of two
ways, either they fed off passing clouds of gas,
eating sparingly over the aeons and building
new stars at a sustainable rate, or they were

gluttons and cannibalized other galaxies.
In the latter case, they wanted it all right there
and then. They hid their victim's stars amongst
their own and used any spare gas quickly,
mixing it with their own and transforming it
into a sudden raft of new stars.

___Our Milky Way was more inclined
towards the careful line, growing steadily to
prominence, and the gravity of this central
region was responsible for this circumspect
behaviour. In the process, it crafted the spiral
pattern of arms that the Sun sits within.

___Now the core forms the gravitational
fulcrum of the Milky Way, providing the
massive hub around which the curved spokes
of the Galaxy rotate. The bestiary of stars that
populate the central region swarms across
this part of space.

___Within the central three light years of the
Galaxy's centre there are thousands of stars,
most of them are extremely long-lived, having
been formed in ancient times. This is confirmed
by the fact that they contain only small
amounts of the chemical elements heavier
than hydrogen and helium. As these elements
are the ones to build up in space with each
successive generation of stars, paucity is a
clear sign of having been born early in the
Galaxy's history.

___But not all the stars found here are ancient.
There are more than 100 examples of high-
mass stars, all short-lived individuals that must
have been created within the last few million
years. It is somewhat ironic that the oldest part
of the Galaxy contains the largest single
collection of young stars.

LIGHT SECONDS
LIGHT MINUTES
LIGHT YEARS
KILO LIGHT YEARS
MEGA LIGHT YEARS
GIGA LIGHT YEARS

Dark heart

The bright white bloom at the centre of this image represents the deadliest radiation field in the Galaxy. And at its very centre, lurks a supermassive black hole, its crushing gravity poised to ambush any celestial object that strays too close.

It is known as Sagittarius A* and, cloaked in a blinding fog of X-rays [1], it has lurked unseen [2] at the centre of our galaxy since the very beginning. It may even be the gravitational seed that pulled together the surrounding swathes of gas that become our Galaxy, but now it is a force of destruction.

___Containing more than 4 million times the Sun's mass, the black hole is crushed into a sphere no bigger than the orbit of Mercury around the Sun. From Earth, it should look no larger than a beach ball on the Moon. Not surprisingly, no one has yet seen it but we know it's there, silently going about its destructive purpose because of the havoc it is wreaking on its surroundings.

___Nothing is immune: stars are being hurled through space by the powerful gravity of the black hole, and any that stray too close are being ripped to shreds and devoured, otherwise parallel filaments of gas are sucked sharply downward towards the bright blob cocooning Sagittarius A* [3].

___Surrounding the black hole is a melting pot of ancient stars, white dwarves, neutron stars, smaller black holes as well as more than 100 of the Galaxy's highest-mass, shortest-lived stars. But how could they get there?

___There is no sign of current star formation. Perhaps they formed out of the debris of other stars pulled to pieces and strewn into a disc surrounding the black hole. No one yet knows. However they got there, they are now in a race against time: will they live out their short lives to explode as supernovae before they are wrenched into their constituent atoms and devoured?

___That's where the X-rays come in. As the stars are pulled apart and the gas races to destruction, it heats up and pours out X-rays. These powerful bursts are the final luminous reminder of the oblivion that lies beyond the black hole's event horizon.

___The event horizon marks the celestial Rubicon. Pass this boundary, and there is no escape. No force in the Universe could propel you back out to safety. Not even light can escape. The only place to go is down towards the singularity, the impossibly compacted region of spacetime that possesses the paradoxical qualities of being infinitely small, yet infinitely dense. Once there, all matter is squeezed out of existence in a process that science cannot yet explain

NGC 6981

GLOBULAR CLUSTER

DIAMETER: 50 LY

LIGHT SECONDS
LIGHT MINUTES
LIGHT YEARS
KILO LIGHT YEARS
MEGA LIGHT YEARS
GIGA LIGHT YEARS

1

2

3

Stellar survivor

One of the loneliest outposts of the Milky Way, globular cluster M72 is a survivor. Where once there were thousands of similar celestial cities in the sky, now just 150 or so remain. The rest have fallen prey to the Milky Way's unmerciful gravity, been dismembered and scattered to the stellar winds.

In common with other globular clusters – M4 [1], M30 [2], NGC 6397 [3] – M72 follows an inclined orbital path around the central hub of the Galaxy. Usually this keeps it out of harm's way, well separated from the Galaxy's other stars. But every 100 million years or so, M72 must run the galactic gauntlet.

___It plunges through the Milky Way, where it is subjected to stronger gravitational forces than it is used to withstanding. These forces tear at its innards, drawing out vast streams of stars and stringing them across tens of thousands of light years of space. For most of the other globular clusters that once surrounded the Milky Way, this has proved

fatal, eviscerating them to the point of utter destruction as the aeons have passed.

___No one knows how the globular clusters formed. By the ages of the stars they contain, they must have attended the very birth of our Galaxy. In fact, they are older than any surviving structure in our Galaxy. And very few show progressive populations of stars. It seems that the stars in most globular clusters formed at the same time, long ago. Yet although their antiquity is obvious, the other secrets of their formation are under a lock that remains unpicked.

___Globular clusters do, however, prove that the Solar System is not in the centre of the

Galaxy. If we were at the centre of things, the globulars would be distributed randomly around us. As it is, most are located in the southern sky, betraying the centre of the galaxy to be located in that direction.

___Today, just 100,000 stars cling together in M72. It is one of the most distant globular clusters, which has surely helped its survival. As time has marched on, so the stars die off one by one. And they will continue to do so until, where there was once a glittering ball of stars, there will be a black mass of stellar corpses. The price of survival, it seems, is to simply fade away.

INTER
GALACTIC

It is time to leave the glittering stars and their coloured cloaks of gas. As the Galaxy falls away behind us, the magnificent objects that once dominated our view merge into one and we can discern the exquisite finesse of the Galaxy's overall design. Its sweeping spiral arms of blue stars punctuated by the red light of the nebulae, and laced with a tracery of dust.

Turning outwards, we see it is a pattern that is repeated throughout the Universe. The next facsimile galaxy is Andromeda, and a bounty of others grace the night; but to reach them, we need to accelerate again. Andromeda itself lies 2.3 million light years away. Although it is the nearest large galaxy, the first galaxies we encounter on our outward journey are much smaller. They are the Magellanic Clouds, so-called because in the night sky from Earth they appear to be detached fragments of the Milky Way. From our vantage point on the journey we see them as dwarf galaxies a few hundred thousand light years from our Galaxy, close enough for us to see details in their interiors.

___Each Magellanic Cloud serves as a home to a few billion stars, and they are both busily making more. Here we encounter the first surprise in our survey of intergalactic space. Despite their relatively diminutive size, they contain regions of star formation that dwarf anything the Milky Way possesses. If the mighty Tarantula Nebula were to replace the Orion Nebula in our own Galaxy it would dominate the night sky and cast shadows on Earth.

___To truly appreciate the population of intergalactic space we have to reach tens and hundreds of millions of years into the Universe. Here we will find that, as well as the majestic spirals such as the Milky Way and Andromeda, there are barred spirals that support their heavy arms of stars on broad dusty shoulders, and the elliptical galaxies where the stars swarm like bees around a hive. Then there are the irregulars, just fuzzy patches of stars. We will encounter them all, revel in their compelling similarities and wonder at their marked differences. From the scars of dust that score some galaxies, to the deadly wildfire of creation that engulfs others, to the incomprehensible violence of galactic collisions, each galaxy has its own story to tell.

___There is IC 342, turning serenely on its axis, while displaying the grand design of its spiral arms for the Universe to see. The Sombrero Galaxy has had its time of magnificence, and is now losing its spiral arms to contract and fade into a lens-shaped retirement home for old stars. And then there is NGC 1275. There is no growing old gracefully here, it is tearing itself apart from the inside out by blasting bullets of hot gas outwards, drawing colder streams behind them to hang like a freeze-framed firework.

___All the galaxies people could see were once thought to be part of the Milky Way. Their spiral shapes were imagined to be whirlpools of matter settling into a solar system of planets around a central forming star. The image was a seductive one with each galaxy's central bulge of stars resembling an airy star. Then in the early 20th century, the distances of these spiral nebulae were determined and they turned out to be huge.

___They were banished from the Milky Way altogether and shown to be not just far away but vast in size as well. Far from being denizens of our Galaxy, they are whole 'Milky Ways' in their own right; enormous star cities that house hundreds of billions of lustrous stars.

___Galaxies exist across a broad range of size scales. The titans are the elliptical galaxies. In a rich collection of galaxies, one giant elliptical will often be found to have sunk to the dead centre of the cluster, having grown to enormous proportions on a cannibalistic diet. Its vast bulk now forms the fulcrum around which the other galaxies rotate. Spent of any further gas, it has completely lost its ability to breathe life into any new stars. The only way it can replace those that it loses, as they come to an end of their natural lives, is to consume more galaxies. Anything that comes too close will be shown no mercy. They will be dismembered; their lifeblood of stars spilled across space until the giant elliptical mops it all up, using its strong gravity to absorb everything that was once in the other galaxy.

___At the opposite end of the size spectrum, the dwarf galaxies may prove to be some of the most scientifically valuable galaxies existing today. Being so small, they have not produced stars with anything like the profligacy of their much larger brethren. As a result the stellar alchemy that drives the composition of the galaxies to change with each new generation of stars has been arrested. This has preserved the conditions of the early Universe, turning these diminutives into windows onto the distant past.

___The further we journey, the more the arrangement of galaxies becomes apparent. At a scale of hundreds of millions of light years, so the clusters of galaxies come into clear view. Each grouping is the cosmic equivalent of the coliseum, where the galactic gladiators fight to the death.

___Inexorably drawn together into these groups and clusters by the gravity they generate, the galaxies are revealed to be aggressive individuals, always spoiling for a fight. As the galaxies circle, sizing each other up, they rake their gravitational fields across their opponents. Sometimes it is one-on-one, as in the case of M51 and NGC 5196. This David versus Goliath contest sets the smaller NGC 5196 up against a mighty spiral. In contrast to the biblical tale, there is unlikely to be poetic justice here. Unless NGC 5196 can race away, it will be destroyed by M51.

___When two galaxies are evenly matched, as with Antennae Galaxies, there can be no winner. Along the front line where these two spiral galaxies clash, the terrible fires of star formation are ignited. For hundreds of thousands of years, these fires will spread until each cloud of gas is transformed into new stars, as if in a desperate attempt to reinforce each galaxy's army. Finally, drained of energy and reserves, the two warring galaxies will coalesce, reborn as an exhausted, elliptical galaxy.

___At other times, these galactic brawls are pitched battles between numerous galaxies. Stephan's Quintet sees five galaxies all tearing at each other. But not every galactic fight needs to end in the destruction of elegance.

___In a few rare cases, sublime splendour results from these cosmic smash-ups: a ring galaxy, in which the collision creates a ripple of star formation that moves outwards from the bull's eye to the edge. Hoag's Object, 600 million light years away, is one such galaxy, perhaps the best example yet found, with its perfect circular symmetry.

___The galaxies are as individual as human beings. Each possesses its own character and idiosyncrasies, and each has a unique narrative spanning billions of years of cosmic history.

Right: NGC 7217, a tightly bound spiral galaxy in the constellation Pegasus, 41 mega light years distant.

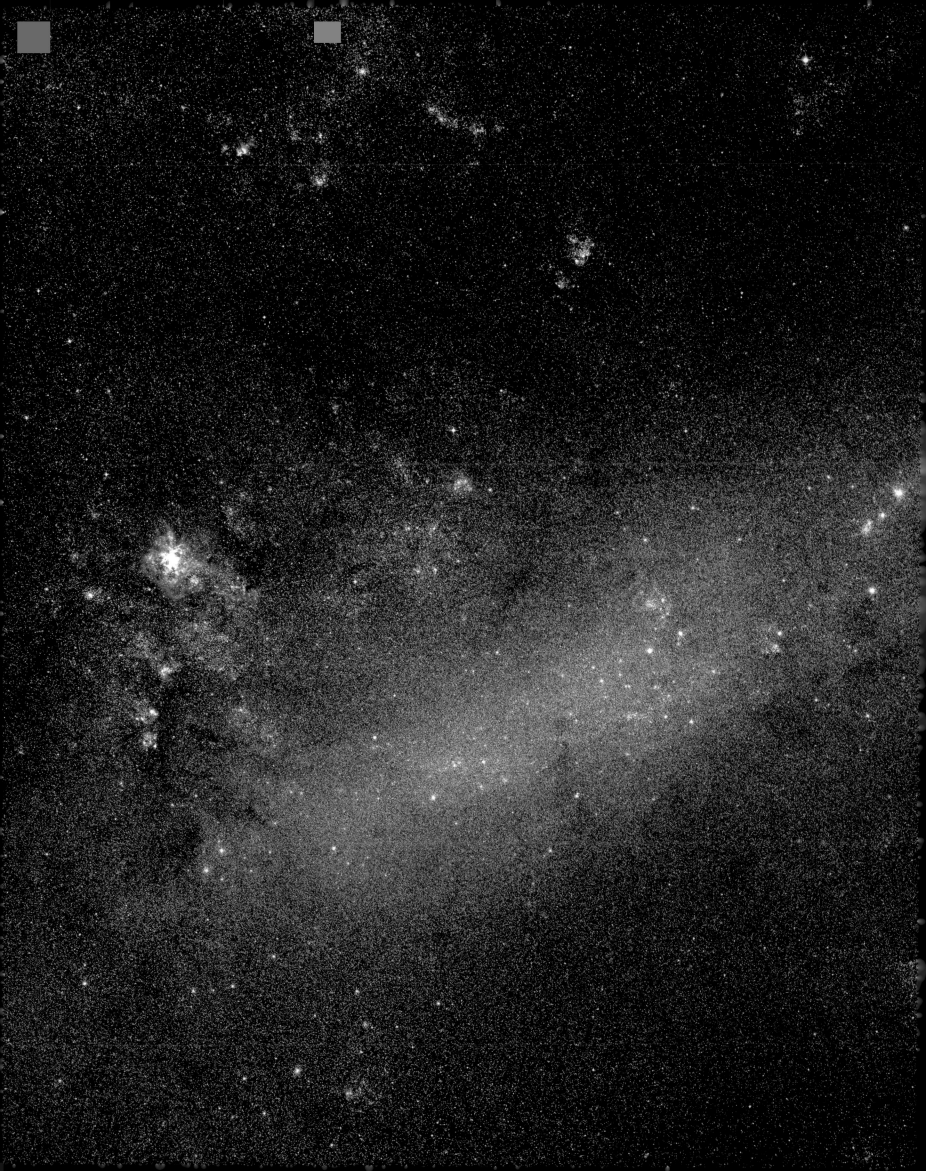

Large Magellanic Cloud
SATELLITE GALAXY
DIAMETER: 14,000 LY

LIGHT SECONDS
LIGHT MINUTES
LIGHT YEARS
KILO LIGHT YEARS
MEGA LIGHT YEARS
GIGA LIGHT YEARS

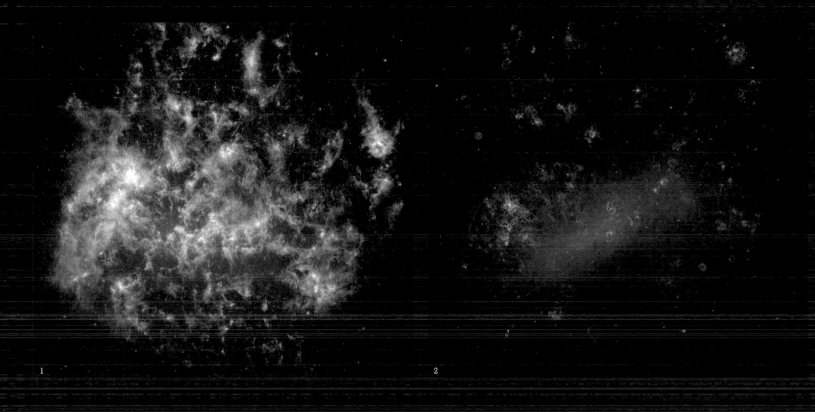

1

2

Intergalactic visitor

Heralded as one of the Milky Way's finest outposts, the Large Magellanic Cloud is big enough to be thought of as a galaxy in its own right. And the Milky Way may not enslave this satellite galaxy after all; it could be its own master.

Much larger than the globular clusters that surround the Milky Way, and ten times further away, the Large Magellanic Cloud (LMC) displays the trappings and behaviour of a galaxy in its own right. Whereas globular clusters are spent forces and can no longer make stars, the LMC has a full stellar ecosystem at work.

___The entire stellar lifecycle of the LMC is on display here. The smaller stars contribute a suffused glow to a bar across the centre of the galaxy. All told, they number around a few billion. That they are in a bar suggests that this galaxy once had spiral arms of stars, too. They would have curved out from the ends of those bars but are absent today, perhaps ripped away by the gravity of the Milky Way.

___The LMC's heavyweight stars are less ordered, scattered at random around the galaxy. Enshrouded in dust, they show up best at infrared wavelengths, manifesting as glowing knots of red [1]. The green coloured clouds are reservoirs of cooler gas harbouring molecules. These sites are where the next generation of stars will form. Where stellar production is ramping up, bright magenta nebulae gleam with the light of fluorescing hydrogen [2].

___If the globular clusters are the Milky Way's attendants, then the LMC and its smaller cousin the Small Magellanic Cloud (SMC) are honoured guests. However, where they were once thought to be permanent residents, now it seems that they are only paying us a fleeting visit.

___Both galaxies are whipping past at double the speed previously calculated. In the case of the LMC, the speed is nearly 380 km/s. For the SMC progress is a little more sedate: just 300 km/s. At these speeds, the gravity of the Milky Way, huge in reach though it is, would not be able to corral these smaller galaxies into orbit.

___So, instead of satellites, they are merely passers-by, taking in the view before their haste carries them on their intergalactic way. And what a view it is.

___The Milky Way fills a large portion of the sky with its striking spiral shape, arms outlined in silver blue and curled around a core of golden yellow starlight. Glowing red star-forming regions dot those arms and intricate bindings of dust appear to thread everything together.

___With a good star map, it would even be possible to spot the Sun, nestled in the trailing edge of the Orion Spur. Our whole life-giving Sun reduced to a seeming pinprick of light.

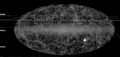

LIGHT-SECONDS
LIGHT MINUTES
LIGHT YEARS
KILO LIGHT YEARS
MEGA LIGHT YEARS
GIGA LIGHT YEARS

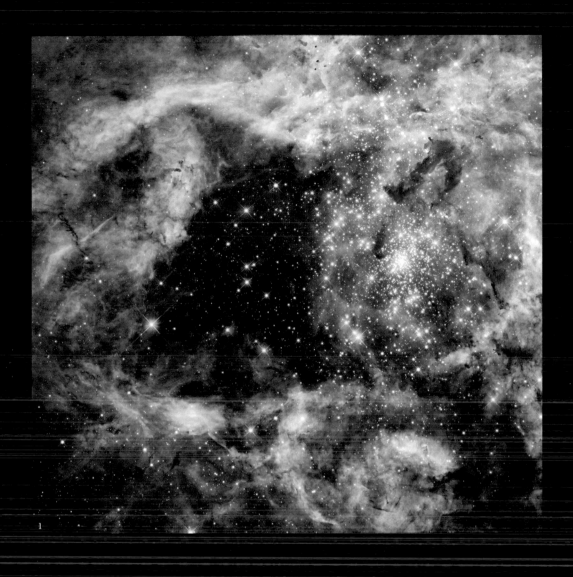

1

Fierce brood

The giant Tarantula Nebula's gaseous limbs reach
out across 1,000 light years of space, illuminated by
the fiercest centre of star formation in the Local Group
of galaxies.

We have seen star-forming regions in our own
Galaxy, but nothing like this. The Tarantula
Nebula is 20 times bigger than the Orion Nebula.
If the two were to swap places, the Orion
Nebula would be completely undistinguished,
virtually lost amongst these distant stars.
But the Tarantula would menace the night sky.
It would fill the constellation and cast shadows
across the night-time surface of Earth.

___The Tarantula is so large that no single star
can be responsible for supplying that much
energy to keep it all glowing. Instead, it is
powered by a whole cluster of bright stars [1].
Known as R136, it is a highly compact stellar
bundle. It dates to just a few million years ago
and yet it has already managed to squeeze
stars, to the value of 450,000 solar masses,
into a sphere just 35 light years across.

___Brandishing those statistics, R136 could
be another of the rarest sights in the Universe:
a globular cluster in the process of formation.
Certainly, it is not the first nest of stars that the
Tarantula has built. Another, called Hodge 301,
was born there around 25 million years ago.
That is sufficiently long ago that the more
massive of its stars have already exploded
as supernovae.

___The shock waves from these now dead
stars may have helped R136 to reach its great
proportions by compressing the gas in its
surroundings, thereby forcing more stars to
form while supplying them with plenty of raw
gaseous material. It has led to a dozen stars
with masses more than 40 times that of the Sun;
a couple may be approaching even 100 solar
masses.

___In 1987, a star from the Tarantula Nebula
met its fate. In a sudden nuclear paroxysm,
it was gone: a giant star a dozen times the
mass of the Sun blasted to atoms. Despite
being 160,000 light years away, the light from
the supernova was still powerful enough to
strip a layer of atoms from Earth's atmosphere
when it arrived.

___As the scattered fragments of the former
star reached out into space, travelling much
more slowly than the light from the explosion,
they smashed into a ring of dense gas that
must have been ejected earlier by the star.
As the two debris clouds collided, they lit up
each other in a blaze of X-rays, surrounding
the supernova with a brilliant halo of light. It
will not be the last such event; one by one the
Tarantula's children will meet their own kismet.

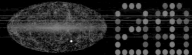

LIGHT SECONDS
LIGHT MINUTES
LIGHT YEARS
KILO LIGHT YEARS
MEGA LIGHT YEARS
GIGA LIGHT YEARS

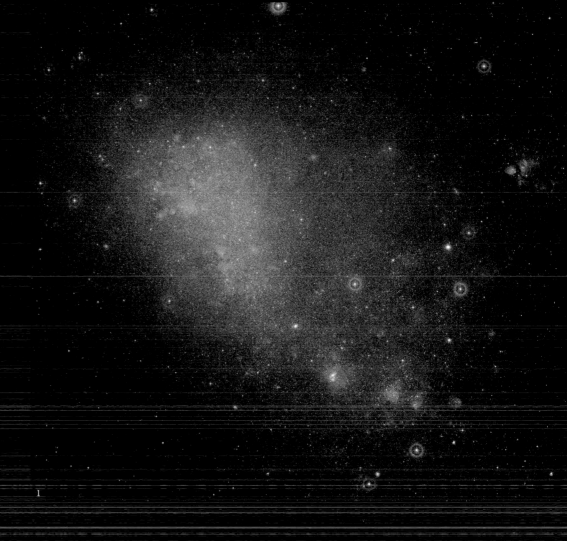

1

A glimpse of the past

Two and a half thousand pristine new stars burn with
the blue light of stellar youth in this giant interstellar
cloudbank. What kind of giant galaxy houses such a
colossal region of star formation? Not a giant at all,
one of the smallest in the Local Group.

The Small Magellanic Cloud (SMC) [1] contains
only a few hundred million stars. It may
once have had some small measure of spiral
structure but these days it is an irregular fuzzy
ball of stellar light. However, settling down to
a life of quiet mediocrity is not an option. While
most stars in this galactic minnow were created
around 4.5 billion years ago, unknown forces
triggered a new bout of stellar creation some
5 million years ago.

___The emission nebula NGC 346 is the
result of this new episode. Despite its relative
youth it is a celestial time machine, offering a
glimpse into the mighty forces that engulfed
the Universe early in its history. During the
Universe's first billion years, star formation
swept through the cosmos, lighting stellar

fires across the void, populating the Universe
with the first stars.

___NGC 346 has already disgorged one
stellar cargo, with a rippling conglomeration
of massive stars as the vanguard, and it is
preparing its next production run. Embedded
in the dark ribbons of dust that weave through
the blue illumination is a second generation
of new stars in the making. They are busily
pulling together enough mass to take their
place on the nebula's shining stage.

___Because star formation stalled for billions
of years, the SMC has a skewed overall stellar
population. Nevertheless, the trappings of this
latest bout are there for all to see in the shining
nebulae that litter the galaxy.

___Beyond the stars is a rarefied 'atmosphere'

of hydrogen gas. Not only does it surround the
SMC but it reaches to cover the neighbouring
Large Magellanic Cloud, and then extends to
span a much larger volume of space as well.
This common envelope suggests the two
galaxies share a bond; that they are held
together by gravity and travel through space
in company with one another.

___It probably came about when the two
galaxies suffered a near miss some 2.5 billion
years ago. Had they actually collided, the
two would have merged in a lavish display
of star formation that would have smothered
the resulting galaxy in a heat of star formation
regions, all resembling the fires of NGC 346.

LIGHT SECONDS
LIGHT MINUTES
LIGHT YEARS
KILO LIGHT YEARS
MEGA LIGHT YEARS
GIGA LIGHT YEARS

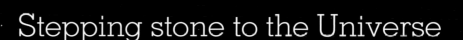

2

Stepping stone to the Universe

This beautiful island of stars was the stepping stone to the wider Universe. The furthest object to be visible to the naked eye, it became the subject of serious argument during the early 20th century, as astronomers debated whether it lay inside our Galaxy – or was itself another galaxy in a vastly larger cosmos than had been previously imagined.

The Andromeda Galaxy vies with the Milky Way for domination of the Local Group of galaxies. Locked in combat, the two galactic behemoths are screaming towards each other at 500,000 km/h. In 4 billion years they will collide. In the meantime, Andromeda is harassed by an armada of satellite galaxies that have suceeded in disrupting its spiral structure. In visible light everything appears normal, but infrared wavelengths reveal rings of dust like ripples on a pool [1] and dark arcs devoid of stars within the disc [2]. These are tell-tale signs of a galactic shapeshifter caught between spiral and ring forms.

___The Andromeda Galaxy has always invited speculation about its nature. Dimly visible to the unaided eye as a fuzzy pocket of light, the earliest known recording dates from AD 964 by Persian Astronomer al-Sufi in his *Book of Fixed Stars*, although people must surely have seen it before.

___Viewed through the developing telescopes of the early 20th century, Andromeda intoned a siren's song. To some, its swirling arms convinced them that it was a nearby gaseous whirlpool, perhaps forming a new star. Others wondered whether it could be a whole galaxy, far off in space. But that would mean a revolution in thought, an acknowledgement that the Universe was not just a single collection of stars but broken into

islands and strewn across space as a cosmic archipelago. What was at stake was our understanding of the scale of the Universe.

___Astronomer Edwin Hubble irritated his American colleagues. Originally from Missouri, he studied at University of Chicago and then at Oxford, where the dress sense and pipe smoking that rankled his peers took root. After serving in the US army during the First World War, Hubble turned full time to astronomy.

___He was inspired by observations that showed Andromeda and other spiral nebulae were rotating. His breakthrough came when he identified individual twinkling stars in Andromeda – and not just ordinary stars, but pulsating ones that varied their brightness in regular ways. By comparing them to similar, nearby stars, he showed that Andromeda was a whole galaxy in its own right, containing billions of stars and lying farther away than anyone had previously dared to imagine. This was the true triumph from Hubble's work.

___He showed the world that the Universe extends way beyond the collection of stars that comprises the Milky Way. Our continuation of the work he started has shown that the cosmos is punctuated by billions or even trillions of other galaxies, each containing their own collection of billions of stars. He made the Universe a richer, more detailed place for us all.

1

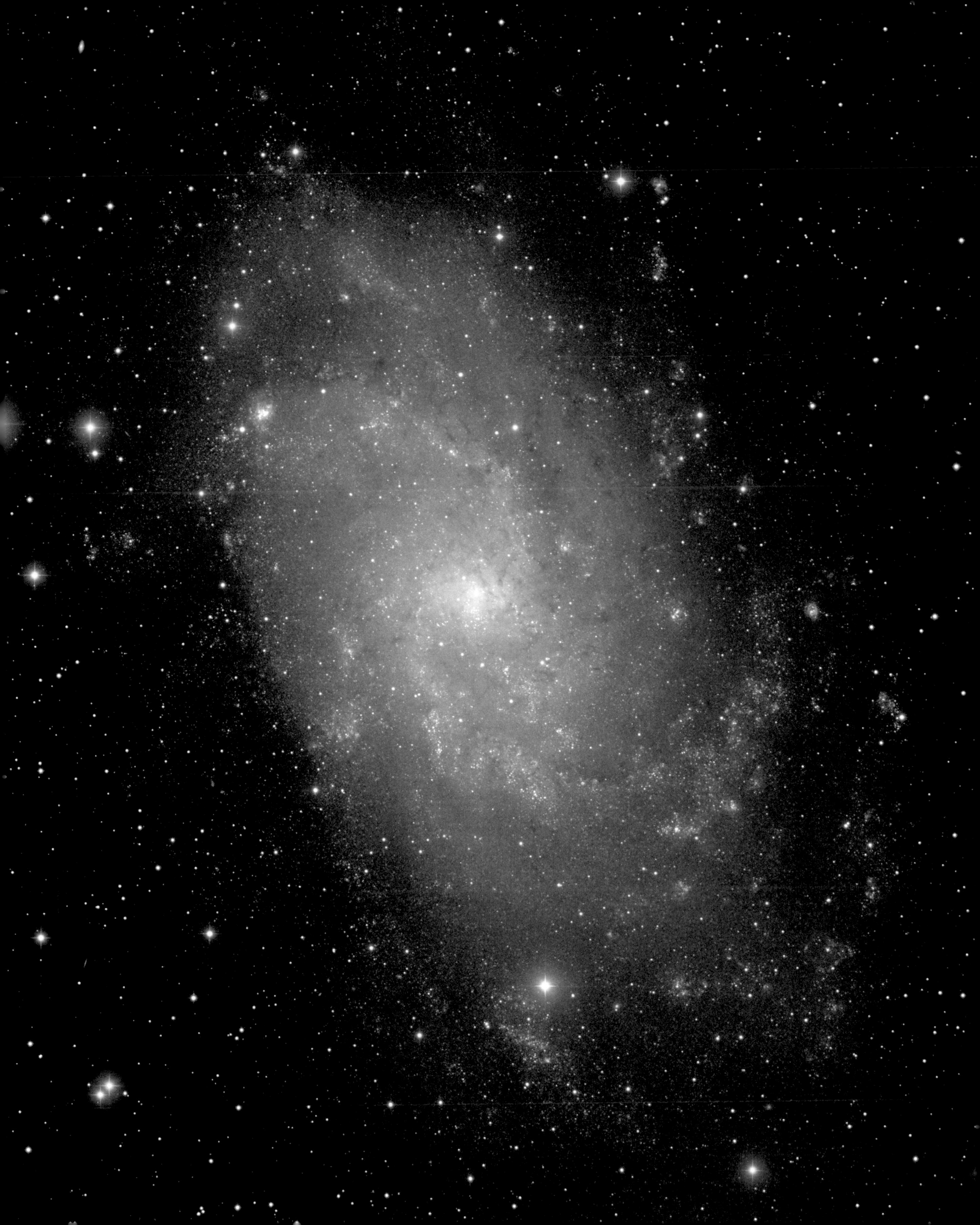

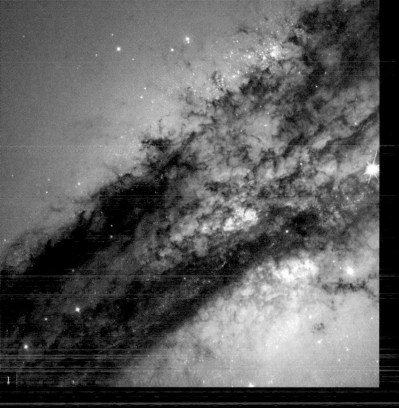

1

2

Galactic glutton

Remarkable jets of particles shoot from the centre of this galaxy. As they interact with the surrounding magnetic fields, so they cry out with radio waves, making them luminous. They are the visible signs of over-indulgence, poorly digested.

Centaurus A almost bit off more than it could chew. One hundred thousand years ago, a smaller companion galaxy drew too close. It was seized and swallowed whole, but it has been giving the greedy galaxy some serious indigestion ever since.

___The remains of the companion can be seen in the obscuring dusty 'tyre-track' that runs across the centre of Centaurus A [1]. But an infrared 'X-ray' [2] provides an even better view of the swallowed galaxy – a bright parallelogram – writhing within its captor. The collision has ignited a maelstrom of star formation, with more than a hundred sites easily visible across the disc. But move away from this disturbed region and there is an air

of false calm. The galaxy's main bulge is composed of old stars, still quietly following their normal orbits.

___The mayhem is repeated in the very heart of the galaxy, for the other winner in this situation lurks there: a billion solar masses compressed into a black hole that is just waiting to devour any stray stars or gas knocked its way. And during the ongoing absorption of the ill-fated companion galaxy, there is plenty for it to feed from.

___As the gas speeds to its deadly rendezvous with the black hole, so it screams out across the Universe, releasing a final cry at radio wavelengths. Somehow, it is also managing to generate sufficient energy to squirt two

enormous jets of electrically charged particles to their salvation, away from the black hole and clean out of the galaxy.

___These jets extend for some 13,000 light years into space and are only slowed because they plough into tenuous gas clouds surrounding the galaxy. A beautiful blue bow shock can be seen surrounding the lower jet, as the faint intergalactic medium is pushed out of the way and set glowing.

___Eventually, when the feeding frenzy is over, Centaurus A will settle down. The black hole and the jets will quieten and the dust lane will disappear, transforming in a plethora of sparkling stars. All will be calm. Order will have been restored.

Bode's Galaxy

M81

SPIRAL GALAXY

DIAMETER: 60,000 LY

LIGHT SECONDS
LIGHT MINUTES
LIGHT YEARS
KILO LIGHT YEARS
MEGA LIGHT YEARS
GIGA LIGHT YEARS

Might is right

You would be forgiven for thinking that we have turned to look back at the Milky Way. Our own Galaxy certainly shares a similar construction to this one, with its central bulge and winding arms. But no, we are far from home. This is M81 – galactic tyrant.

This beautiful spiral galaxy forms a triumvirate with two other large galaxies. Together, they appear to form a peaceful band of galactic brothers.

___Yet despite its wholesome appearance, there are hints that Bode's Galaxy is a bad apple, and hiding a propensity for violence. There is an ultraviolet surge of new star formation, which is helping to reinforce its spiral arms [1]. The stars are playing the role of the white water on the crests of its density waves. Such events do not just happen by accident; something must be feeding it.

___A central black hole resides at the heart of this galaxy, brooding with a mass of 70 million

suns. Although it stands poised, ready to gorge on any star that strays too close, it is quiet for now. So, this is not the reason for the stellar surge.

___More tellingly, the speed of the galaxy's rotation gives away that there are deep reservoirs of matter in the disc and nucleus. Not all of it can have been there from the start or else it would have long since been transformed into stars. So, this spare matter has to be coming from somewhere. Again, this provides an indicator that the galaxy is not the innocent bystander it appears to be.

___The real clue is subtle. In a few places the starry arms break up into mackerel clouds

And to the left of the nucleus, scars of dust cut across the disc, defying its spiral curve and hinting at a violent past.

___Indeed, not everything is as peaceful as it looks. M81 is ripping two companion galaxies to pieces. Invisible gas is streaming into this galaxy, bolstering its mass, and feeding it with fuel to grow larger and make more stars [2 & 3]. When it comes to satiating its appetite for more gas, this galaxy knows no bounds. But you have to look at its victim, the neighbouring galaxy M82, to truly appreciate the rapacity of its craving.

160
161

LIGHT SECONDS
LIGHT MINUTES
LIGHT YEARS
KILO LIGHT YEARS
MEGA LIGHT YEARS
GIGA LIGHT YEARS

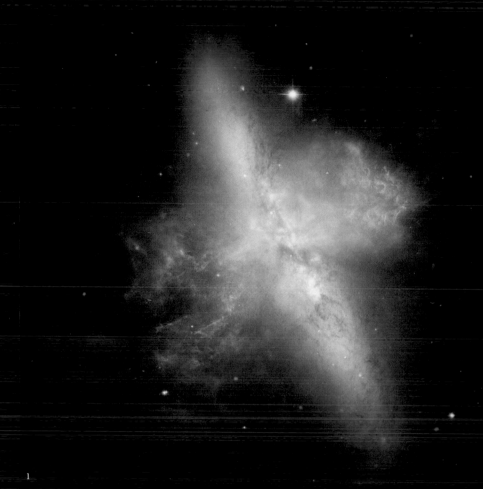

1

Into the inferno

Once a spiral galaxy, M82 has been reduced to wreckage. Beginning a few hundred million years ago, a close pass with a neighbouring galaxy stripped it of its finery and transformed it into an inferno of star formation. It has metamorphosed into a galactic throwback.

Star formation in M82 is running hot. In a central region 1,500 light years in diameter, the stellar production line is racing ahead ten times faster than in most galaxies today. Indeed, the Cigar Galaxy is five times brighter than the entire Milky Way, although only a quarter of the size.

___It began during a raid a few hundred million years ago, during which its larger neighbour M81 snatched away vast quantities of gas from M82. This left the remainder of M82 to collapse into itself, kindling a wave of stellar genesis that continues to this day.

___Almost 200 giant star clusters are known to exist in M82, each one holding enough mass to make 20,000 sun-like stars. Much of this mass is locked away temporarily into extremely high-mass stars. These live for just a few tens of millions of years before blowing themselves to pieces in powerful detonations that contribute even more terrible energy to the centre of the galaxy.

___The result is that the galaxy is now eviscerating itself in fusillade after fusillade of supernovae. This gives rise to the Cigar Galaxy looking like a gigantic galactic explosion, with gaseous debris that has been dragged or blasted from the galaxy now hanging above and below the main disc. This material is now beginning the slow process of raining back down onto the galaxy, helping to trigger a new round of star formation. Higher-temperature gas, colour-coded blue [1], leaves the galaxy altogether, destined to be scooped up by M81.

___Such a cacophony of stars and gas could be what most galaxies looked like 10 billion years ago. Back in those ancient cosmic times, the star formation was uniformly higher in almost every galaxy; the result of smaller galaxies colliding and merging in the bid to grow into the mature galaxies of today. In some cases the stellar output was several hundreds of times the current average.

___As this tremendous starburst engulfed the Universe, so the flood of ultraviolet radiation ripped apart almost every atom, sundering the outer particles, called electrons, from their atomic nuclei. Only one in every thousand atoms escaped.

___This watershed in history is known as the Reionization. It set the stage for the modern cosmos of today, when galaxies came of age and settled into a general state of quiescence, allowing their constituent atoms to combine once more.

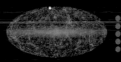

LIGHT SECONDS
LIGHT MINUTES
LIGHT YEARS
KILO LIGHT YEARS
MEGA LIGHT YEARS
GIGA LIGHT YEARS

1

2

Firecracker galaxy

Like firecrackers on New Year's Eve, chains of new stars
are bursting into life throughout this galaxy. Baubles of
red gas mark areas of active star formation, indicating
that the stellar production line is in full swing.

NGC 4449 bears a remarkable similarity to
the Milky Way's Large Magellanic Cloud. It is
about the same size as our neighbour, has a
similar number of stars and, most interestingly,
has an elongated shape rather than a
spherical one.

___Such elongated structures are called bars
and are often seen near the centre of much
larger galaxies joining the spiral arms to the
nucleus. In the case of NGC 4449, and indeed
the LMC, the spiral arms are completely missing.

___At invisible radio wavelengths, NGC 4449
no longer seems such a dwarf. The galaxy
sits in the centre of a gigantic bubble of
unilluminated hydrogen, 14 times the
expanse of the visible portion.

___At the core of the galaxy is a tinge of yellow
light, indicating the presence of long-lived
stars. This signals that stars have been forming

here for several billion years, but most of the
visible stars in the rest of the galaxy are vibrant
blue and date to within the last 5 million years.

___Hundreds of thousands of these sparkling
gems now inhabit the galaxy, each one destined
to burn its fuel so quickly that it will exist for
only a hundred million years at the most.
These short-lived stars cluster together into the
equivalent of cities and towns, with the rural
expanses marked out by dark clouds of dust,
held in silhouette against the flaming starlight.

___The huge number of these stars signals an
unusually intense bout of star formation – a
starburst that is continuing to this day. Brilliant
twists of red hydrogen are the heralds of yet
more newly minted stars. If the current rate of
creation continues, the galaxy will transform
all its spare gas into stars within a billion years.

___Such widespread activity is thought to

resemble the primordial galaxies that grew by
merging with one another billions of years ago.
It is highly likely that the same is happening
here, with NGC 4449 sent into frenzy by a
collision with a smaller galaxy.

___Today, no hint of the galactic bullet remains
but its effects are brilliantly visible for all to see.
Whereas starbursts are usually confined to the
central regions of the stricken galaxy, in NGC
4449 they have spilled outwards into streamers
that wind through the whole assemblage.

___Starbursts can rekindle otherwise faded
dwarfs. NGC 1313 [1] is a sickening spiral
galaxy being rejuvenated by a new wave of
starburst activity sweeping round its limbs.
NGC 1569 should be an insignificant island
of stars. Instead, it is being tormented into
blazing activity by a group of 10 surrounding
larger galaxies [2].

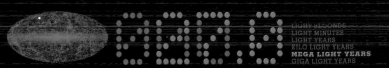

LIGHT SECONDS
LIGHT MINUTES
LIGHT YEARS
KILO LIGHT YEARS
MEGA LIGHT YEARS
GIGA LIGHT YEARS

Grand designs

The spiral pattern of some galaxies is no accident. They result from waves of denser gas passing round the galaxy, acting like stellar flypaper and sparking star formation in their wake. But what triggers these density waves remains elusive.

Only 10 percent of spiral galaxies display a grand design, making them rare beauties to be cherished. The grand design spirals are those that display prominent arms of blue stars. In many cases, these arms can be traced from the nucleus to the outer edges of the galaxy.

___Seldom do grand designs come much bigger than that at work in the Pinwheel Galaxy. Its sweeping arms curve across 170,000 light years of space. The galaxy rotates, trailing these giant arms and taking about 250 million years to complete one revolution.

___The arms in all spiral galaxies can be more or less tightly wound, suggesting that the pattern is produced by rotation, rather like the way cream swirls in a stirred cup of coffee. But it cannot be this simple. Stars closer to the centre of the galaxy do indeed move faster than those on the outer edges, but this would wind the spirals up within just a few revolutions and there are too many grand design spirals to believe that they have all been observed during this transition phase.

___Instead, the spiral arms are like stellar flypaper, somewhat denser regions of the disc, which attract old stars into them. These stars eventually move back out of the arms but their lingering passage concentrates their starlight, helping the arm to glow.

___Unlike flypaper, the spiral arms also stimulate the growth of new stars. They do this by attracting and compressing clouds of gas that might have not otherwise burst into star formation. As the clouds fall into the spiral arm, they will also tend to collide with one another. Such smash-ups are certain to provoke them into forming stars.

___In this way, the spiral pattern moves around the galaxy at a fixed speed, maintaining its shape by inveigling the help of existing stars.

___But what creates these denser regions in the first place remains unclear. They could be instilled in the galaxy when it first forms as ripples in the primordial gas, or they could be fostered later by the gravitational perturbation of a nearby companion galaxy.

LIGHT SECONDS
LIGHT MINUTES
LIGHT YEARS
KILO LIGHT YEARS
MEGA LIGHT YEARS
GIGA LIGHT YEARS

Missing limbs

A spiral galaxy but without spiral arms. This is not the only distinction making the Sombrero Galaxy unusual. A large dust lane without star formation, a giant central black hole without activity; it's a galactic enigma.

The Sombrero Galaxy breaks all the rules. The most striking feature of this galaxy is the dust lane that cuts across its equator. Mixed in with this dust are large quantities of cold hydrogen gas, and on the face of it, this should supply plenty of material from which to make stars but there are no clouds of glowing hydrogen to signal any widespread stellar manufacture.

___Its lack of interest or ability in making stars has led to the Sombrero losing its spiral arms – if it ever had any in the first place. The result is a confusing galaxy that displays similarities to both spiral and elliptical galaxies. Like an elliptical, it possesses a large central bulge of stars, but like a spiral it then surrounds this with a disc of older stars, dust and gas [1]. In total, the Sombrero is home to some 800 billion stars, four times the number in the Milky Way, yet it spans only half the size: 50,000 light years.

___The distended central bulge conceals a sleeping giant of a black hole. Judging by the speed at which stars are orbiting the centre of

the galaxy, the Sombrero plays host to one of the largest supermassive black holes in the nearby Universe. Clocking up an impressive one billion solar masses, this dark behemoth has certainly been busily devouring other celestial objects. But now, it seems to have lost its appetite.

___There are no jets of gas or cataracts of X-rays shooting from this monster. For now it seems replete, reassuring the stars around it they are safe. Nevertheless, there is a mystery here. A short-wavelength form of radio emission is coming from the centre of the galaxy. Investigation shows it's not coming from the dust, nor the gas, nor the particles caught in the galaxy's magnetic fields. So at present, its origin is completely unexplained.

___Just to complete the picture of this enigmatic galaxy, it is surrounded by a plethora of globular clusters. Estimates place the census at between 1,200 and 2,000, roughly 10 times as many as are gathered around our own Galaxy. No one knows why this should be the case.

LIGHT SECONDS
LIGHT MINUTES
LIGHT YEARS
KILO LIGHT YEARS
MEGA LIGHT YEARS
GIGA LIGHT YEARS

1

Sinister beauty

Looking for all the world like a whirlpool of stars being sucked down into the centre of the galaxy, M51 is one of the grandest of the grand design spiral galaxies. But beauty is a fragile thing; M51 could so easily have become an ill-defined mess.

M51 is not the largest of galaxies; it spans just 40,000 light years, about half the size of our Galaxy. Yet its bulk almost equals the Milky Way at some 160 billion solar masses, and it boasts equally mighty coiled arms rendering it one of the most pronounced spiral galaxies in the Universe.

___Two broad arms of brilliant stars wrap themselves around the nucleus, displaying blisteringly hot stars in blue and stellar nurseries in glowing red. One of these stretches onwards, all the way to the faded yellow glow of a dwarf galaxy that sits close by [1]. The smaller galaxy, NGC 5195, has been significantly distorted by the gravitational

might of M51. It may once have been a lenticular shape, but now it is an amorphous clump that defies classification.

___It has made two close passes to M51. The first took place as it approached from behind around 500 million years ago, and the second about 50 million years ago. Now it lies just slightly further away from us than the big spiral.

___Had it smashed into M51, the glorious spiral pattern would have been destroyed, torn apart by the dramatic clash of gravitational forces. The orderly stars would have been thrown from their orbits, creating a random mess that would have settled eventually into an elliptical shape

___As it was, NGC 5195 missed by just 10,000 light years or so – a hair's breadth in galactic terms. Maybe it was this close shave that bestowed such extreme beauty upon M51. As the weaker gravitational field of the companion swept across the disc of the larger galaxy, so it could have generated or strengthened the ripple of gas that has so clearly defined the spiral arms.

___Now M51 looks as if it is extending an arm to comfort its errant companion. In reality it is probably preparing to drag it the rest of the way to its doom. The bully's crushing strength of gravity has already begun the process of dismembering and devouring the dwarf

Spindle Galaxy

NGC 5866

LENTICULAR GALAXY

DIAMETER: 60,000 LY

LIGHT SECONDS
LIGHT MINUTES
LIGHT YEARS
KILO LIGHT YEARS
MEGA LIGHT YEARS
GIGA LIGHT YEARS

1

On the edge

Turn this galaxy through 90 degrees, so that it appeared face-on, and it would present a moon-face. Pale and round, it would be almost indistinguishable from an elliptical galaxy. However, viewed from the side, the difference becomes clear: it is rake-thin.

The Spindle Galaxy is only a spindle from this angle. In actuality, it is a flat disc, like NGC 2787 [1], that we happen to be seeing exactly edge-on. It is another example of a spiral galaxy that has lost its spirals.

It has undoubtedly been a vigorous exponent of star formation in the past because the milky glow of starlight lies all around this galaxy. But over the past few hundreds of millions of years, so the pace has slowed and the spiral shape has disappeared. Now all that remains is a central bulk of stars, an almost featureless disc and a diffuse halo of older stars.

What this lenticular galaxy lacks in spiral structure, however, it more than makes up for in dust. A dense dust lane runs around its nucleus. It is mostly condensed towards the central regions of the galaxy, petering out in the outer extremities. But this could be enough. Close inspection of this reservoir reveals that all may not be lost for the Spindle Galaxy.

There are dusty projections that stand proud of the main disc. These elephantine trunks reach outward for hundreds of light years and are more like giant geysers of dust that are being blown upwards to rain down over a large area of the galaxy.

The only celestial objects that can muster the kind of power necessary to drive such fountains are hot, massive stars that are expelling furiously. Their cascade of light and particles is sufficient to loft huge quantities of dust into these celestial fountains.

From the number of them, it appears that there could be a widespread renaissance of star formation taking place. Perhaps it is even enough to begin a rippling pattern of density variations around the galaxy to restore it to spiral splendour. Sadly, even if this were to happen, it would be largely lost to our view, as we will continue to look at it side-on.

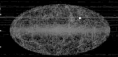

LIGHT SECONDS
LIGHT MINUTES
LIGHT YEARS
KILO LIGHT YEARS
MEGA LIGHT YEARS
GICA LIGHT YEARS

Clash of the titans

In galactic terms this is the ultimate heavyweight clash.
Two evenly matched galaxies are going head-to-head.
Yet, in the harsh reality of the Universe, there cannot
be a winner. What started with an undeniable mutual
attraction, now signals the end for both galaxies; and
also a new beginning.

The bout began billions of years ago, when these galaxies felt the first tentative caress of each other's gravity. At that stage they were both preening spirals, basking in the glow of the Universe. Gently at first they began to edge towards one another. With each onward step, so the attraction became stronger until it was impossible to avoid their destiny to be together.

___They began racing onward at an ever-accelerating rate, gripped by an unalloyed gravitational passion to be together. But as they drew nearer so the true nature of the impending encounter became apparent. This was not to be a tender embrace, but a confrontation, a fight to the death.

___When they first touched, just over a billion years ago, the mayhem truly began. They ripped away each other's spiral arms and scattered them to the stellar winds. A firestorm of star formation flared in both galaxies, and the interstellar clouds clashed in mighty collisions.

___Two long tails of stars [1], which give the system its name, mark where these galaxies have cut through space on their way to this deadly embrace. Many other stars in the bulk of the galaxy have yet to be directly affected by the titanic fight going on around them because the space between the stars is so wide. Most stars never actually collide, even during the closest of passes.

___The galaxies have already travelled through each other once, and are now falling back together again for the final round in this match. They are within just 400 million years of becoming one indistinguishable mass of stars. As this conglomeration settles into a new equilibrium, and the spree of star formation subsides, so the two original shapes will entirely disappear, the once spiral grandeur lost for evermore.

___But this is not the very end. In their place will be a mighty elliptical galaxy, presiding over the other galaxies in the locality, youthful beauty replaced by age and the wisdom of having lived through a titanic event.

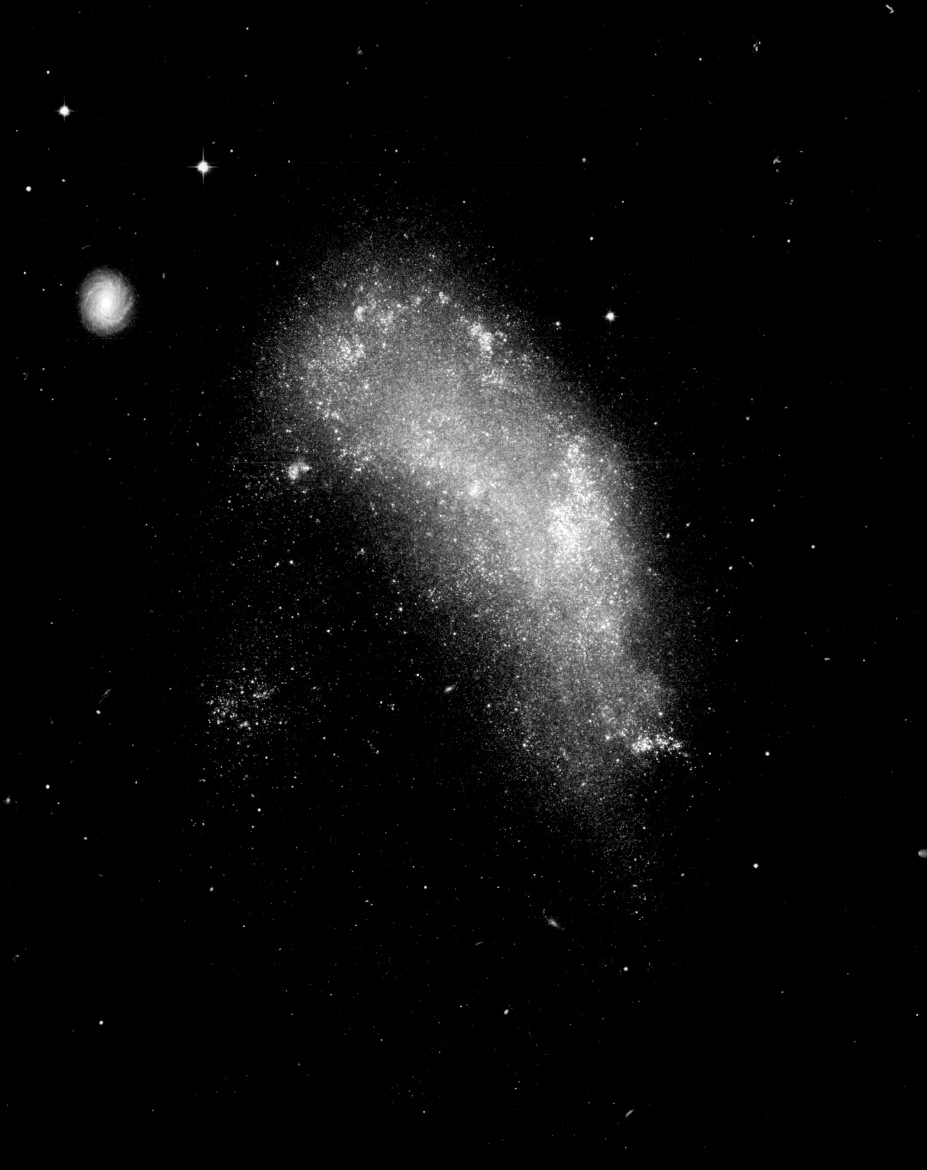

LIGHT SECONDS
LIGHT MINUTES
LIGHT YEARS
KILO LIGHT YEARS
MEGA LIGHT YEAR
GIGA LIGHT YEARS

Surreal stars

It looks like the way Salvador Dali would have painted a galaxy, with one part of it melting away. But this is reality. The brush that fashions NGC 1427A's surreal aspect is a tidal force. On Earth, tides produce the ebb and flow of the ocean; in space they rip galaxies apart.

Doomed is the only word to describe this dwarf galaxy. Its journey through space has taken it too close to a cabal of galaxies called the Fornax Cluster, and their combined gravity has pulled it off course. Now, they are dragging it down into their midst at speeds of more than 600 km/s.

The galaxy owes its distorted appearance to gravity accelerating its forward edge faster than its rear. This is because gravity weakens progressively with distance and the galaxy, although classified as a dwarf, is still roughly 30,000 light years long. So, the strength of gravity acting on the front is much greater than on the rear, with the result that the galaxy is being stretched.

This has created a so-called tidal force. These are at work throughout the Universe, from the oceans of Earth to the moons of Jupiter and beyond; but on intergalactic scales, their power is exaggerated.

As time goes on, and NGC 1427A dips deeper into the cluster, it will be elongated even more. Eventually it will be pulled into a piece of stellar spaghetti, before losing any final semblance of coherence.

As it falls, the galaxy is being forced through the cluster's envelope of gas. This creates the intergalactic equivalent of air resistance, and helps to define the 'arrowhead' shape of the galaxy. It also promotes a final round of star formation in NGC 1427A. Short-lived bright blue stars now outline the galaxy, where the intergalactic gas has impacted the margins and compressed the dwarf's own clouds of gas into new stars.

These stars and the older ones in the centre of the dwarf will eventually be cast off randomly into the cluster. Some will be attracted to the other galaxies and captured by them. Taking their places in the stellar complement, only their eccentric orbits will betray that they were not formed there in the first place.

Other stars will escape the galaxies' clutches to spend the rest of their lives wandering the cluster in isolation. There must be vast numbers of lonely stars drifting in the orphaned expanses of intergalactic space. However, being such tiny motes against the vastness of the cosmic night, they are rendered almost invisible by sheer distance, and so remain as yet undiscovered.

LIGHT SECONDS
LIGHT MINUTES
LIGHT YEARS
KILO LIGHT YEARS
MEGA LIGHT YEARS
GIGA LIGHT YEARS

Spiral evolution

The overwhelming feature of this galaxy is its elongated shape. It has what amounts to a bar of stars running between its nucleus and the beginning of the spiral arms. These elongated galaxies could be the next step in a spiral galaxy's evolution.

The spiral arms themselves are a relatively poor feature of this galaxy, even though they number four in total with two being far more prominent than the others. Overwhelming them all is the large bar that spans more than 60,000 light years and accounts for most of the width of NGC 1672. Rejig the catalogue numbers and you have NGC 6217, another fine specimen of a barred spiral galaxy [1].

___Barred spiral galaxies are more prevalent in the modern Universe. They account for nearly two-thirds of nearby spirals. Tellingly, their numbers have tripled during the last 7 billion years of cosmic history, about half the age of the Universe. This suggests that bars represent the final mature shape of a spiral galaxy.

___The mass of the galaxy helps to determine how quickly a bar can form with the most massive spiral galaxies developing so fast that they manifest bars early. Nowadays, the other spirals are catching up. For example, our Milky Way has a modest bar connecting its nucleus to its spiral arms.

___Bars form in a galaxy when otherwise circular stellar orbits are perturbed and begin to take on elliptical shapes. They start lingering along certain paths and this leads to a bar beginning to build. As the bar forms, so it ensnares more and more stars in it, reinforcing its durability. It also becomes a trap that can funnel dust and gas down into the centre of the galaxy.

___In NGC 1672 this sudden arrival of edible matter has woken up the supermassive black hole in its core. It measures somewhere between 10 million and 100 million solar masses and is presently eating its way through a celestial meal. Being a typically messy eater, it is splashing quantities of hydrogen, helium, nitrogen and oxygen all over the place, which is then lighting up under the glare of the doomed matter nearby.

___Not that the doomed matter is going without a final hoorah. As it is progressively squeezed toward its gravitational Rubicon, so it is giving birth to a teeming mass of new stars. This starburst entirely surrounds the black hole providing its own brilliant radiation.

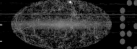

LIGHT SECONDS
LIGHT MINUTES
LIGHT YEARS
KILO LIGHT YEARS
MEGA LIGHT YEARS
GIGA LIGHT YEARS

Swimming upstream

NGC 4522 knows what it is like to swim against the current. It is being inexorably pulled down into a morass of giant galaxies. As it is being dragged faster and faster through the surrounding gas, so it is being stripped of its contents.

Spiral swirls of dust and stars lift from this galaxy, apparently forced upwards by the pressure of the surrounding gas through which it is travelling. The galaxy is falling like a stone. Its downward plunge has been clocked at more than 10 million km/h.

___It is just one of the 1,300 members of the Virgo Cluster of galaxies. The great round bulks of the elliptical galaxies are concentrated towards the centre of the cluster, while the flighty spirals are more evenly distributed around the edges, spread throughout a lozenge-shaped region of space that spans millions of light years.

___This is the nearest large grouping of galaxies to the Milky Way, and it dominates the nearby Universe. The Virgo Cluster contains around ten trillion solar masses

of material and is so immense that it is even tugging on our own Local Group of galaxies. So, if we can feel the gravitational attraction towards Virgo, some 60 million light years away, then NGC 4522, situated within it, stands no chance.

___The hapless spiral galaxy is fighting against the pressure of the tenuous mist of gas known as the intergalactic medium. Although this gas is only very sparsely spread through space, it exerts a stinging force when encountered head on at high speed. While it is not enough to lift whole stars out of the galaxy, it is doing a good job of cleaning out the gas.

___As they levitate away from the galaxy, the fleeing gas clouds are being sufficiently compressed to sire new stars, and as these

burst into radiant life they give the illusion that the galaxy is evaporating away.

___While the density of the intergalactic gas is tantamount to nothing, a million billion times more rare than fresh air, it still mounts up when the enormous volumes of space are considered. The pressure from the surrounding gas has actually curved NGC 4402 at the edges; another victim of the Virgo Cluster's titanic pull of gravity [1].

___Fully half of the atoms in the Universe are thought to be located within the intergalactic gas. If the gas stays there, none of it will ever transform into clumps dense enough to form stars and galaxies. Eventually, some may be pulled into nearby galaxies and thus finally take part in the gravitational game of star formation there.

LIGHT SECONDS
LIGHT MINUTES
LIGHT YEARS
KILO LIGHT YEARS
MEGA LIGHT YEARS
GIGA LIGHT YEARS

Swimming upstream

NGC 4522 knows what it is like to swim against the current. It is being inexorably pulled down into a morass of giant galaxies. As it is being dragged faster and faster through the surrounding gas, so it is being stripped of its contents.

Spiral swirls of dust and stars lift from this galaxy, apparently forced upwards by the pressure of the surrounding gas through which it is travelling. The galaxy is falling like a stone. Its downward plunge has been clocked at more than 10 million km/h.

___It is just one of the 1,300 members of the Virgo Cluster of galaxies. The great round bulks of the elliptical galaxies are concentrated towards the centre of the cluster, while the flighty spirals are more evenly distributed around the edges, spread throughout a lozenge-shaped region of space that spans millions of light years.

___This is the nearest large grouping of galaxies to the Milky Way, and it dominates the nearby Universe. The Virgo Cluster contains around ten trillion solar masses

of material and is so immense that it is even tugging on our own Local Group of galaxies. So, if we can feel the gravitational attraction towards Virgo, some 60 million light years away, then NGC 4522, situated within it, stands no chance.

___The hapless spiral galaxy is fighting against the pressure of the tenuous mist of gas known as the intergalactic medium. Although this gas is only very sparsely spread through space, it exerts a stinging force when encountered head on at high speed. While it is not enough to lift whole stars out of the galaxy, it is doing a good job of cleaning out the gas.

___As they levitate away from the galaxy, the fleeing gas clouds are being sufficiently compressed to sire new stars, and as these

burst into radiant life they give the illusion that the galaxy is evaporating away.

___While the density of the intergalactic gas is tantamount to nothing, a million billion times more rare than fresh air, it still mounts up when the enormous volumes of space are considered. The pressure from the surrounding gas has actually curved NGC 4402 at the edges; another victim of the Virgo Cluster's titanic pull of gravity [1].

___Fully half of the atoms in the Universe are thought to be located within the intergalactic gas. If the gas stays there, none of it will ever transform into clumps dense enough to form stars and galaxies. Eventually, some may be pulled into nearby galaxies and thus finally take part in the gravitational game of star formation there.

The archetype

So beautiful it's used as a galactic archetype, NGC 1300
is a fine example of a barred spiral galaxy. But that's not
all. It is an ordinary spiral galaxy, too. The spiral within
a barred spiral can be found embedded in the centre of
the galaxy.

At 110,000 light years across, NGC 1300 is
large for a spiral galaxy and contains myriad
fine details across its arms, bar and nucleus.
The entire galaxy is bejewelled with blue
and red supergiant stars, clusters of stars,
and star forming regions. Dust lanes braid
the arms and the bar, showing marked
asymmetries between the opposing sides
of the galaxy. The dark dust lanes show up
almost like a skeleton, with the starry surrounds
providing the celestial equivalent of flesh.

___Star formation is particularly active in the
inner regions of the spiral arms, where matter
is thought to be queuing up to flow along the
bar and into the central bulge of the galaxy.

___And it is in the core of NGC 1300 that there
lies a surprise. The central nucleus displays a
distinct 'grand design' spiral structure, a small
version of the grandest of the spiral galaxies [1].
This miniature replica is about 3,300 light years
wide. It could have formed because matter is
being funnelled along the bars and into these
central regions; certainly on one side of the
galaxy, the rate of star formation seems to be
much higher than on the other.

___The spiral within a spiral is not the only
mystery here. The other is found or, more
accurately, not found in the very centre of the
galaxy. With all the matter that is supposedly
being channelled down that way, one should

expect the supermassive black hole there to
be wide awake.

___But the centre of this galaxy is as quiet as
the grave: no untoward radio waves or X-rays
springing from it. Could this be a galaxy
without a central black hole? Maybe, but that
would seem to go against everything known
about galaxy formation. Yet, if there is a black
hole then it is a peculiarly fussy eater, refusing
all that is presumably being handed to it.

___Something doesn't add up about NGC 1300.
Perhaps it is not quite the archetype it was
once thought.

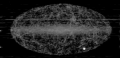

LIGHT SECONDS
LIGHT MINUTES
LIGHT YEARS
KILO LIGHT YEARS
MEGA LIGHT YEARS
GIGA LIGHT YEARS

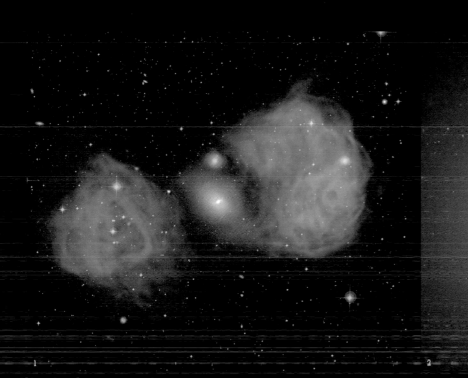

1

2

Dusty chimera

Here's another galactic puzzle: NGC 1316 looks like an elliptical galaxy except that it is riven with dust. Such lanes of raw stellar ingredients are more in keeping with a spiral galaxy. So, just what kind of galaxy is NGC 1316?

Take away the dark markings of dust and NGC 1316 would be an archetypal elliptical galaxy. It is a little on the small side at just 60,000 light years in diameter but, in keeping with the larger ellipticals, it shows no sign of recent star formation and glows with the pale light of older stars.

___However, it does not live in the elliptical galaxy neighbourhood of the Fornax Cluster. Instead of plumping for the centre of town, it chooses a place in the suburbs, where the majority of spiral galaxies can be found.

___Tuning into the celestial radio frequencies shows that, while the galaxy is only modest at visible wavelengths, in reality it is a giant. Two fat lobes of radio emission sit on opposite sides of the galaxy [1]. Individually, each is bigger

than the galaxy itself. In total, from the outer edge of one lobe, across the galaxy to the outer edge of the other, the distance is a million light years.

___The radio lobes themselves must have been excited by incredibly accelerated jets of particles generated in some way near the supermassive black hole at the centre of the galaxy. The particles will have bored their way through the galaxy and out into intergalactic space. Now, however, there is no sign of these jets. The lobes themselves are probably the fading remnants of the previous activity that once lit up this galaxy.

___In the visible outer regions of the galaxies, many structures can be seen: ripples, loops and arcs of stars all point to the idea that two

galaxies are in the final phase of merging here. In the centre of the galaxy is a compact disc of gas that rotates faster than the stars. It is probably what is left of the gas that slid into the central black hole, and created the radio lobes in the process.

___So what is NGC 1316? Is it a stellar shambles that has yet to make up its mind which way it is going? Most likely, it is an elliptical galaxy merging with a spiral galaxy and, like the chimera of lore, it now shows features of both. Galactic chimeras are not uncommon, many galaxies display such mixed features, like the dusty ring wrapped around the otherwise elliptial NGC 7049 [2].

LIGHT SECONDS
LIGHT MINUTES
LIGHT YEARS
KILO LIGHT YEARS
MEGA LIGHT YEARS
GIGA LIGHT YEARS

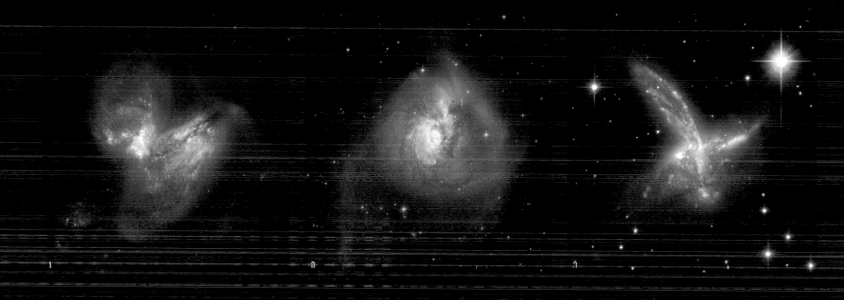

Tug of war

It's a tug of war between two galaxies. They've been locked into this Herculean struggle for millions of years, and the rope they are using is nothing less than a whole other galaxy.

Not every cluster of galaxies is huge. While it is the giant clusters that most easily grab the attention, there are far greater numbers of smaller galactic groupings. Our own Local Group is one such example with its 30 or so members. But even this looks big compared to the compact groups.

___Each one of these modest galactic gatherings contains from three or four galaxies to just half a dozen or so, but they are every bit as capable of drama as their far-larger cousins. In the case of the Hickson Compact Group (HCG) 90, two of its members are fighting for possession of the third.

___NGC 7173 and NGC 7176 are smoothly contoured elliptical galaxies, existing without much excess gas or dust. Now, they have

developed new appetites for these components and have set about their companion galaxy NGC 7174 to provide them. They have mangled its spiral shape as they continuously plunder its contents, drawing it on a gravitational rack into a long braiding of light and shade.

___These days, the damaged NGC 7174 barely clings to an independent existence, and it will not be long in cosmic terms before it is decimated. The strong tidal forces surging through the galaxy from both of its so-called companions will rip it to pieces. Already significant numbers of its stars have been strewn around the group, forming a diffuse glowing halo.

___So intent on their tug of war are the competing elliptical galaxies that they may

already have crossed the point of no return and are even now heading for their own destruction. Drawn too close together by their greed for NGC 7174, they run the risk of collision. If so, where there was once a group, eventually there will be a single giant galaxy, providing a home for tens to hundreds of times the number of stars in the Milky Way. Such apparently catastrophic collisions are a natural, necessary and not unusual part of galactic life: deep space resounds to the clash of galaxies **[1, 2 & 3]**.

___But it is not always like this. Sometimes, these modest groupings can be elegantly dispersed so that each galaxy has its own space to perform a graceful minuet, rather than HCG 90's feverish tarantella.

NGC 4696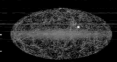
ELLIPTICAL GALAXY
DIAMETER: 50,000 LY

LIGHT SECONDS
LIGHT MINUTES
LIGHT YEARS
KILO LIGHT YEARS
MEGA LIGHT YEARS
GIGA LIGHT YEARS

The memory of youth

If our eyes could see in X-rays, this is what galaxies would look like. Their stars hidden away, all that remains to be seen are the high-temperature gas clouds. At the centre of this throng, directing its motion, lies a supermassive black hole.

One in ten of all galaxies displays some sort of remarkable activity springing from its core. It cannot be coming from stars alone because the quantity and type of light does not match. Instead, the central engine is a supermassive black hole containing anything from a few million to a few billion times the mass of the Sun.

___The black hole itself cannot release energy. Once matter crosses the outer boundary known as the event horizon, it ceases to be able to communicate in any way with the outside Universe – this is what makes a black hole black. But on the way to their doom, the gases heat up significantly and radiate copious quantities of farewell energy.

___In the supermassive black holes found in the young galaxies called quasars, this energy shines across space as ultraviolet and visible wavelengths. It is so intense that, despite being billions of light years away, the quasars were initially confused with stars. This even gave rise to their name, which stands for quasi-stellar object.

___In this particular galaxy, things are a little more sedate even though the black hole is still clearly in charge. NGC 4696 [1] is an elliptical galaxy and the brightest member of the Centaurus Cluster, a conglomeration of hundreds of galaxies located about 150 million light years from Earth.

___The X-rays show up as red and betray vast mottled clouds of hot gas. The blue lobes on either side of the galaxy's core are 10,000-light-year-wide bubbles, hollowed out by particle jets generated by the strong magnetic fields that are formed in the vicinity of the black hole.

___The turbulence that this creates within the galaxy's corpus of gas is enough to prevent new stars from forming. Any small knots of gas that do begin to form will soon by swept away and dispersed back into the galaxy.

___In its youth, this galaxy was almost certainly a tearaway, blazing across space as a quasar during those formative years. Even though it has now settled down, the X-ray glow at its heart shows that it still remembers what it was like to be young and powerful.

Perseus A
NGC 1275
ACTIVE GALAXY
DIAMETER: 100,000 LY

LIGHT SECONDS
LIGHT MINUTES
LIGHT YEARS
KILO LIGHT YEARS
MEGA LIGHT YEARS
GIGA LIGHT YEARS

Magnetic monster

Like a circular saw slicing through a tree trunk, a spiral galaxy has scythed its way into a larger elliptical. The resulting catastrophe has unleashed a powerful response from the black hole at the heart of the elliptical galaxy.

The dark dust lanes of the attacking galaxy's spiral arms symbolize the teeth of this particular saw blade. It appears to have gone straight for its victim's heart, aiming for the very centre and colliding headlong with the destructive black hole lurking there.

___It has made a particularly foolhardy choice of victim. NGC 1275, also known as Perseus A, is a monumental elliptical galaxy. It sits at the centre of the Perseus Cluster and directs the movement of the other galaxies. Its response to this vicious assault has been immediate and devastating.

___The interplay of titanic forces around Perseus A's central black hole has resulted in the creation of magnetized bubbles of gas, only visible at X-ray energies [1], that have grown to enormous size. Each one now spans

50,000 light years, half the width of our Galaxy.

Smaller bubbles have risen faster and further, drawing out colder gas behind them to create shining threads that stretch for 20,000 light years into the surrounding intergalactic space. Typically just 200 light years wide, and containing enough gas to make a million stars like the Sun, the threads are so long they must have been forming for 100 million years.

___It is initially baffling that the threads can be this old. The gaseous strands are tens of millions of degrees cooler than the surrounding intergalactic gas and so they should have been buffeted and blown about, losing their carefully delineated shapes long ago. If the winds in the 70,000,000 °C intergalactic medium failed to disrupt them, then the gravity of the parent galaxy should have ripped them apart. But no

something is magically holding them in place.

___In fact, it is not magic but magnetism. Magnetic fields must be corralling these threads, binding them together and strengthening them against the destructive forces that would otherwise seek to bring them down. The more fragile-looking the filament, the stronger the magnetic bracing required to keep it stable.

___The pulled threads of NGC 1275 are a striking example of intergalactic magnetic fields and highlight another way, other than gravity, that the supermassive black holes in giant galaxies reach out and attempt to control their wider environments.

190

990.0
LIGHT SECONDS
LIGHT MINUTES
LIGHT YEARS
KILO LIGHT YEARS
MEGA LIGHT YEARS
GIGA LIGHT YEARS

Towards the Great Attractor

Galaxies glow green in this colour-coded image of the
Norma Cluster. Thousands of galaxies are estimated to live
here. Moreover, this is no ordinary galaxy cluster; it sits in
a gravitational anomaly known as the Great Attractor.

Many galaxies are part of larger groupings.
If the group contains more than 100 individual
galaxies it is known as a cluster, and the
Norma Cluster is one of the largest in the
local Universe. It is estimated to contain the
equivalent of several thousand galaxies the
size of the Milky Way.

___It sits in a region that was dubbed the Great
Attractor because, when the movement of all
the galaxies in the nearby Universe is taken
into account, they are clearly streaming
towards the Norma Cluster at speeds of
hundreds or even thousands of kilometres
per second. Millions of galaxies are involved
in this headlong rush through space, tiny
trails of hot gas streaming behind them [1].

___The cluster, while massive, does not
seem to contain anything like the necessary

abundance of galaxies to perform this feat of
attraction and so, for a while, it was thought
that this region of space must contain an
egregious quantity of extra matter, and most
of it probably in a form unknown on Earth.
Such 'dark matter' would outweigh the normal
matter by ten to one.

___Calculations showed that it must be
spread over an area 400 million light years
across. However, fate has rendered the region
largely invisible as it sits hidden behind the
bulk of the Milky Way in the Zone of Avoidance,
locked away from further investigation.
To underline this cosmic censorship, the
stars of the Milky Way in this direction appear
as dense as snowflakes in a blizzard, as if
occupied in the attempt to conceal the distant
galaxies from view.

___Recently, however, the Great Attractor has
been shown to be an imposter. While there is
a clear enhancement of matter in this region
of space, it is not as large as first thought. We
were being fooled by an even larger collection
of galaxies lurking behind the Norma Cluster.

___Called the Shapley Supercluster this
gargantuan grouping is responsible for
dragging the Milky Way and all the other
galaxies in the nearby groups and clusters.
Approximately 650 million light years away,
the supercluster is a cluster of galaxy clusters,
containing 20 times the number of galaxies
as there are in our immediate galactic
neighbourhood. It is the largest concentration
of galaxies in the nearby Universe and it is
making sure we don't ignore it.

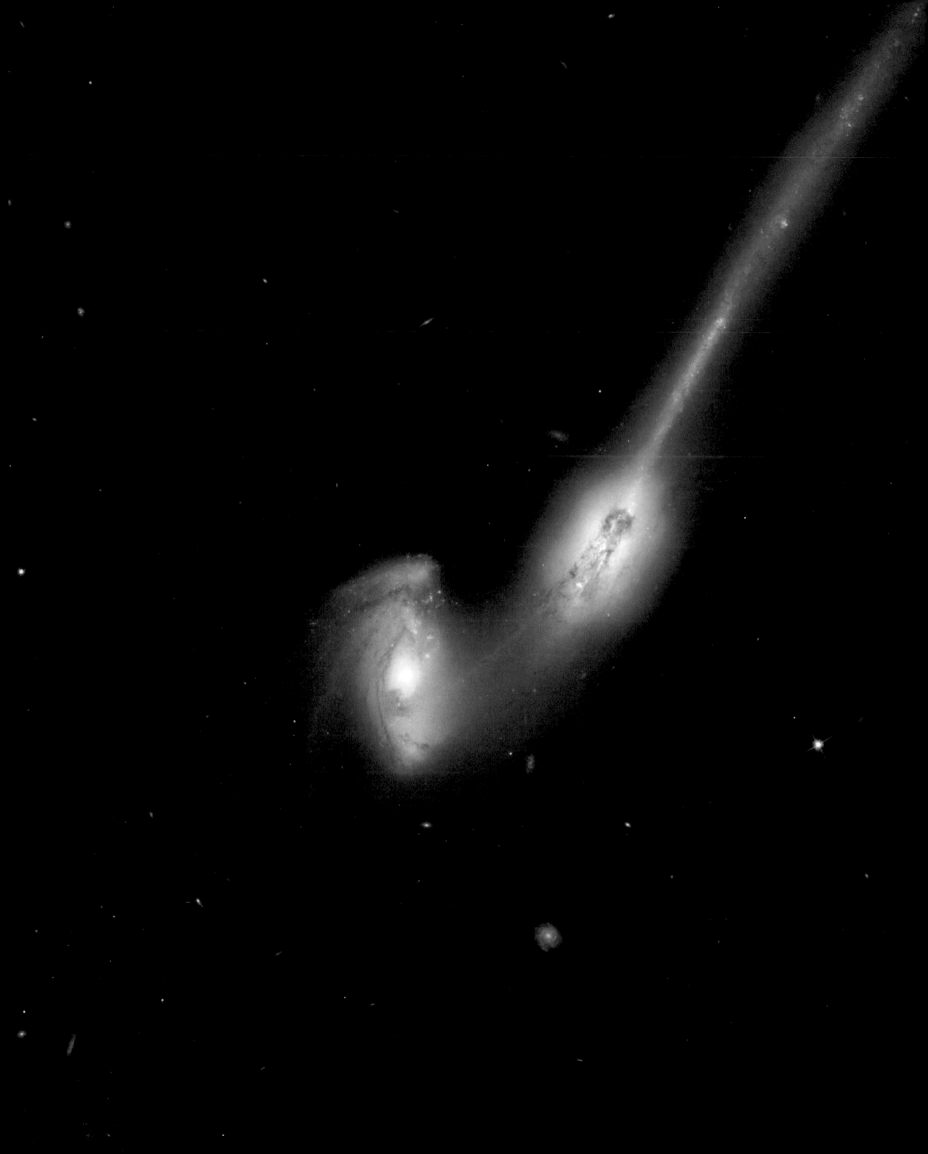

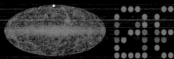 

LIGHT SECONDS
LIGHT MINUTES
LIGHT YEARS
KILO LIGHT YEARS
MEGA LIGHT YEARS
GIGA LIGHT YEARS

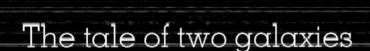

1   2   3

The tale of two galaxies

These colliding galaxies are known as the Mice because
of the starry tails that stretch out behind them, but if you
were to speed up time they would remind you more of a
massing flock of starlings swooping and merging as the
fancy took them.

In reality, the drama of these merging galaxies
will play out in apparent slow motion over
the course of billions of years. But if the cosmic
film could be speeded up, then their behaviour
would seem very different. Its the old story:
galaxy meets galaxy against the cold backdrop
of space, they feel an immediate attraction,
but then it all starts to go horribly wrong.
Snapshots of three other merging galaxies
stand in to provide the opening frames of
the story, showing this first encounter [1, 2 & 3].
___Then, as the Mice circle each other, so the
tails lose their blue sheen as the massive stars
die. They tarnish to the dull yellow of longer-
lived stars, before experiencing a final flush
as those stars swell into red giants and die.
___The galaxies draw ever closer and their
stars surge this way and that like flocks of
birds until eventually the two galaxies plunge

together forming a single system of stars.
The newly formed gestalt galaxy wobbles
like a jelly, as the stars jostle for position,
acclimatizing to the suddenly cramped
environment in which they find themselves.
___But the real drama is just starting. Across
the galaxy, the individual clouds of dust and
gas are ploughing into one another, triggering
giant compression waves as they slam
together. As they merge, growing darker and
more menacing with each passing moment,
eventually something has to give. When the
celestial thunderhead finally bursts, jagged
forks of star formation leap across the clouds.
Initially red with the hue of fluorescent
hydrogen, they turn almost immediately to
blue as the searing brilliance of the most
massive stars reveals itself. Then abruptly
the fireworks really start.

___Star after star bursts vividly and then
disappears from view. These are supernovae.
They blast bubbles in the galaxy, transforming
the dense environs into Swiss cheese. Dust
and gas are launched away into space, only to
form fountains of matter as the galaxy jealously
grabs them back, pulling them down into the
fold once more.
___Eventually, when all the spare dust and
gas have been used up and the maelstrom
has died down, the surviving stars are left to
huddle together. Comforted by the warm glow
of their fellows, they apparently settle to their
new way of life as an elliptical galaxy. But the
newly enlarged galaxy is constantly alert. Its
bolstered gravitational field is ready to grasp
and consume any tasty galactic morsel that
strays too close.

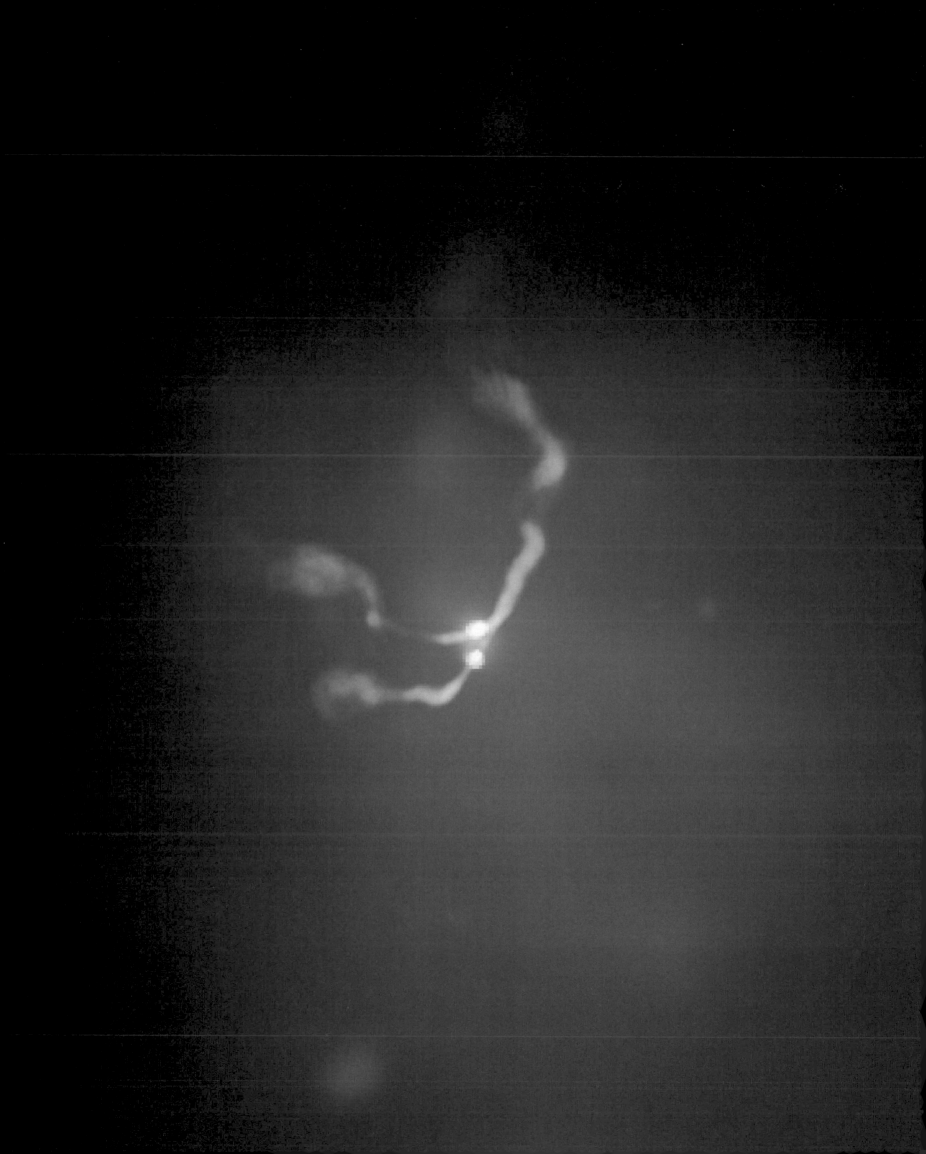

LIGHT SECONDS
LIGHT MINUTES
LIGHT YEARS
KILO LIGHT YEARS
MEGA LIGHT YEARS
GIGA LIGHT YEARS

1

2

Black hole collision

This cosmic X-ray of a colliding galaxy pair sees right
through the stars and into the guts of the system. It
shows a brace of supermassive black holes heading
for a deadly heart to heart – a collision that will unleash
a blast of energy more powerful than the light of every
single star in the Universe combined.

Trailing devil horns of gas, these two gigantic black holes are heading for Armageddon. Once upon a time, each was the heart of a separate galaxy. Now the galaxies are merging to form a larger collection of stars, and the black holes are circling each other like predators, sizing each other up before a duel.

___As they complete each revolution of the other, so they inch closer. They are spiralling together, separated now by just 25,000 light years and plunging headlong through their ever-decreasing orbits at 1,200 km/s. This is just the first of three phases.

___The second phase happens quickly and is known as the plunge. This is the moment when the black holes touch. Exactly what happens next is unknown for sure because black holes continue to defy our understanding, but most likely there will be an extraordinary release

of energy – bad news for the merging galaxy in which they live.

___The calculated quantities of energy that will be liberated in the plunge defy imagination. Such an event is second only to the Big Bang itself in terms of the energy that is released. In the case of the Big Bang, the Universe was created and all of cosmic history was set in motion. For a black hole merger, the burst could spell death and destruction for hundreds of thousands of star systems. The radiation will vaporize nearby stars and planets, rip atmospheres off otherwise habitable worlds, and blast away clouds of star-forming material. Not only this, it will set the very fabric of space quivering in this third and final phase, known as the ringdown.

___Space itself acts like netting, supporting

the Universe's various celestial heavyweights. Catastrophic meetings of extreme mass, such as black-hole mergers, set off disturbances in this netting that ripple through space at the speed of light. They distort the shape of everything they pass through: stars, planets, moons – nothing escapes their temporary warping ability.

___But the size of the distortion is so small, being just a fraction of the width of a hydrogen atom's nucleus, that so far such ripples have completely evaded detection.

___3C 75 is not the only object doomed to suffer this fate. NGC 6240 also harbours two supermassive black holes spiralling towards each other [1]. Already their interaction has lit X-ray fires that threaten to engulf the galaxy [2].

The time of giants

This is the shape and size of things to come. Across the
Universe, where currently there are whole groups of
galaxies, eventually only gargantuan ellipticals will
remain. The subtle dwarfs and the splendid spirals that
once ruled space will all have merged together, giving
rise to giant unstructured galaxies.

Although referred to as a fossil group, NGC
1132 really demonstrates a taste of things
to come. It was once a collection of dozens
of galaxies, all bound in gravitational
brotherhood. But as time has passed, so the
brothers lost energy and inched towards
the centre of the group, making things more
crowded and pushing up the chances of
collision. One-by-one, the galaxies slammed
into one another. In the resulting havoc,
stars were flung from their established orbits
and the bulk of the galaxies merged together
into a single indistinguishable clump of stars.

____The survivors of those numerous collisions
are the thousands of orphaned globular
clusters that now swarm around this galaxy,
each parent digested somewhere inside
NGC 1132's lustrous bulk. The globulars
themselves look like stars in this image but,
by pinpointing them, subtle differences such
as the age of their stars and their compositions,
can reveal how many galaxies went into the
making of this giant.

____Switch to X-ray wavelengths [1] and NGC
1132 becomes larger still, sitting in an ocean of
hot gas ten times larger than the collection of
stars. This gas has been heated by the violence
of the collisions and spread throughout space
as a tenuous mist, far too insubstantial to clump
together to form new stars. As future aeons

pass it will gradually cool and sink back
down towards the giant elliptical.

____Our own Galaxy seems destined to become
a giant elliptical. The process may already
have begun, because the Milky Way and the
Andromeda Galaxy are heading towards each
other. The two spirals are closing at a speed
of 120 km/s but, given that there are 2.5 million
light years separating the two, any collision
is still more than 3.5 billion years in the
future. By this time, the Earth will already be
uninhabitable because of the Sun's evolution
to higher temperatures.

LIGHT SECONDS
LIGHT MINUTES
LIGHT YEARS
KILO LIGHT YEARS
MEGA LIGHT YEARS
GIGA LIGHT YEARS

Fountain of youth

Anaemic is the only word that can describe this galaxy. Its pallid arms are revealed in infrared as glowing milky white, and star formation has all but stopped. With no new stars to replenish its bulk, this galaxy could even be dying.

NGC 4921 is undoubtedly a faded beauty. Its remaining structure, while delicate, is a mere palimpsest of what it must have been. In its prime, this galaxy would have drawn attention to its graceful arms by draping them in azure-blue stars, bold indicators of youth and beauty. Now, the only signs of stellar vigour are to be found in a dusty necklace surrounding the nucleus. Here, massive stars are visible, radiating their characteristic blue light.

___The rest of the galaxy is simply fading away as the stars die out. In another billion years or so, the arms will probably have withdrawn completely into the shadows. At that point, NGC 4921 will have to be reclassified as a lenticular galaxy. All that will remain is the central stock of stars in the elongated nucleus.

___As if that were not bad enough, the galaxy is bleeding hydrogen into space, losing the very gas that could make new stars. But there may just be a fountain of youth from which to revive this galaxy.

___It exists in a rich assemblage of other galaxies called the Coma Cluster [1]. The galaxies float like islands in a vast ocean of gas and are composed almost exclusively of large ellipticals and lenticulars.

___In dense clusters such as Coma, spiral galaxies tend to be endangered species. The crowded environment promotes interactions and mergers that erode the delicate patterns and transform the spirals into messy elliptical galaxies. As a result there are fewer spirals in this 1,000-strong grouping than in other quieter

corners of the Universe. Of those that do live here NGC 4921, despite its palid appearance, remains the brightest.

___But encounters need not always be destructive. As the myriad galaxies weave their orbits, they often draw close without actually colliding. Proximity allows the galactic neighbours to gravitationally reach out and touch each other. Such interactions can reignite quiescent galaxies, breathing new fire into them by prompting the remaining gas clouds to collapse in frenzies of star formation.

___If this were to happen to NGC 4921 it would experience a brief renaissance, a final lease of life before the inevitability of age caught up with it once and for all.

LIGHT SECONDS
LIGHT MINUTES
LIGHT YEARS
KILO LIGHT YEARS
MEGA LIGHT YEARS
GIGA LIGHT YEARS

1

Another brick in the wall

Unlike the larger, richer clusters, which tend to destroy their spiral galaxies in collisions, Hercules is more sedate and the pace of life is slower. But, this doesn't mean that the Hercules Cluster is some galactic backwater, it is actually part of the largest structure we have yet come across.

A hundred galaxies gather together in loose association in the Hercules Cluster. Most of them are spirals, affording us a look at what many clusters used to be like before infighting produced populations of mostly elliptical galaxies.

___Within the extended family of this cluster, there are a number of smaller units. Arp 272 is a beautiful pair of galaxies [1]. Look closely and they appear to be cradling a third, smaller galaxy in their arms. Yet these galaxies are anything but loving parents; the same old fights are kicking off, driven by the same gravitational jealousies and greed.

___These two galaxies are in a neck-and-neck race to consume the smaller galaxy. Not even that will satiate their appetites, once they have despatched their hapless victim, they will turn on each other, each galaxy attempting to

cannibalize the other. The only winners in this dog-eat-dog situation will be the three giant black holes, one from each galaxy. They will gorge themselves on as much of the stellar carrion as they can before merging into a single supermassive black hole. When that has happened, the galaxy will take its place with the other ellipticals in the cluster.

___There is a marked difference in the colours of the different galaxy types. Blue marks out the recently formed, short-lived stars in the spirals while gold denotes the older, long-lived stars, which dominate elliptical galaxies. Yet, 400 million light years from Earth, individual galaxies are becoming less important, relegated to the status of building blocks for the clusters of galaxies that dominate the Universe on this scale.

___The Hercules Cluster itself is the densest

collection of galaxies within a larger gravitationally bound structure called the Hercules Supercluster. Whereas the clusters and the superclusters are cloud-like, their three dimensions being roughly equal, there is a marked change of shape in the larger groupings. There are no cloud-like mega-clusters. Instead there are long wall-like filaments and sheets of galaxies, and the Hercules Cluster is just another brick in the Great Wall.

___Stretching for a length of at least 500 million light years and a height of 300 million light years, this extraordinary structure of galaxies is just 15 million light years deep. And the length of the Great Wall is a conservative estimate, because it disappears behind the Milky Way's Zone of Avoidance and is lost from view.

LIGHT SECONDS
LIGHT MINUTES
LIGHT YEARS
KILO LIGHT YEARS
MEGA LIGHT YEARS
GIGA LIGHT YEARS

Knight in shining armour

This galactic knight is ready for the joust. Its lance of stars is poised, 280,000 light years long. But there is something missing from this contest. While the galaxy has obviously been damaged from a previous round, at first sight there is no sign of its opponent.

Tadpole-like tidal tails are not uncommon [1&2], but there is something unusual about this particular one. Wherever they appear, they are a sure sign of a grand gravitational conflict between two galaxies. But in this image only one somewhat battered barred spiral is obvious. Six thousand other galaxies share the image but not one of them can be the missing combatant because they are all much further away. They are there simply to provide a tapestry backdrop.

The mystery of the missing galaxy deepens. For a while it was thought that perhaps an entirely invisible galaxy was crossing swords with the Tadpole, and we were seeing just the visible portion of this galaxy's struggle with the dark side.

A plethora of star clusters have been kindled by the galaxy collision. These are not just visible along the tidal tail but around the spiral arms too. Each one of these stellar associations can contain around a million stars, each one 10 times hotter than the Sun and a million times brighter.

But wait, there is something bigger buried in there too – much bigger – near the nucleus of the Tadpole. Just to its top left is a knot of stars much too large to be a star cluster. It is the core of the interloping galaxy. It must be a dense galaxy, punching well above its weight to take on the whole Tadpole. It has passed by once, drawing out the tidal tail and is currently 300,000 light years behind the Tadpole.

No one knows whether the small galaxy has finished harassing the larger one or whether it has more mischief in mind. Assuming that it now decides against a second pass, then the Tadpole Galaxy, just like its terrestrial namesake, will eventually lose its tail as the bright stars fade away. But a legacy will remain; a couple of dwarf galaxies are forming within the tail. They will linger in train with the main galaxy, or may even begin orbiting around it.

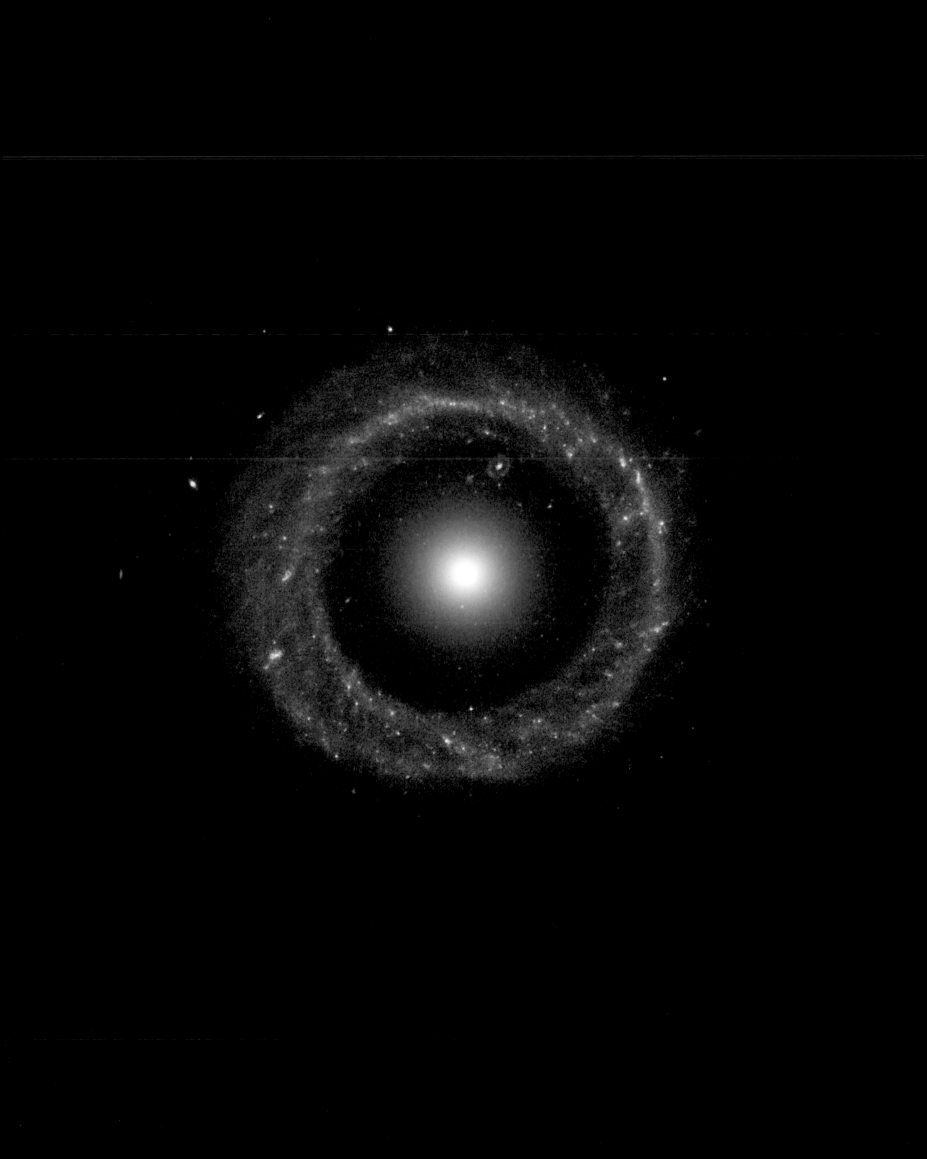

600.0
LIGHT SECONDS
LIGHT MINUTES
LIGHT YEARS
KILO LIGHT YEARS
MEGA LIGHT YEARS
GIGA LIGHT YEARS

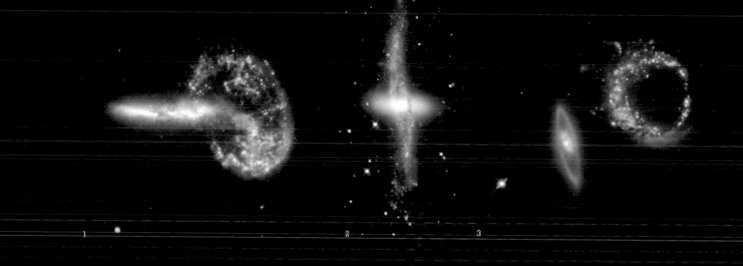

1 2 3

Direct hit

Hoag's Object took it on the chin. Another galaxy
smacked it fairly and squarely, passed straight through
and continued on its way. In response, a shockwave
developed around Hoag's old nucleus, creating this
shimmering halo of new stars.

Such intergalactic bull's eyes are rare events,
afflicting far less than one percent of the
galaxies in the Universe. Even when such a
ring galaxy forms, it is usually distorted in
some way. Hoag's Object is remarkable for its
delectable symmetry: a spherical nucleus in
the dead centre of the perfectly circular ring
of stars.

___As rare as ring galaxies are, by the luckiest
of cosmic coincidences another one appears in
the background, reddened by its distance and
shrunken by perspective. Nevertheless, it is
another almost perfect ring galaxy.

___Most ring galaxies are thought to form
as one galaxy passes through another. Such
an encounter is dramatically captured in
Arp 148 [1]. Like a bullet through a bubble, the

target galaxy gives the illusion of having been
shattered by the impact. Both galaxies have
been distorted by the collision but, in this case,
only one will emerge as a ring galaxy.

___An incredible double pair of ring galaxies
form the Arp 147 system [3]. Although they
lack the perfect symmetry of Hoag's Object,
they are a vanishingly rare sight. The starry
blue ring, some 30,000 light years in diameter,
was most probably created when the galaxy
on the left dived through an existing spiral
galaxy. The orange knot at the lower left of the
blue ring is the vestige of the target galaxy's
original nucleus. But most fittingly, in a rare
case of poetic justice, the left-hand intruder has
also been transformed by the encounter into
a ring galaxy.

___There is a subset of galaxies that are
more puzzling. They are called the polar
ring galaxies [2] and, as the name suggests,
their adornments are not equatorial but
perpendicular. They are still formed when
two galaxies approach each other too closely
but, instead of one galaxy slamming through
the other, the larger one drapes the smaller
around itself like a scarf on a winter's day.
Or it draws out a seam of gas, transforming
it into a starry necklace.

___Some polar rings are to be found around
elliptical galaxies. However, most of them
surround lenticular galaxies, indicating that
the central galaxy paid for its adornment by
losing its spiral arms,

INTER
TEMPORAL

we finally reach the largest scales of the Universe.
Just as planets gave way to stars, which gave way
to galaxies as our vista expanded, now the galaxies
give way to the clusters. On distances of over a billion
light years, we see a significant fraction of the cosmos,
and the large-scale structure is revealed: a cosmic
web of galaxy clusters that string themselves across
the entire Universe.

Each cluster contains from a few hundred to
a few thousand galaxies. These collections
can be elongated or spherical in shape, and
can contain predominantly spirals or be
overwhelmingly composed of elliptical
galaxies. There are numerous smaller groups,
each of a few dozen galaxies or so, but on these
cosmic scales they are too small to concern us.

___It is the distribution of the clusters that
catches the eye on these scales. They are but
individual enhancements in the much larger
grouping, superclusters that twist through
space. They are strung into filaments that
weave around large empty bubbles of cosmic
wasteland, the voids.

___Also at this scale, gravity begins to lose its
overwhelming influence. So far in our journey,
all the celestial objects we have encountered
have been bound together by this universal
force. Now, the distances are vast enough that
gravity is so weakened that other factors come
into play. One of the most obvious is the
expansion of the Universe.

___In the big bang, our Universe's most
extraordinary moment of creation, all matter
and energy were created and hurled outwards
at tremendous force. It set the Universe into a
state of expansion that continues to this very
day. Early in Universal history, all matter
followed this expansion, carried along like
so much flotsam on the cosmic ocean. But as
gravity went to work, so pockets of gas drew
themselves together, becoming islands in
which gravity was the master.

___Today these islands are the clusters of
galaxies, in which the cosmic drama plays out
on the individual stages of galaxies, stars and
planets, and the clusters are bound to others
creating the archipelagos of the superclusters.

___Mysteries abound at these scales, not
only are we pushing the limits of our ability
to see, we are also encountering the current
boundaries of human knowledge. There are
strong hints that other forces are at work on
these scales, forces that build up and only
become apparent over cosmic distances.
For example, the movement of galaxies
within individual clusters is much faster than
we expect. Something must be pulling them
harder than our understanding of gravity
allows. Could this mean that we simply do
not understand how gravity works on these
distances? Or does it mean that there is more

matter hidden in the galaxies themselves? If it
is extra matter, it must be invisible and totally
different to normal atoms or our understanding
of the way the chemical elements have built
up in the Universe will be invalidated. To
differentiate the hypothetical stuff from atoms,
it is called dark matter.

___Just as galaxies occasionally collide,
so whole galaxy clusters can smash into
one another. Such impacts give us clues that
can either be interpreted in favour of dark
matter or in favour of a modified theory of
gravity. As yet, there is no way to tell, although
the weight of modern opinion rests on the side
of dark matter.

___As the space between superclusters
continues to expand, driving them ever further
away from one another, so the fate of the
Universe rests in the strength of gravity versus
this expansion. Gravity is subtle, and has time
on its side. It will tenaciously attempt to still
the cosmic expansion, clawing back the
superclusters little by little. If there is sufficient
matter – atomic or dark – to generate enough
gravity, then the expansion will be reversed
and everything will eventually fall back
together, creating an inescapable Armageddon
called the big crunch. If there is not enough
mass, then the Universe will continue to
expand forever, eventually driving the
superclusters so far away from one another
that they become lost to each other's sight.

___In the fight over the fate of the Universe
another dark force has come to light. Although
its nature is dimly perceived at present, it
appears that a weak form of antigravity may
permeate the universe. This unanticipated
force of nature has been termed 'dark energy'
to emphazize its unknown nature. If it exists, it
is not predicted by any current theory. It might
not be a force; it could be a form of energy in
space, or an unanticipated aspect of gravity.

___Or it could simply be an illusion brought
about because we happen to live in a lower
density region of the cosmos. With less gravity
being generated around, so the expansion of
space can move faster.

___Distances and motions are not the only
confounding issues in the intertemporal zone.
As the name suggests, our perception and
treatment of time needs to be taken into account.
At the simplest level, this means that light has
taken billions of years to cross these distances

and that in that time, not only have the celestial
objects changed but the expansion of space
has driven them ever further away. So what we
perceive to have been located at 13 billion light
years distance, will in reality be much further
away, out to some 45 billion light years or so.

___As if that was not brain-bending enough,
the rate at which time passes changes from
place to place as well. This is because time
is affected by gravity, which behaves like
molasses, retarding every natural process
and effectively slowing down time.

___If we were to measure the age of the
cosmos in a region of space with a greater
density of galaxies and other matter, we would
register a younger Universal age because the
gravity in that region has forced the clock to
run more slowly. If so, it means our perception
of the age of the Universe may not tally with
other age estimates elsewhere. In this case, the
Universe would not just be a cosmic landscape
but a cosmic timescape as well.

___At the furthest limits of our view is the
cosmic microwave background radiation.
This universal barrier prevents us looking any
further through time or space; it walls off the
big band from our direct view. The cosmic
microwave background shows us what the
Universe looked like just 380,000 years after the
big bang, when all space was filled with just
a diffuse ocean of gas. A few slight crests and
troughs were the only variation that existed
and they became the large-scale structure of
galaxies that we see today.

___But what of the big bang? What was it?
What set it into motion? In other words,
why did our Universe begin? No one knows.
Ideas abound; from believing that it is just a
statistical quantum fluke, to the idea that it is
the aftermath of two whole universes colliding.
But as yet, we have no real evidence for
either. Only when our ideas of space and
time, matter and energy, force and motion
are more developed will we stand any chance
of moving towards a wider understanding.

___And it is this journey that makes the
Universe such a rewarding thing to study.
The more we look, the more we find, the more
knowledge we possess, the richer the ever
wider Universe becomes.

Right: a computer simulation reveals a web of dark
matter filaments flecked with bright galaxies

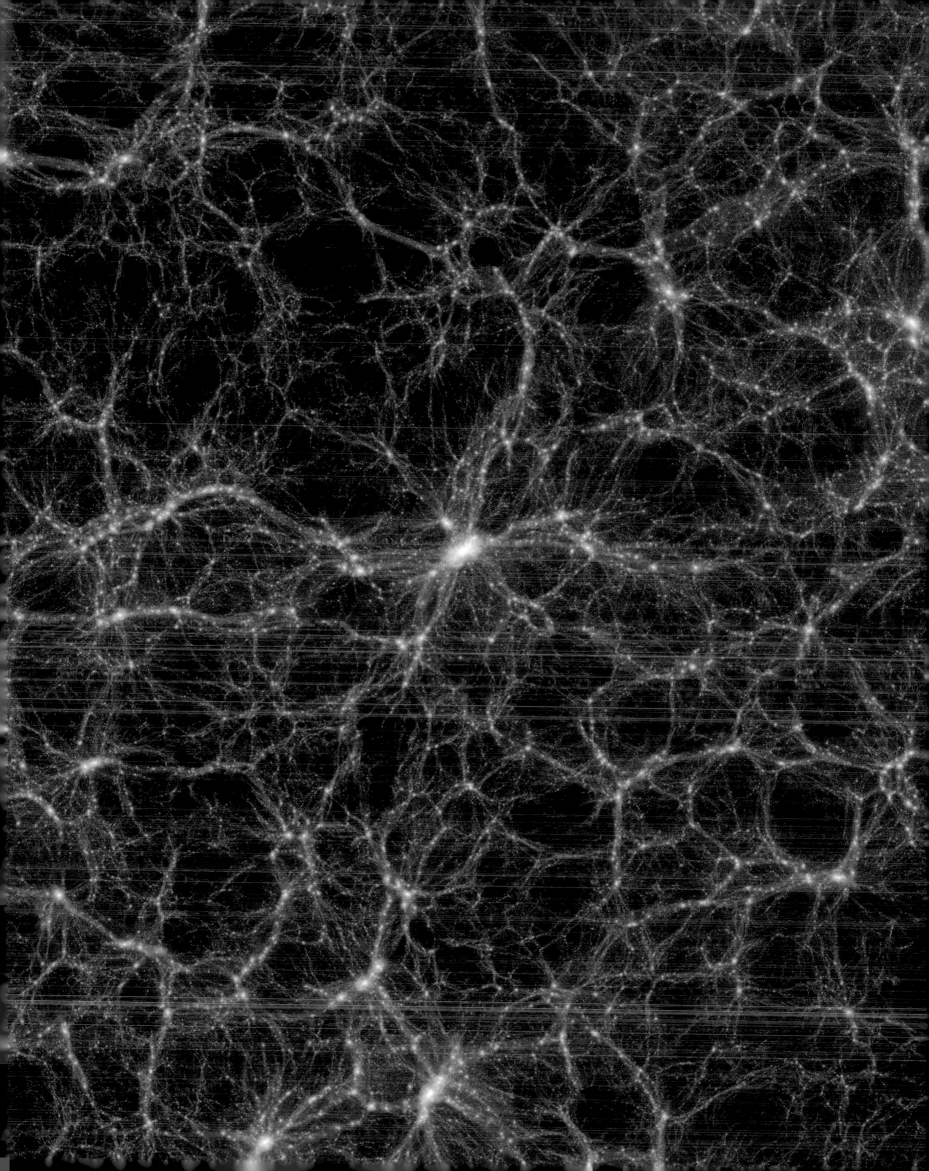

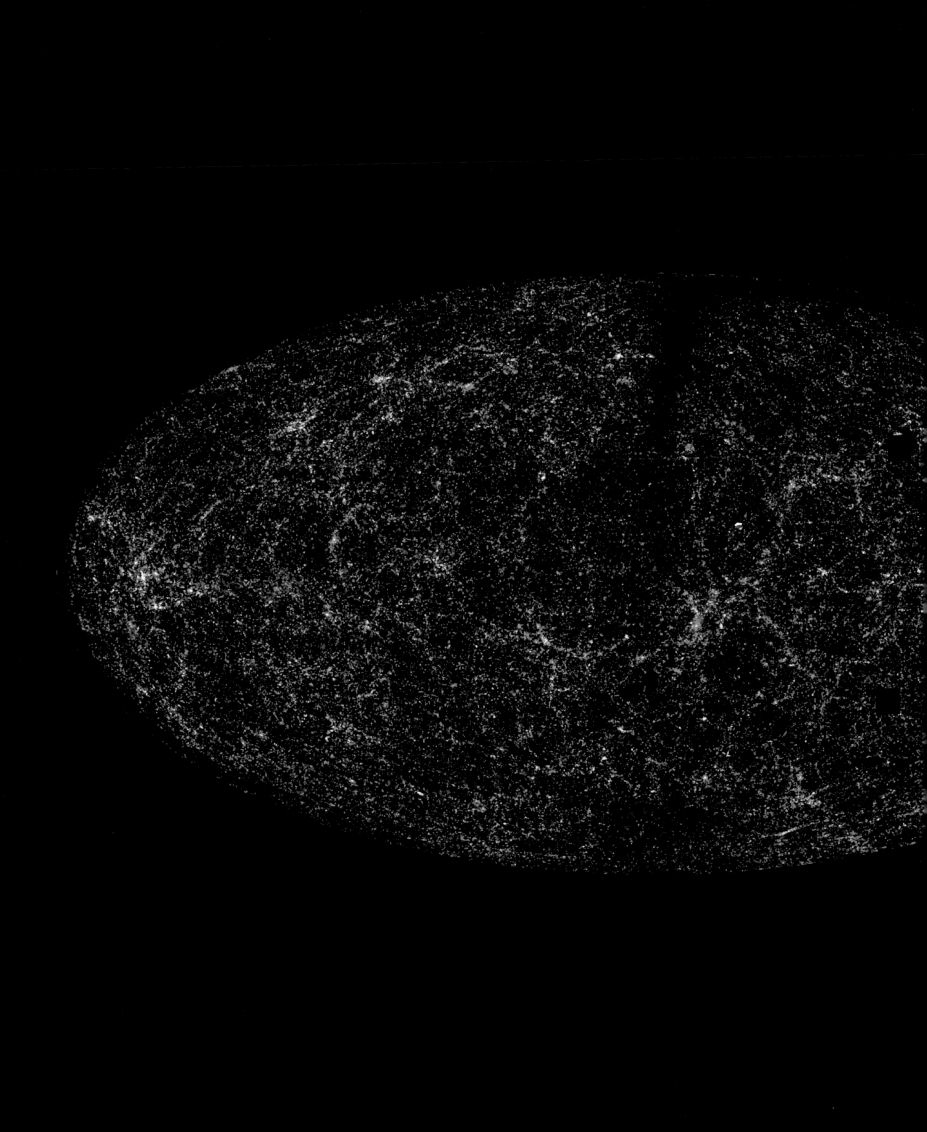

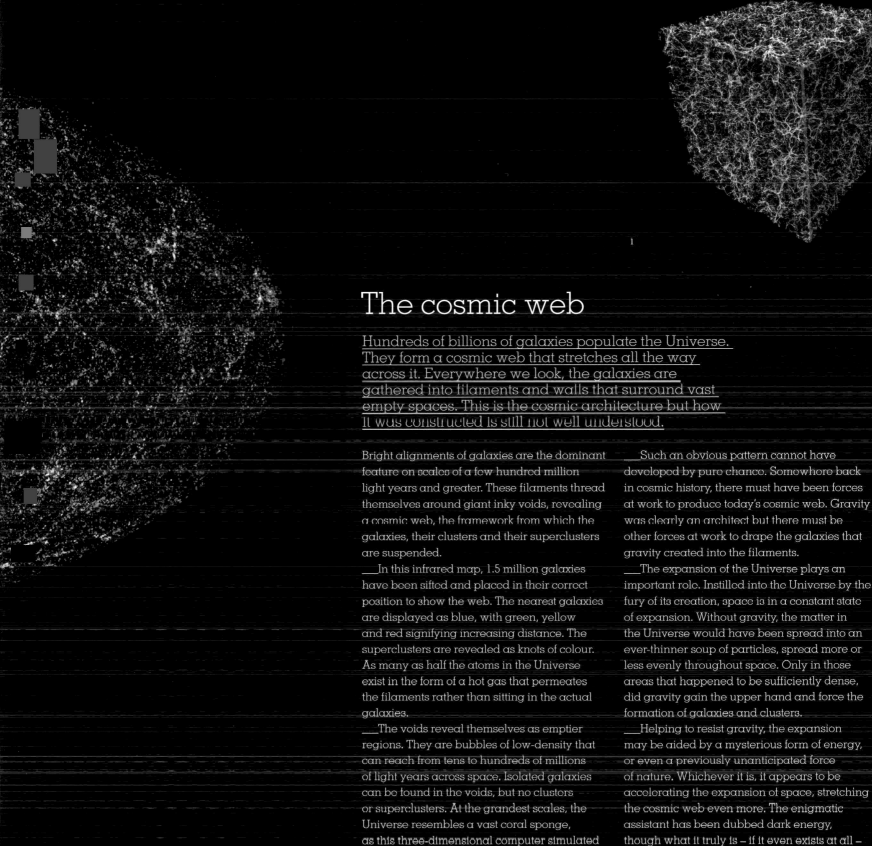

The cosmic web

Hundreds of billions of galaxies populate the Universe. They form a cosmic web that stretches all the way across it. Everywhere we look, the galaxies are gathered into filaments and walls that surround vast empty spaces. This is the cosmic architecture but how it was constructed is still not well understood.

Bright alignments of galaxies are the dominant feature on scales of a few hundred million light years and greater. These filaments thread themselves around giant inky voids, revealing a cosmic web, the framework from which the galaxies, their clusters and their superclusters are suspended.

___In this infrared map, 1.5 million galaxies have been sifted and placed in their correct position to show the web. The nearest galaxies are displayed as blue, with green, yellow and red signifying increasing distance. The superclusters are revealed as knots of colour. As many as half the atoms in the Universe exist in the form of a hot gas that permeates the filaments rather than sitting in the actual galaxies.

___The voids reveal themselves as emptier regions. They are bubbles of low-density that can reach from tens to hundreds of millions of light years across space. Isolated galaxies can be found in the voids, but no clusters or superclusters. At the grandest scales, the Universe resembles a vast coral sponge, as this three-dimensional computer simulated chunk of spacetime shows [1].

___Such an obvious pattern cannot have developed by pure chance. Somewhere back in cosmic history, there must have been forces at work to produce today's cosmic web. Gravity was clearly an architect but there must be other forces at work to drape the galaxies that gravity created into the filaments.

___The expansion of the Universe plays an important role. Instilled into the Universe by the fury of its creation, space is in a constant state of expansion. Without gravity, the matter in the Universe would have been spread into an ever-thinner soup of particles, spread more or less evenly throughout space. Only in those areas that happened to be sufficiently dense, did gravity gain the upper hand and force the formation of galaxies and clusters.

___Helping to resist gravity, the expansion may be aided by a mysterious form of energy, or even a previously unanticipated force of nature. Whichever it is, it appears to be accelerating the expansion of space, stretching the cosmic web even more. The enigmatic assistant has been dubbed dark energy, though what it truly is – if it even exists at all – remains unknown.

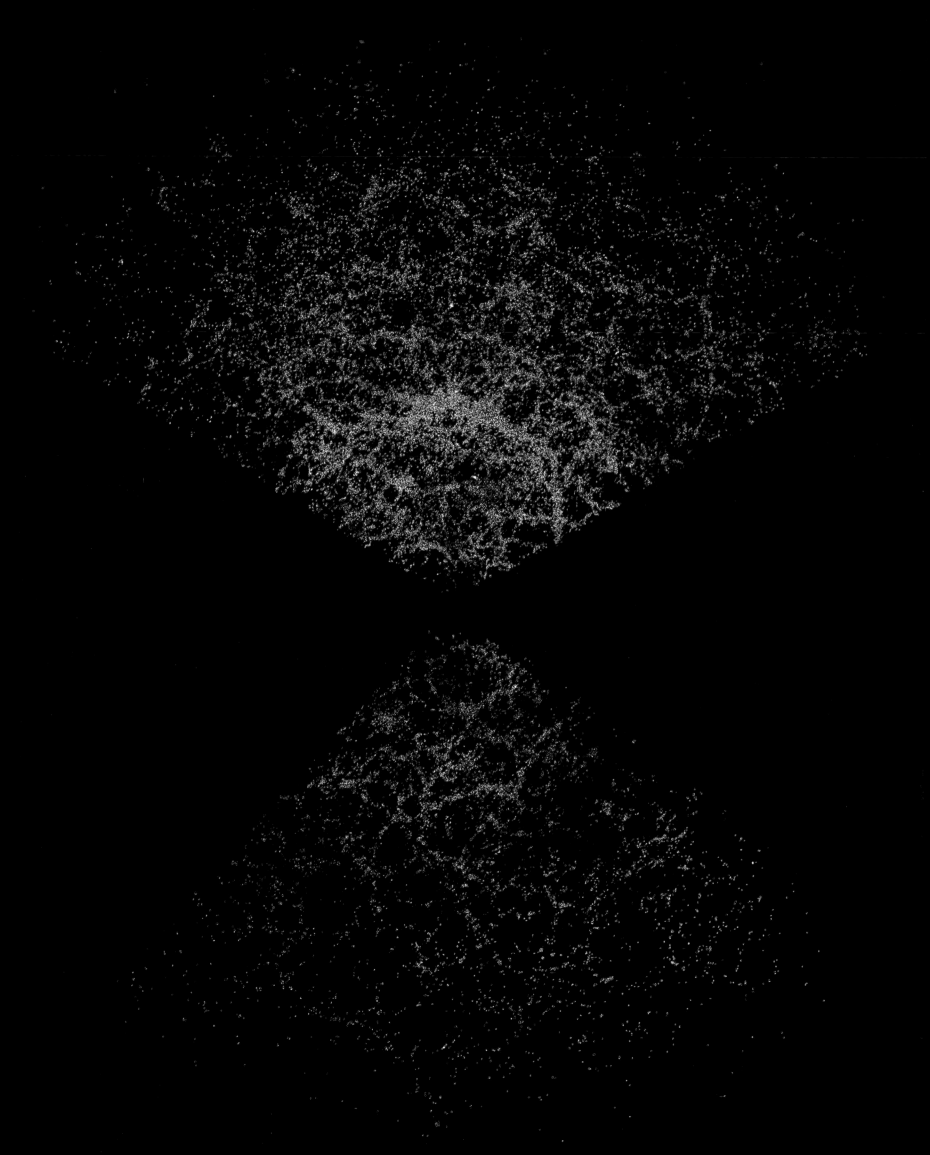

LIGHT SECONDS
LIGHT MINUTES
LIGHT YEARS
KILO LIGHT YEARS
MEGA LIGHT YEARS
GIGA LIGHT YEAR

The end of greatness

The Sloan Great Wall of galaxies measures approximately 1.37 billion light years across, at least twice the size of the previously encountered Great Wall. Situated a billion light years from Earth, and visible in this map as a bright arc across the top cone, Sloan is the largest known structure in the Universe. But is it really a structure?

The great walls are gargantuan sheets of galaxies, hundreds of millions of light years or more in length and width. Yet they are only tens of millions of light years deep. Five have been positively identified, with a handful of others under investigation. Our own Galaxy could be part of a great wall that stretches through the Local Supercluster and off in the direction of the southern constellation Centaurus. Verifying this association is difficult, however, because it passes through the Zone of Avoidance, behind the Milky Way.

___The Sloan Great Wall is so large that the gravity from one side has reduced to virtually nothing by the time it reaches the other. This means it cannot be a gravitationally bound object. Instead, it may be just a chance alignment of galaxy superclusters, a lingering memory of where they happened to form.

___It signals the end of greatness, a strange term perhaps to apply when we arrive at the very grandest scales of the Universe. But by greatness we mean the ability of gravity to bind objects together. At this scale or larger, the lumpiness created by gravity gives way to a more or less smooth distribution of matter. Each volume of space larger than 300 million light years contains roughly the same amount of mass as any other volume of a similar size.

___This is crucial to our understanding of the Universe as a whole because our current level of mathematical ability only allows us to calculate the behaviour of the cosmos if the distribution of matter is roughly uniform. Fluctuations will be present because of the random way the structures collapsed in the first place. Hence there will be chance alignments like the Sloan Great Wall and the mighty Eridanus Supervoid, which some estimates suggest stretches for almost a billion light years across space.

___Such deviations from uniformity are known as the cosmic variance and they will impact upon our understanding, making the Universe behave somewhat differently from the idealized calculations. But, by and large, the mass of the Universe on these scales can be thought of as homogeneously distributed.

LIGHT SECONDS
LIGHT MINUTES
LIGHT YEARS
KILO LIGHT YEARS
MEGA LIGHT YEARS
GIGA LIGHT YEARS

A secret matter

Thousands of galaxies from across space and time
dot this image. Only a few stars from our own Galaxy
show up; everything else represents individual
collections of billions of stars, shrunken to almost
point-like stellar proportions by their extreme distance.

The yellow galaxies in the lower left section of the image form the galactic metropolis called Abell 315. They are the galactic equivalent of bees around a hive, each travelling on a curving path but never straying too far away – and that's a riddle looking for a solution.

The paths these galaxies take should be dictated by the combined mass of their companions, which creates a cluster-wide gravitational field. The problem is that they are all moving too fast to be corralled by the gravity of their companions, even though each galaxy contains the mass of a few hundred billion stars. Taken at face value, this would mean this cluster is in the process of disintegration with each of the galaxies now intent on forging its own path through space. But such behaviour is repeated in every single

other galaxy cluster strewn throughout the entire universe.

They can't all be flying apart otherwise there would not be any left in the Universe today. So what does this mean? Either our understanding of gravity breaks down on the largest scales and the force pulls a little harder in those realms, or there are vast reserves of matter hiding in every galaxy and galaxy cluster.

If it is matter rather than the behaviour of gravity, then it cannot be formed from ordinary atoms or there would be many more galaxies – and the ones that we do have would be much bigger. Instead, it is possible that this invisible matter could be made up of undiscovered particles that played crucial roles during the origin of the Universe and the establishment of

its physical laws but are now relics, sitting in space like ash at the bottom of a fire. As such particles would not emit or absorb light (otherwise we would have seen them), their sole way of communicating with the rest of the Universe would be through the gravity they generate. As a result, they are collectively referred to as dark matter.

If this picture is true then each galaxy is the equivalent of an iceberg – a brightly visible tip atop a great bulk of hidden matter.

If, however, a misunderstanding of large-scale gravity is responsible for the gulf between a galaxy's mass and its gravitational influence, then we are going to need a contemporary Newton or Einstein to move our knowledge onwards.

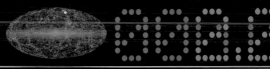

LIGHT SECONDS
LIGHT MINUTES
LIGHT YEARS
KILO LIGHT YEARS
MEGA LIGHT YEARS
GIGA LIGHT YEARS

1

2

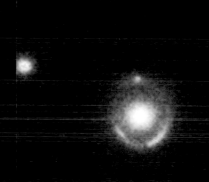

3

4

Space warp

The combined mass of this cluster of galaxies is so great that it visibly warps space around it. Light can no longer travel in straight lines through these buckled realms and so becomes distorted and even duplicated – but this offers an enormous bonus.

The thin blue cobwebs surrounding Abell 1689 are the malformed images of exceptionally distant galaxies, brought into view only because the gravity of this galaxy cluster acts like a gigantic natural zoom lens and amplifies the light.

___Just as diverging light rays are bent to a focus by a normal lens, be it a glass lens in a telescope or an organic one in an eye, so space can perform a similar feat. It takes the combined mass of trillions of stars, all held in a giant cluster of galaxies, to distort space so much that it takes on the shape of a lens two million light years wide.

___The more massive the cluster, the better it acts as a gravitational lens. Even then, it is a slightly peculiar one. Unlike a normal lens, it does not bring light to a sharp point but instead tries to spread it into a halo. If the alignment is perfect between the observer, the lens and the target object, then the image produced is a circle, known as an Einstein ring [1]. When the alignment is not ideal, arcs are created [2, 3 & 4].

___Abell 1689 lens sits 2.2 billion light years away and shows us hundreds of galaxies much further away, spread into the concentric threads of a cosmic spider's web. Some of these distorted galaxies date from the beginning of galaxy formation, a billion or so years after the big bang.

___The distribution of the cobwebs, especially where they deviate from a symmetrical pattern, allows the gravitational field of the lensing cluster to be mapped out. Such efforts corroborate the realization that our understanding of gravity is flawed. Calculating the amount of mass needed to generate the lensing seen leaves the cluster wanting. There are simply not enough galaxies in there to do the job. So again, either there is an enormous stock of dark matter in there, outweighing the normal matter ten to one, or our understanding of the way gravity is generated on the large scale is flawed.

___Regardless of how they manage the task, gravitational lenses provide a way of seeing further into the cosmos than would otherwise be currently feasible.

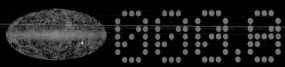

LIGHT SECONDS
LIGHT MINUTES
LIGHT YEARS
KILO LIGHT YEARS
MEGA LIGHT YEARS
GIGA LIGHT YEARS

Taking a bullet

As if galaxy collisions weren't big enough, the Bullet Cluster is the head-on smash between a pair of whole galaxy clusters. Thousands of billions of solar masses of gas have been ripped out of each cluster, and the elusive dark matter may have been revealed.

Like two charging armies, a pair of galaxy clusters has ripped right through each other and both clusters are currently speeding out of the other side. The collision took place 150 million years ago and, whereas all the galaxies have survived, the surrounding oceans of hot gases have been dragged out of each cluster. Coloured in red, the gas blisters at 70–100 million °C. The smaller cluster has had its gas forged into a bullet shape as it powered through the large one.

The blue areas are colour codings that show where the majority of each cluster's mass should be, according to the way they behave as gravitational lenses. Both regions still clearly surround the two galaxy clusters involved in the collision indicating that most of the mass contained in each remains intact.

The amount of lensing also allows the mass within each cluster to be calculated and it is much more than can be contained within just the visible parts of the galaxies. So could this be another piece of evidence for dark matter? Maybe, maybe not.

The collision speed has been estimated at 10 million km/h and this is faster than expected for two clusters of this type. It is as if something is pulling them a little harder than anticipated from our understanding of gravity.

Another galaxy cluster collision that displays a similar pattern to the Bullet Cluster is MACS J0025.4-1222 [1]. The hot gas has been stripped from the galaxy clusters in a textbook example of how you would expect dark matter to behave in a cosmic collision. But not every galaxy collision is so simple.

Abell 520 is a chaotic mess [2] with hot gas and supposed dark matter intermixed to such an extent that the only way to explain it is by postulating that a new force of nature must exist to pull on the dark matter. Alternatively, perhaps gravity behaves differently from the way we expect on the largest of the cosmic scales and maybe dark matter does not exist at all.

Yet another, MACSJ0717.5+3745, is a multiple pile-up of four galaxy clusters [3]. Here too is a confusing picture, with two of the galaxy clusters having been separated from their supposed dark matter.

Like the expressionist paintings they resemble, these images capture the grandeur of cluster collisions, yet only hint at the physical reality that underpins them.

LIGHT SECONDS
LIGHT MINUTES
LIGHT YEARS
KILO LIGHT YEARS
MEGA LIGHT YEARS
GIGA LIGHT YEARS

1

Ring of truth?

The Universe just got weirder, a lot weirder. The blue shading surrounding this cluster of galaxies shows where space is warped the most. But it should be in the centre of the cluster, not spread around the outer edges.

In the battle to uncover the invisible behaviour of dark matter, the warping of space is now a front-line weapon. A menagerie of distant galaxies exists in every direction one looks [1] and can be analyzed for subtle contortions that betray the curvature of space.

____Each crooked galactic visage is the result of a weak version of gravitational lensing. Analyzed across a whole cluster they map out hills and valleys in the fabric of space. This can then be colour coded and overlain on images of the same region to see whether the topography corresponds to luminous groupings of matter.

____Around galaxy cluster Cl 0024+17 it does not. The dark matter thought responsible for the majority of its mass does not appear to be concentrated in the centre of the cluster.

Rather, it is spread around its outskirts in a ring that measures 2.6 million light years across. Such an arrangement runs against the grain of traditional theory and begs an explanation.

____One possible solution is that this cluster of galaxies collided with another between one and two billion years ago. The smash took place directly in our line of sight so that one cluster is now directly behind the other and difficult to see. Somehow, this collision set the dark matter rippling outwards to become the ring-like structure now revealed by the weak lensing. But if so, it would seem to pull in the opposite direction to some of the other galaxy cluster collisions that suggest that dark matter particles pass straight through each other undisturbed.

____So, how should the blue areas be interpreted if dark matter does not exist? They could show where the curvature of space is greater than expected from the mass contained in that volume. And if that were to be the case, our fundamental understanding of gravity on the large scale would have been wrong.

____For the moment, although the weight of opinion swings towards the dark matter explanation for all gravitational anomalies in the Universe, it is by no means proven. Ambiguous findings, such as in Cl 0024+17, do not help and while they remain inexplicable, the mystery continues.

LIGHT SECONDS
LIGHT MINUTES
LIGHT YEARS
KILO LIGHT YEARS
MEGA LIGHT YEARS
GIGA LIGHT YEARS

1

A vision of infinity

This is what infinity looks like. Vast stretches of the darkest night punctuated by the occasional island of light. These particular islands are the first galaxies, the first motes of hope in a previously black existence, the first inklings of the grandeur that was to burst across the cosmos.

This is the end of the dark ages. Before this moment, the giant oceans of gas created in the big bang had yet to fall together to become the first stars and galaxies. But here we see the moment when star formation truly ignited across the Universe and galaxies were born.

___They are unmasked from the blackness in the deepest image of the Universe ever taken. No existing ground-based telescope can see these galactic youngsters; only the Hubble Space Telescope so far has the power – and then only by staring myopically at the same patch of sky for eleven and a half days.

___Light from the very faintest of these objects trickled in at just one photon per minute, compared with the usual rate of millions per minute from nearer galaxies. Having completed its 13-billion-year-long journey, each photon was recorded and amassed until

the galaxies responsible for these dim celestial fires materialized.

___Many of those galaxies appear as they did just 800 million years after the Big Bang, or around 13 billion years ago; some may be as they appeared just 400 million years after the big bang. They are youthful, perhaps even foetal galaxies, just emerging from their first growing pains to begin to resemble the fully fledged adults they will become. Yet astronomers search in vain for familiar galactic shapes. There are no grand spirals or giant ellipticals. These shapes will come later, over the course of billions of years, as these galactic infants collide and merge.

___There are 10,000 galaxies in this image alone, each one home to billions of stars. For all it can tell astronomers about our cosmic origins, it is still the poorest scrap of information

about the Universe at large. This is because the whole panorama only covers one fiftieth of the area of the full moon in the night sky. To observe the whole sky at this level of precision would take almost a million years of uninterrupted observing time with the Hubble Space Telescope.

___Stepping back from the Hubble Space Telescope's unprecedented level of detail, a widefield view of deepest space from the Herschel Space Observatory is just as astounding [1]. It reveals a pointillist blizzard of 10–12 billion-year-old galaxies, reminiscent of densest starfields of the Milky Way. In actual fact, there are many more galaxies in the Universe than there are stars in the Milky Way. Clearly we are a long way from mapping the entire Universe, and there are secrets enough in eternity to keep us busy for aeons.

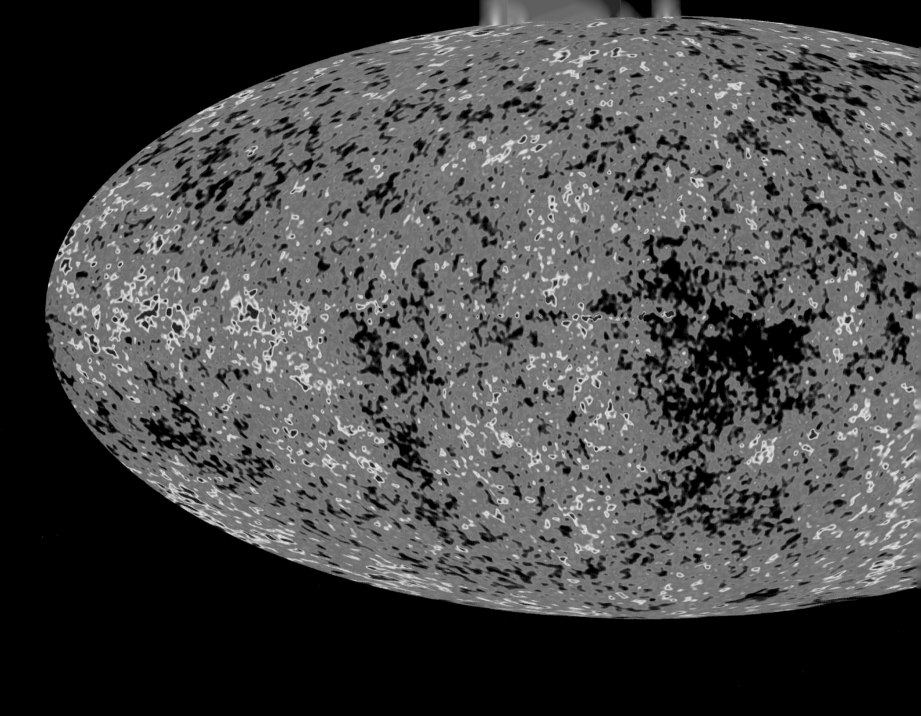

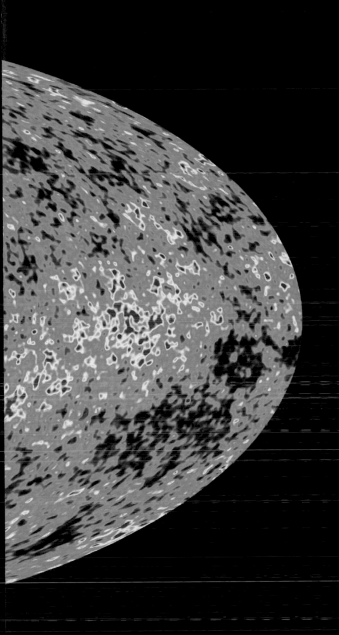

WMAP survey
COSMIC MICROWAVE
BACKGROUND RADIATION
DIAMETER 46.5 GLY

LIGHT SECONDS
LIGHT MINUTES
LIGHT YEARS
KILO LIGHT YEARS
MEGA LIGHT YEARS
GIGA LIGHT YEARS

The cosmic blueprint

This is what the Universe looks like to microwave eyes. Gone are the planets, the stars and the galaxies. In their place is an all-pervading glow of microwaves that shows up as a faint hiss on Earthly radios. But make no mistake, this static is significant: it is the echo of the Big Bang and the blueprint for the Universe.

This is what the Universe looked like just 380,000 years after the Big Bang. Before any celestial objects were born there were only atoms and light. The light was a flood of X-rays that, enfeebled with age and distance, now appears as this wall of microwave radiation.

___We can see no further than this, it is an impenetrable barrier that blocks our view of the creation of the Universe. The energy locked in this all-pervading radiation was produced when more than a billion times the amount of matter in the entire Universe today annihilated itself against an equal quantity of antimatter just a fraction of a second after the Big Bang.

___This galactic cataclysm produced a tiny residue of matter that has been sufficient to build every planet, every star and every galaxy in the Universe around us. But for the first few hundreds of thousands of years, the clouds of gas and energy fought for supremacy. Then, as atoms formed, so the radiation broke free and flooded space.

___Now it is everywhere, having been travelling for about 13.7 billion years. In all that time, roughly the age of the Universe, space has expanded greatly, stretching the radiation and transforming it from X-rays to microwaves. In the far future, it will be stretched even further into radio waves.

___The blotches on this all-sky view represent small differences in gas density at the moment of the radiation's escape. The cooler, denser regions went on to become the filaments, the great walls and the superclusters of galaxies.

___The expansion has also driven this barrier ever further from the Milky Way. Now it sits at a distance of 46.5 billion light years. For all practical purposes, it marks the edge of our observable universe and the end of our journey. As befits the weirdness of intertemporal space, we have come the furtherest possible distance in order to see the youngest possible image.

GLOSSARY

ABSOLUTE ZERO
The lowest theoretical temperature possible.
It is equivalent to –273 °C, and known as zero
on the Kelvin scale. There is no upper limit on
temperature.

ABSORPTION NEBULA
A sufficiently dense cloud of interstellar dust
and gas which can block the light from more
distant celestial objects.

ACCRETION DISC
A disc of dust and gas formed as material
spirals down into the gravitational field of a
body, such as a forming star or a black hole.

ACTIVE GALACTIC NUCLEUS (AGN)
The core of an active galaxy. The energy
generated inside an AGN can outshine all
the other stars in that galaxy. There is now
persuasive evidence that an AGN is powered
by the heating of an accretion disc as it spirals
into a supermassive black hole. Although most
galaxies are thought to contain a supermassive
black hole, only one in ten display activity.

ACTIVE GALAXY
A galaxy that emits more energy from its
centre than can be accounted for by its normal
components: stars, dust and gas. It is thought
that a central supermassive black hole is
feeding, creating an AGN.

ASTEROID, NEAR-EARTH ASTEROID
A small rocky body orbiting the Sun, each one
up to 1,000 km in diameter. Most are found in
the Asteroid Belt between Mars and Jupiter
but some have more elliptical orbits and swing
past the inner planets. Eros is a good example
of such a near-Earth asteroid.

ASTRONOMICAL ICES
Water, ammonia and methane. When found
beyond the Asteroid Belt, they are so far from the
heat of the Sun that they are usually in solid form.

ATMOSPHERE
A shell of gas around a planet or moon.
Atmospheres exist in a variety of combinations
and densities.

AURORA
Incoming solar particles can excite the atoms in
a planet's atmosphere, usually near the poles
of a planet with a magnetic field, to produce
vivid colours.

BARRED SPIRAL GALAXY
A form of spiral galaxy in which the arms do
not connect directly to the central bulge.
Instead, they peel off from a central bar of stars
running across the bulge.

BIG BANG
The event that marks the origin of the Universe
13.7 billion years ago. At this time, the Universe
exploded into existence and has been
expanding ever since.

BILLION
10^9 or 1,000,000,000 (a thousand million).

BLACK HOLE
A dense celestial object with a gravitational
field so strong that within a certain radius,
known as the event horizon, nothing can
escape. Even light is trapped inside. At the
end of its life, a particularly massive star
collapses under its own weight to form a black
hole. A supermassive black hole can form in
the centre of a galaxy, either from collapsing
gas clouds or from black hole mergers.

BLUE SUPERGIANT STAR
The most massive stars, often containing
between 30 and 150 solar masses of material.
With a surface temperature greater than
30,000 °C, their light appears bluish-white.

BOK GLOBULE
A dark, dense cloud of dust and gas in which
star formation is taking place.

BROWN DWARF
A failed star, containing less than eight
percent of the Sun's mass. Unable to sustain
the nuclear fusion of hydrogen atoms, brown
dwarfs probably look like somewhat larger
versions of the planet Jupiter.

CALDERA
A volcanic crater, found in the top of a volcano.

CELSIUS
A scale of temperature that places zero as the
freezing point of water.

CEPHEID VARIABLE
A type of variable star that undergoes cyclic changes in its brightness, closely related to its average luminosity. By measuring the periods of variation in Cepheids in distant galaxies, astronomers can estimate their average luminosities and then calculate their distances.

COMET, LONG-PERIOD, SHORT-PERIOD
Leftovers from the formation of the Solar System, comets are kilometres-wide chunks of dust and ice. Those that orbit the Sun in less than 200 years are termed short-period comets; long-period comets can take millions of years to return. They are the icy, outer Solar System equivalent of the asteroids.

CORE
The densest centre of a moon, planet or star.

COSMIC MICROWAVE BACKGROUND RADIATION (CMBR)
A faint glow of microwave radiation across the entire sky. It is believed to be the afterglow of the big bang itself, now cooled to –270 °C or just 2.7 °C above absolute zero by the expansion of the Universe.

CRATER
The usually circular scar left by an impact on the surface of rocky body.

CRUST
The uppermost solid layer on a rocky body.

CRYOVOLCANISM
Volcanic activity involving astronomical ices rather than molten rock.

DEEP FIELD
An extremely long exposure to reveal faint galaxies, usually located billions of light years away in space.

DUST
Tiny particles of chiefly silicates and carbon occupying deep space alongside gas. Dust clouds absorb visible light but infrared wavelengths can pass through them.

DWARF GALAXY
A small, faint galaxy, either irregular or elliptical in structure.

DWARF PLANET
A small round object orbiting the Sun. The definition of small means that it is incapable of controlling its wider environment through gravity.

ELECTROMAGNETIC RADIATION
A form of energy that propagates across the Universe as a combination of electrical and magnetic waves. The most familiar form is visible light, whose colours correspond to different wavelengths and energies. The full electromagnetic spectrum runs from extremely energetic gamma rays, via X-rays, ultraviolet, visible and infrared light, and microwaves to low-energy radio waves. Electromagnetic radiation can also be described as a stream of particles known as photons.

ELLIPTICAL GALAXY
A galaxy that appears spherical or American football shaped, with no specific internal structure. Its constituent stars are all in randomly inclined orbits.

EMISSION NEBULA
A cloud of gas that shines with its own light, usually by absorbing ultraviolet radiation from blue supergiant stars and re-emitting it at visible wavelengths. Planetary nebulae, supernova remnants, and many star-forming clouds are all emission nebulae.

GALACTIC HALO
A spherical region around a spiral galaxy that contains dim stars and globular clusters. It is also thought to contain dark matter. The radius of the halo surrounding the Milky Way extends some 50,000 light years from the galactic centre.

GALAXY
A gravitationally bound system of dust, gas and stars. Galaxies range in size from a few hundred, to hundreds of thousands of light years across, and are classified according to their appearance. The most common types are spiral, barred spiral, elliptical, lenticular and irregular.

GALAXY CLUSTER
A collection of hundreds or thousands of galaxies bound together by gravity.

GALAXY SUPERCLUSTER
A grouping of perhaps a dozen or more neighbouring galaxy clusters.

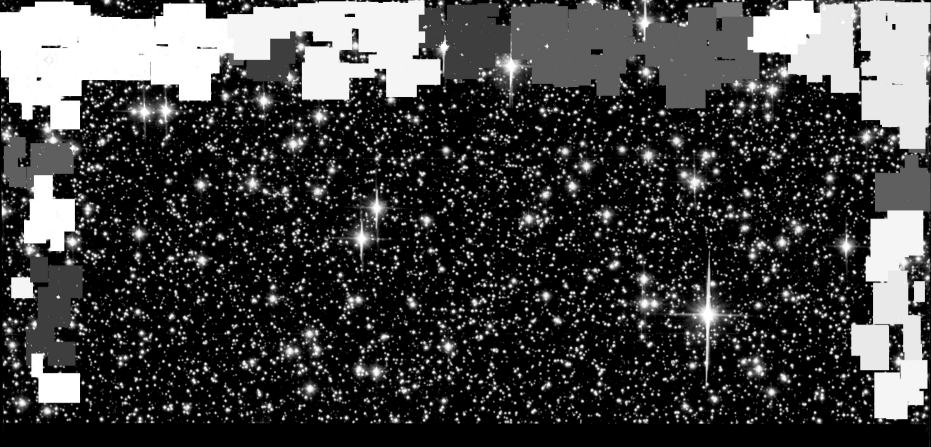

GAMMA RAY
The most energetic form of electromagnetic radiation.

GAMMA RAY BURST
A brief but immensely powerful burst (measured in minutes at most) of gamma rays from space. Usually seen to emanate from the distant realms of the Universe, they are believed to be triggered by the detonation of the first stars to form in the Universe, or the collisions between neutron stars or between black holes.

GAS GIANT PLANET
Vast planets, such as Jupiter or Saturn, with extraordinarily thick atmospheres.

GENERAL RELATIVITY
Albert Einstein's theory that explains gravity as a distortion or warping of space and time.

GLOBULAR CLUSTER
A distinct, densely packed ball of mostly old stars in orbit around a central galaxy. These are some of the oldest objects found in the Universe.

GRAVITY
A mutual attraction between masses, proportional to the masses and the distance between them, manifesting itself as a force.

HICKSON COMPACT GROUP
A collection of a handful of galaxies that is unusually compact. Often, the galaxies in a compact group will be close enough to interact with one another.

ICE GIANTS
Gas giant planets with a high proportion of astronomical ices in their make-up. Uranus and Neptune are ice giants.

INDEX CATALOGUE (IC)
A two-part supplement, published in 1895 and 1908, adding 5,386 astronomical objects to the New General Catalogue (NGC).

INFLATION
An event just after the big bang in which, for a fraction of a second, the entire Universe was driven to expand much faster than normal.

INFRARED RADIATION
A section of the electromagnetic spectrum invisible to human eyes but sensed as heat or thermal radiation.

INTERSTELLAR MEDIUM
The rarefied material scattered through the space between the stars, typically consisting of 90 percent hydrogen, 9 percent helium and 1 percent dust.

IONIZATION
The process that produces ions – atoms that are electrically charged by the capture or loss of electrons. Atoms can be stripped of their electrons by high-energy radiation (from stars, for example). Material that has been completely ionized is known as plasma.

IRREGULAR GALAXY
Any galaxy that lacks the necessary structures to be classified as an elliptical, spiral or lenticular galaxy. Despite their lack of form, irregular galaxies are typically rich in gas, dust and young stars.

LANDER
A man-made vehicle designed to safely land on the surface of a celestial body and take scientific measurements.

LENTICULAR GALAXY
A galaxy that resembles a spiral galaxy, with a central nucleus and a disc, but without spiral arms.

LIGHT
The electromagnetic radiation detectable to the human eye. However, the term is loosely applied to other forms of electromagnetic radiation, especially in the ultraviolet and infrared.

LIGHT SECOND
The distance covered by light in a vacuum during one second: 299,791 km.

LIGHT MINUTE
The distance covered by light in a vacuum during one minute: 17.9 million km.

LIGHT HOUR
The distance covered by light in a vacuum during one hour: 1 billion km.

LIGHT YEAR
The distance covered by light in a vacuum during one year: 9.5 trillion km.

LOCAL GROUP
A collection of approximately 30 galaxies spread over 10 million light years, dominated by our own Milky Way and the Andromeda Galaxy.

LOOK-BACK TIME
The time difference associated with looking at a distant object, due to the finite speed of light. Look-back time is just an interesting curiosity within our cosmic neighbourhood, but on the largest scales, when it amounts to billions of years, it reveals the Universe in a significantly earlier stage of its development.

MAGELLANIC CLOUDS
Two nearby irregular galaxies that could be in orbit around the Milky Way, or simply passing through space close to us.

MAGMA
Hot material shot up from under the crust of a body during a volcanic eruption.

MAGNETIC FIELD
The region of influence of the magnetic force of a body.

MANTLE
An intermediate shell of material covering the core but beneath the crust of a rocky body.

MASS
In astronomy there is a careful distinction between mass, the amount of matter in a body, and weight, defined as the force acting on a body in a gravitational field.

MESSIER CATALOGUE (M)
A list of about 100 nebulous-looking astronomical objects compiled by French astronomer Charles Messier between 1758 and 1781. Most were later identified as galaxies or gaseous nebulae; a few as star clusters.

METEORITE
A piece of rock ejected by one planetary body that lands on another.

METEOR SHOWER
The lights in the sky created by the Earth's atmosphere travelling through debris left by a comet, as the particles burn up.

MILKY WAY
Our Galaxy: the name is derived from our perception of it as a misty band of stars that divides the night sky. The Milky Way is, in fact, a large barred spiral galaxy spanning 100,000 light years and containing around 200 billion stars. Our Solar System lies about two-thirds of the way towards the edge of its disc, in a truncated spiral arm.

MILLION
10^6 or 1,000,000 (a thousand thousand).

MOLECULAR CLOUD
An accumulation of dust and gas, significantly denser than the interstellar medium, which spans hundreds of light years and is the site of star formation.

MOON, SHEPHERD MOON
A moon is a natural satellite of a planet. There are more than 140 in the Solar System of which the Moon orbits Earth. Shepherd moons affect rings around a planet.

NEUTRON STAR
An extremely dense stellar remnant produced during a supernova explosion when huge gravitational forces compress electrons and

NEW GENERAL CATALOGUE (NGC)
A compilation of 7,800 astronomical objects published in 1888 by JLE Dreyer and based on earlier observations made by William and John Herschel.

NUCLEAR FUSION
The process that powers stars. Two or more atomic nuclei are forced together, forming a single larger nucleus and releasing energy. Most stars spend the majority of their lives converting hydrogen into helium; more massive, hotter stars can fuse heavier elements.

OBSERVABLE UNIVERSE
That part of the Universe that we are able to study, limited by look-back time to a sphere of space apparently 13.7 billion light years in radius, but really much larger (45 billion light years), centred on our own location. At the edge of the observable Universe in every direction, we are looking back to within 400,000 years after the Big Bang itself.

OORT CLOUD
The swarm of comets surrounding the Solar System at a distance of half to one light year from the Sun.

OPEN STAR CLUSTER
A group of young stellar siblings, born from the same molecular cloud but only loosely bound together by gravity. Such clusters are usually dominated by short-lived brilliant blue stars, but are fated to disperse over a period of several hundred million years.

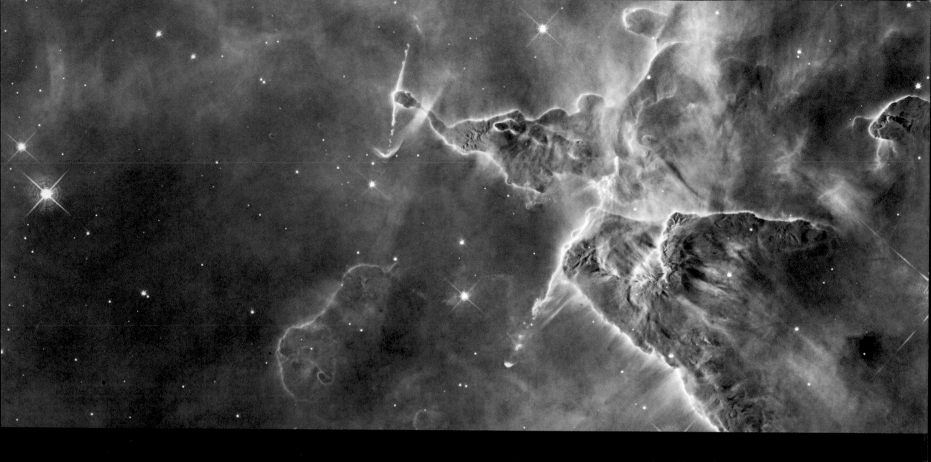

ORBIT, ORBITAL PERIOD

The trajectory of one celestial body around another. The time it takes one body to travel all the way around another body is called the orbital period.

PHOTON

A particle of light; the quantum (smallest possible) unit of the electromagnetic force.

PLANET

A large body in orbit around a star that can control its wider orbital environment with gravity. Pluto has recently been re-classified as a dwarf planet because it shares a similar orbit with a group of smaller, icy asteroids known as Plutinos.

PLANETARY NEBULA

A shell of debris flung out by a red giant star as it becomes unstable, which fades over 100,000 years as the remaining white dwarf star cools. Misnamed because of their appearance through early telescopes.

PULSAR

A rotating neutron star that emits a sweeping beam of high-energy radiation from its magnetic poles.

QUASAR

The very bright, very distant core of an extremely powerful active galaxy. The name is derived from 'quasi-stellar radio source' – so-called because this class of object was first identified through its radio emissions.

RADIATION

The transmission of energy or matter. See also electromagnetic radiation.

RADIATION PRESSURE

The pressure exerted on an object by a stream of photons; it sculpts gas clouds in space.

RADIO GALAXY

A type of active galaxy, usually elliptical, that emits large quantities of radio radiation. Often this is in the form of jets from the centre of the galaxy that create vast clouds of radio emission on either side of the galaxy, hundreds of thousands of light years across.

RED DWARF

A small and relatively cool star with a diameter and mass of less than one-third that of the Sun. Red dwarfs comprise the vast majority of stars.

RED GIANT

An ageing star that has exhausted all the hydrogen in its core and is supported by a thin spherical shell of hydrogen fusion around the core or, later, the fusion of heavier elements within the core. This change of processes boosts the star's brightness, but also causes it to balloon in size, allowing its surface to cool and turn red.

REFLECTION NEBULAE

A cloud of dust and gas in space, where the dust scatters the light from nearby stars.

ROCKY WORLDS

Planets formed predominantly from rock, sometimes with an atmosphere around them.

ROTATION PERIOD

The time it takes a body to spin once on its axis.

SAGITTARIUS A*

The supermassive black hole at the centre of the Milky Way; it is a source of intense radio and X-rays.

SEYFERT GALAXY

A spiral galaxy with an unusually bright core. The activity around a central supermassive black hole is the cause of the bright core. Seyfert galaxies are a type of active galaxy.

SOLAR MASS

A comparative unit used to express the mass of other stars in relationship to our Sun. One solar mass is equal to 2×10^{30}kg.

SOLAR SYSTEM

The Sun and its family of planets, moons and smaller bodies. Many stars could have associated solar systems.

SPIRAL GALAXY

A galaxy with a spherical central bulge of older stars; surrounded by a flattened disc containing a spiral pattern of young, hot stars. The Milky Way is a spiral galaxy.

STAR

A massive ball of hydrogen and helium bound together by gravity and shining for most of its life with the light of nuclear fusion. Stars of many different sizes are born in nebulae and open clusters, and spend most of their lives, sometimes in pairs, fusing hydrogen into helium before evolving into red giants. Depending on their mass stars die as planetary nebulae or supernovae. The stellar remnants they leave behind may be white dwarfs, neutron stars or black holes.

STAR CLUSTER

A loose formation of stars born at the same time from the same cloud.

STAR FORMATION

The process by which stars gravitationally condense from molecular clouds.

STARBURST GALAXY

A galaxy (often irregular in structure) experiencing an intense burst of star formation. Most starbursts are triggered by interaction – or even collision – with other galaxies.

STELLAR WIND

A stream of particles radiated away from a star.

SUN

The star at the centre of our Solar System.

SUPERGIANT

An extremely massive star that has exhausted the supply of hydrogen in its core, increased in luminosity as it enters a phase equivalent to a red giant, and ballooned in size. While the expansion of Sun-like stars means their surfaces cool down to become red or orange, some supergiants produce so much energy that their surface remains hot, and they can have almost any colour.

SUPERMASSIVE BLACK HOLE

A black hole with a mass of millions or billions of solar masses. Most, if not all, galaxies are thought to harbour a supermassive black hole at their core.

SUPERNOVA

The explosive demise of a star. Supernovae come in two types: Type I and Type II. A Type I supernova involves the collapse of an existing white dwarf into a neutron star; a Type II supernova is the explosion that marks the demise of a star of eight solar masses or more. Depending on the mass of the star, either a neutron star or a black hole is left at the centre of the conflagration.

SUPERNOVA REMNANT

An expanding shell of dust and gas – the debris of a supernova explosion, mixed together with swept-up interstellar matter.

TRILLION

10^{12} or 1,000,000,000,000 (a million million).

ULTRAVIOLET RADIATION

Electromagnetic radiation with a shorter wavelength than violet light.

UNIVERSE

The entirety of space, time and everything that it contains. See also observable Universe.

WAVELENGTHS

Electromagnetic radiation is emitted at many different wavelengths, collectively known as the electromagnetic spectrum. Radio wavelengths are the longest. Infrared is invisible to human eyes but sensed as heat. Visible wavelengths are detected by the human eye as light. Ultraviolet radiation has a shorter wavelength than violet in the visible spectrum. X rays are higher energy than ultraviolet radiation but less energetic than gamma rays, which are the shortest wavelengths of all.

WHITE DWARF

The dense, cooling ember of a star that has exhausted its nuclear fuel and collapsed under the force of its own gravity. All but the most massive stars will end their days as white dwarfs.

WOLF–RAYET STAR

A particularly massive, short-lived star, usually containing more than 25 solar masses of material. Wolf–Rayets have powerful stellar winds that strip away the outer layers of their own atmospheres, leaving their interiors exposed.

X-RAYS

High-energy electromagnetic radiation. Less energetic than gamma rays, but more so than ultraviolet radiation.

INDEX

CREDITS

p2: NASA; p11: [1] ESA/LFI & HFI Consortia; p13: [1] Atlas Image courtesy of 2MASS/UMass/IPAC-Caltech/NASA/NSF/G. Kopan, R. Hurt, [2] ESA & SPIRE Consortium & HerMES consortia; p14: NASA/JPL/Space Science Institute; p17: NASA; p18: NASA; p19: [1] NASA/Science Faction, [2] Image Analysis Laboratory/NASA Johnson Space Center; p20: Image Analysis Laboratory/NASA Johnson Space Center; p21: [1] Mike Constantine/NASA; p22: NASA/JPL/Mosaic by Mattias Malmer; p23: [1] NASA/JPL-Caltech, [2] NASA/JPL-Caltech; p24: NASA/Johns Hopkins University Applied Physics Laboratory/Carnegie Institution of Washington; p25: [1] NASA/Johns Hopkins University Applied Physics Laboratory/Carnegie Institution of Washington, [2] NASA/Johns Hopkins University Applied Physics Laboratory/Arizona State University/Carnegie Institution of Washington, [3] NASA/Johns Hopkins University Applied Physics Laboratory/Smithsonian Institution/Carnegie Institution of Washington; p26: Göran Scharmer, Kai Langhans, Mats Löfdahl, ISP, SST, Royal Swedish Academy of Sciences; p27: [1] NASA/AURA/NSF; p28: NASA/JPL/University of Arizona; p29: [1] NASA/JPL/University of Arizona, [2] NASA/JPL/University of Arizona, [3] NASA/JPL/University of Arizona; p30: NASA/JPL-Caltech/University of Arizona; p31: [1] NASA/JPL-Caltech/University of Arizona, [2] NASA/JPL-Caltech/University of Arizona; p32: NASA/JPL-Caltech; p33: [1] NASA/JPL-Caltech, [2] NASA/JPL-Caltech; p34: Canada-France-Hawaii Telescope/Coelum/J.-C. Cuillandre & G. Anselmi; p35: [1] NASA/JPL/UMD, [2] NASA/JPL-Caltech/UMD; p36: NASA/JPL/Space Science Institute; p37: [1] NASA/JPL-Caltech, [2] NASA/JPL/Space Science Institute; p38: NASA/JPL/University of Arizona; p39: [1] NASA/JPL-Caltech; p40: NASA/JPL/University of Arizona; p41: [1] NASA/JPL/University of Arizona/University of Colorado, [2] NASA/JPL-Caltech; p42: NASA/JPL/Space Science Institute; p43: [1] NASA/JPL/Space Science Institute, [2] NASA/JPL/Space Science Institute, [3] NASA/JPL/Space Science Institute; p44: NASA/JPL/Space Science Institute; p45: [1] NASA/JPL/Space Science Institute; p46: NASA/JPL/Space Science Institute; p47: [1] NASA/JPL/Space Science Institute/Universities Space Research Association/Lunar & Planetary Institute, [2] NASA/JPL/Space Science Institute, [3] NASA/JPL/Space Science Institute; p48: NASA/JPL/Space Science Institute; p49: [1] NASA/JPL/Space Science Institute, [2] NASA/JPL/Space Science Institute, [3] NASA/JPL/Space Science Institute; p50: NASA/JPL/Space Science Institute; p51: [1] NASA/JPL/Space Science Institute; p52: NASA/JPL/Space Science Institute; p53: [1] NASA/JPL/Space Science Institute, [2] NASA/JPL/Space Science Institute, [3] NASA/JPL/Space Science Institute; p54: Voyager 2, NASA; p55: [1] NASA/JPL-Caltech, [2] NASA/JPL-Caltech; p56: NASA/JPL-Caltech; p57: [1] NASA/JPL-Caltech, [2] NASA/JPL; p58: ESO/J. Emerson/VISTA. Acknowledgment: Cambridge Astronomical Survey Unit; p61: NASA, ESA and AURA/Caltech; p62: Robert Gendler, Jim Misti, Steve Mazlin; p63: [1] ESO/S. Guisard, [2] NASA/JPL-Caltech/Harvard-Smithsonian CfA; p64: T.A. Rector/University of Alaska Anchorage, H. Schweiker/WIYN and NOAO/AURA/NSF; p65: [1] J. Morse/STScI, and NASA, [2] NASA/ESA and The Hubble Heritage Team (AURA/STScI), [3] NASA and The Hubble Heritage Team (AURA/STScI); p66: NASA, NOAO, ESA, the Hubble Helix Nebula Team, M. Meixner (STScI), and T.A. Rector (NRAO); p67: [1] L. Hora (Harvard Smithsonian Center for Astrophysics); W. B. Latter (NASA/Herschel Science Center); M. Marengo (Harvard Smithsonian Center for Astrophysics); G.G. Fazio (Harvard Smithsonian Center for Astrophysics); H.A. Smith (Harvard Smithsonian Center for Astrophysics), [2] NASA/JPL-Caltech/J. Hora (Harvard-Smithsonian CfA); p68: Robert Gendler, Jim Misti; p69: [1] Canada-France-Hawaii Telescope/Coelum/J.-C. Cuillandre & G. Anselmi, [2] NASA, ESA, and The Hubble Heritage Team (STScI/AURA), Acknowledgment: P. McCullough (STScI); p70: Image Data: Digitized Sky Survey; Color Composite: Noel Carboni; p71: [1] Robert Gendler, Martin Pugh, [2] Robert Gendler, Jim Misti, Steve Mazlin; p72: Anglo-Australian Observatory/David Malin Images; p73: [1] NASA/SAO/CXC, [2] NASA and The Hubble Heritage Team (STScI/AURA), Acknowledgment: W. Blair (JHU) and D. Malin (David Malin Images); p74: NASA, ESA, the Hubble Heritage (STScI/AURA)-ESA/Hubble Collaboration, and the Digitized Sky Survey 2. Acknowledgment: J. Hester (Arizona State University) and Davide De Martin (ESA/Hubble); p75: [1] T.A. Rector/University of Alaska Anchorage, H. Schweiker/WIYN and NOAO/AURA/NSF; p76: H. Schweiker/NOAO/AURA/NSF and T. A. Rector/University of Alaska Anchorage and NOAO/AURA/NSF; p77: [1] T.A. Rector/University of Alaska Anchorage, H. Schweiker/WIYN and NOAO/AURA/NSF; p78: Robert Gendler; p79: [1] Infrared Processing and Analysis Center, Caltech/JPL, [2] Infrared Processing and Analysis Center, Caltech/JPL; p80: NASA,ESA, M. Robberto (Space Telescope Science Institute/ESA) and the Hubble Space Telescope Orion Treasury Project Team; p81: [1] NASA,ESA, M. Robberto (Space Telescope Science Institute/ESA) and the Hubble Space Telescope Orion Treasury Project Team, [2] NASA,ESA, M. Robberto (Space Telescope Science Institute/ESA) and the Hubble Space Telescope Orion Treasury Project Team; p82: T.A.Rector (NOAO/AURA/NSF) and Hubble Heritage Team (STScI/AURA/NASA); p83: [1] ESO; p84: NASA and The Hubble Heritage Team (STScI); p86: T. A. Rector/University of Alaska Anchorage, H. Schweiker/WIYN and NOAO/AURA/NSF; p87: ESO/IDA/Danish 1.5 m/R. Gendler, J.-E. Ovaldsen, C. Thöne and C. Féron, ESO/J. Emerson/VISTA. Acknowledgment: Cambridge Astronomical Survey Unit; p88: University of Colorado, University of Hawaii and NOAO/AURA/NSF; p89: [1] Digital Sky Survey, Acknowledgment: Charles Shahar; p90: T.A. Rector (University of Alaska Anchorage) and WIYN/NOAO/AURA/NSF; p91: [1] NASA/JPL-Caltech /W. Reach (Caltech); p92: ESO; p93: [1] NASA, H. Ford (JHU), G. Illingworth (UCSC/LO), M.Clampin (STScI), G. Hartig (STScI), the ACS Science Team, and ESA; p94: NASA, ESA, HEIC, and The Hubble Heritage Team (STScI/AURA); p95: [1] ESA/Hubble and NASA, [2] NASA, Andrew Fruchter and the ERO Team [Sylvia Baggett (STScI), Richard Hook (ST-ECF), Zoltan Levay (STScI)][3] Bruce Balick (University of Washington), Vincent Icke (Leiden University, The Netherlands), Garrelt Mellema (Stockholm University), and NASA; p96: T.A. Rector/University of Alaska Anchorage, H. Schweiker/WIYN and NOAO/AURA/NSF; p97: [1] Raghvendra Sahai and John Trauger (JPL), the WFPC2 science team, and NASA, [2] Hubble Heritage Team (AURA/STScI/NASA); p98: NASA, ESA, and the Hubble SM4 ERO Team; p99: [1] NASA and The Hubble Heritage Team (AURA/STScI); p100: ESO/S. Guisard (www.eso.org/~sguisard); p101: [1] ESO/IDA/Danish 1.5 m/R. Gendler, U.G. Jørgensen, K. Harpsøe, [2] A. Caulet (ST-ECF, ESA) and NASA; p102: Daniel López, IAC; p104: T. A. Rector/University of Alaska Anchorage, WIYN and NOAO/AURA/NSF; p105: [1] ESA/PACS & SPIRE Consortium, Frédérique Motte, Laboratoire AIM Paris-Saclay, CEA/IRFU - CNRS/INSU - Uni. Paris Diderot, HOBYS Key Programme Consortia; p106: ESO; p107: [1] NASA/JPL-Caltech/J. Rho (SSC/Caltech), [2] NASA/JPL-Caltech/J. Rho (SSC/Caltech), [3] NASA and Jeff Hester (Arizona State University); p108: T.A. Rector/University of Alaska Anchorage, T. Abbott and NOAO/AURA/NSF; p109: [1] ESO/J. Emerson/VISTA, Acknowledgment: Cambridge Astronomical Survey Unit; p110: T.A. Rector/University of Alaska Anchorage, T. Abbott and NOAO/AURA/NSF; p111: [1] NASA, ESA, and the Digitized Sky Survey 2. Acknowledgment: Davide De Martin (ESA/Hubble); p112: NASA, ESA, J. Hester and A. Loll (Arizona State University); p113: [1] NASA/CXC/ASU/J. Hester et al. And NASA/HST/ASU/J. Hester et al., [2] X-ray: NASA/CXC/J.Hester (ASU); Optical: NASA/ESA/J.Hester & A.Loll (ASU); Infrared: NASA/JPL-Caltech/R.Gehrz (Univ. Minn.); p114: T.A. Rector and B.A. Wolpa (NRAO/AUI/NSF); p115: [1] NASA, ESA and The Hubble Heritage Team (STScI/AURA), [2] NASA, Jeff Hester and Paul Scowen Arizona State University; p116: NASA/CXC/Rutgers/J. Warren & J.Hughes et al; p117: [1] NASA, CXC and S. Holt (F.W. Olin College of Engineering); p118: NASA, ESA, N. Smith (University of California, Berkeley), and The Hubble Heritage Team (STScI/AURA); p119: [1] Jon Morse (University of Colorado), and NASA/ESA, [2] NOAO/AURA/NSF; p120: NASA, ESA, and M. Livio and the Hubble 20th Anniversary Team (STScI); p121: [1] NASA, ESA, and M. Livio and the Hubble 20th Anniversary Team (STScI), [2] NASA/JPL-Caltech/N. Smith (Univ. of Colorado at Boulder); p122: NASA, ESA and Jesús Maíz Apellániz (Instituto de astrofísica de Andalucía, Spain). Acknowledgment: Davide De Martin (ESA/Hubble); p123: [1] Davide De Martin (ESA/Hubble), the ESA/ESO/NASA Photoshop FITS Liberator & Digitized Sky Survey 2; p124: NASA, ESA, and the Hubble Heritage (STScI/AURA)/Hubble Collaboration, Acknowledgment: R. Fesen (Dartmouth College) and J. Long (ESA/Hubble); p125: [1] NASA/JPL-Caltech/O. Krause (Steward Observatory); p126: Canada-France-Hawaii Telescope/Coelum/J.-C. Cuillandre & G. Anselmi; p128: NASA, ESA, and the Hubble Heritage Team (STScI/AURA), Acknowledgment: A. Cool (San Francisco State University) and J. Anderson (STScI); p129: [1] NASA, ESA, and the Hubble SM4 ERO Team; p130: ESO; p132: NASA, ESA, and the Hubble Heritage (STScI/AURA)-ESA/Hubble Collaboration, Acknowledgment: J. Maíz Apellániz (Instituto of Astrophysics of Andalucía, Spain); p133: [1] NASA/JPL-Caltech/UCLA; p134: NASA, ESA, and H. Bond (STScI); p135: [1] NASA and The Hubble Heritage Team (AURA/STScI); p136: NASA, ESA, SSC, CXC and STScI; p137: [1] ESO, Digitized Sky Survey 2 & S. Guisard (www.eso.org/~sguisard); p138: NASA, ESA, SSC, CXC and STScI; p139: [1] NASA/CXC/MIT/F.K. Baganoff et al, [2] ESO/S. Gillessen et al., [3] NRAO/VLA F.Zadeh et al; p140: ESA/Hubble & NASA; p141: [1] NOAO/AURA/NSF, [2] NASA, ESA, [3] NASA, ESA and H. Richer (University of British Columbia); p142: NASA, ESA, and the Hubble Heritage (STScI/AURA)-ESA/Hubble Collaboration; p145: NASA/ESA; p146: ESO; p147: [1] NASA/ESA/M. Meixner (STScI) & the SAGE Legacy Team, [2] C. Smith, S. Points, the MCELS Team and NOAO/AURA/NSF; p148: ESO; p149: [1] NASA, ESA, and F. Paresce (INAF-IASF, Bologna, Italy), R. O'Connell (University of Virginia, Charlottesville), and the Wide Field Camera 3 Science Oversight Committee; p150: NASA, ESA and A. Nota (STScI); p151: [1] ESA/Hubble and Digitized Sky Survey 2. Acknowledgments: Davide De Martin (http://www.skyfactory.org); p152: Robert Gendler; p153: [1] NASA/JPL-Caltech/P. Barmby (Harvard-Smithsonian CfA), [2] NASA/JPL-Caltech/P. Barmby (Harvard-Smithsonian CfA); p154: T.A. Rector (NRAO/AUI/NSF and NOAO/AURA/NSF); p155: [1] NASA/JPL-Caltech, [2] NASA and The Hubble Heritage Team (AURA/STScI); p156: NASA, ESA, and The Hubble Heritage Team (STScI/AURA), Acknowledgment: Y. Momany (University of Padua); p158: X-ray: NASA/CXC/CfA/R.Kraft et al; Submillimeter: MPIfR/ESO/APEX/A.Weiss et al; Optical: ESO/WFI; p159: [1] NASA/JPL-Caltech/J. Keene (SSC/Caltech), [2] E.J. Schreier (STScI) and NASA; p160: NASA, ESA, and The Hubble Heritage Team (STScI/AURA). Acknowledgment: A. Zezas and J. Huchra (Harvard-Smithsonian Center for Astrophysics); p161: [1] X-ray: NASA/CXC/Wisconsin/D.Pooley & CfA/A.Zezas; Optical: NASA/ESA/CfA/A.Zezas; UV: NASA/JPL-Caltech/CfA/J. Huchra et al; IR: NASA/JPL-Caltech/CfA, [2] NASA/Hubble and Digitized Sky Survey 2. Acknowledgments: Davide De Martin (ESA/Hubble), [3] Chynoweth et al., NRAO/AUI/NSF, ESA/Hubble & Digitized Sky Survey 2. Acknowledgments: Davide De Martin (ESA/Hubble); p162: NASA, ESA, and The Hubble Heritage Team (STScI/AURA), J. Gallagher (University of Wisconsin), M. Mountain (STScI), and P. Puxley (National Science Foundation); p163: [1] NASA, ESA, CXC, and JPL-Caltech; p164: NASA, ESA, A. Aloisi (ESA/STScI) and The Hubble Heritage (STScI/AURA)-ESA/Hubble Collaboration; p165: [1] ESO, [2] NASA, ESA, A. Aloisi (ESA/STScI), and A. Aloisi (STScI/ESA); p166: NASA, ESA, K. Kuntz (JHU), F. Bresolin (University of Hawaii), J. Trauger (Jet Propulsion Lab), J. Mould (NOAO), Y.-H. Chu (University of Illinois, Urbana), and STScI; p168: NASA and The Hubble Heritage Team (STScI/AURA); p169: [1] NASA/JPL-Caltech; p170: NASA, ESA, S. Beckwith (STScI), and The Hubble Heritage Team (STScI/AURA); p171: [1] NASA, ESA, S. Beckwith (STScI), and The Hubble Heritage Team (STScI/AURA); p172: NASA, ESA, and The Hubble Heritage Team STScI/AURA); p174: NASA, ESA, and the Hubble Heritage Team (STScI/AURA)-ESA/Hubble Collaboration, Acknowledgment: B. Whitmore (Space Telescope Science Institute); p175: [1] NOAO/AURA/NSF, B. Twardy, B. Twardy, and A. Block (NOAO); p176: NASA, ESA, and The Hubble Heritage Team (STScI/AURA), Acknowledgment: M. Gregg (Univ. Calif.-Davis and Inst. for Geophysics and Planetary Physics, Lawrence Livermore Natl. Lab.); p177: [1] NASA/ESA and The Hubble Heritage Team; p178: NASA, ESA, and the Hubble Heritage Team (STScI/AURA)-ESA/Hubble Collaboration; p179: [1] NASA, ESA, and the Hubble SM4 ERO Team; p180: NASA & ESA; p181: [1] NASA & ESA; p182: NASA, ESA, and The Hubble Heritage Team (STScI/AURA), Acknowledgment: P. Knezek (WIYN); p183: [1] NASA, ESA, and The Hubble Heritage Team (STScI/AURA), Acknowledgment: P. Knezek (WIYN); p184: NASA, ESA, and The Hubble Heritage Team (STScI/AURA), Acknowledgment: P. Goudfrooij (STScI); p185: [1] NRAO/AUI and J. M. Uson, [2] NASA, ESA and W. Harris (McMaster University, Ontario, Canada); p186: NASA, ESA, and R. Sharples (University of Durham); p187: [1] NASA, ESA, the Hubble Heritage Team (STScI/AURA)-ESA/Hubble Collaboration and A. Evans (University of Virginia, Charlottesville/NRAO/Stony Brook University), [2] NASA, the Hubble Heritage Team (STScI/AURA)-ESA/Hubble Collaboration and A. Evans (University of Virginia, Charlottesville/NRAO/Stony Brook University), [3] NASA, the Hubble Heritage Team (STScI/AURA)-ESA/Hubble Collaboration and A. Evans (University of Virginia, Charlottesville/NRAO/Stony Brook University); p188: X-ray: NASA/CXC/KIPAC/S.Allen et al; Radio: NRAO/VLA/G. Taylor; Infrared: NASA/ESA/McMaster Univ/W.Harris; p189: [1] NASA & ESA; p190: NASA, ESA and Andy Fabian (University of Cambridge, UK); p191: [1] X-ray: NASA/CXC/IoA/A.Fabian et al; Radio: NRAO/VLA/G. Taylor; Optical: NASA/ESA/Hubble Heritage (STScI/AURA) & Univ. of Cambridge/IoA/A. Fabian; p192: European Southern Observatory; p193: [1] X-ray: NASA/CXC/UVa/M. Sun, et al; H-alpha/Optical: SOAR (UVa/NOAO/UNC/CNPq-Brazil)/M. Sun et al; p194: NASA, H. Ford (JHU), G. Illingworth (UCSC/LO), M.Clampin (STScI), G. Hartig (STScI), the ACS Science Team, and ESA; p195: [1] NASA, ESA, the Hubble Heritage Team (STScI/AURA)-ESA/Hubble Collaboration and A. Evans (University of Virginia, Charlottesville/NRAO/Stony Brook University), [2] NASA, the Hubble Heritage Team (STScI/AURA)-ESA/Hubble Collaboration and A. Evans (University of Virginia, Charlottesville/NRAO/Stony Brook University), [3] NASA, ESA, the Hubble Heritage Team (STScI/AURA)-ESA/Hubble Collaboration and A. Evans (University of Virginia, Charlottesville/NRAO/Stony Brook University); p196: X-ray: NASA/CXC/AIfA/D.Hudson & T.Reiprich et al; Radio: NRAO/VLA/NRL; p197: [1] X-ray (NASA/CXC/MIT/C.Canizares, M.Nowak); Optical (NASA/STScI), [2] X-ray (NASA/CXC/MIT/C.Canizares, M.Nowak); Optical (NASA/STScI); p198: NASA, ESA, and the Hubble SM4 ERO Team; p199: [1] X-ray (NASA/CXC/CfA/E.O'Sullivan); Optical (Canada-France-Hawaii-Telescope/Coelum; p200: NASA, ESA, and The Hubble Heritage Team (AURA/STScI); p201: [1] Kirk Borne (STScI), and NASA; p202: NASA, ESA and the Hubble Heritage (STScI/AURA)-ESA/Hubble Collaboration. Acknowledgment: M. West (ESO, Chile); p203: [1] NASA, ESA, M. West (ESO, Chile), and CXC/Penn State University/G. Garmire, et al; p204: NASA, ESA, K. Cook (Lawrence Livermore National Laboratory, USA); p205: [1] NASA, ESA, and the Hubble Heritage Team (STScI/AURA) Acknowledgment: D. Carter (Liverpool John Moores University) and the Coma HST ACS Treasury Team; p206: Canada-France-Hawaii Telescope/Coelum/J.-C. Cuillandre & G. Anselmi; p207: [1] NASA, ESA, the Hubble Heritage Team (STScI/AURA)-ESA/Hubble Collaboration and K. Noll (STScI); p208: NASA, H. Ford (JHU), G. Illingworth (UCSC/LO), M.Clampin (STScI), G. Hartig (STScI), the ACS Science Team, and ESA; p209: [1] NASA, ESA, the Hubble Heritage Team (STScI/AURA)-ESA/Hubble Collaboration and A. Evans (University of Virginia, Charlottesville/NRAO/Stony Brook University), [2] NASA, ESA, the Hubble Heritage Team (STScI/AURA)-ESA/Hubble Collaboration and A. Evans (University of Virginia, Charlottesville/NRAO/Stony Brook University), K. Noll (STScI), and J. Westphal (Caltech), [2] The Hubble Heritage Team (AURA/STScI/NASA), [3] NASA, ESA, and M. Livio (STScI); p212: MacFarland, Colberg, White (Munchen), Jenkins, Pearce, Frenk (Durham), Evrard (Michigan), Couchman (London, CA) Thomas (Sussex), Elstathiou (Cambridge), Peacock (Edinburgh)/National Science Foundation/Max-Planck-Institute for Astrophysics; p216: 2MASS/T. H. Jarrett, J. Carpenter, & R. Hurt; p217: [1] NASA, ESA, and E. Hallman (University of Colorado, Boulder); p218: Acknowledgment: Richard Gott et al; p220: ESO/J. Dietrich; p222: NASA, N. Benitez (JHU), T. Broadhurst (Racah Institute of Physics/The Hebrew University), H. Ford (JHU), M. Clampin (STScI), G. Hartig (STScI), G. Illingworth (UCO/Lick Observatory), the ACS Science Team and ESA; p223: [1] NASA, ESA, A. Bolton (Harvard-Smithsonian CfA) and the SLACS Team, [2] NASA, ESA, A. Bolton (Harvard-Smithsonian CfA) and the SLACS Team, [3] NASA, ESA, A. Bolton (Harvard-Smithsonian CfA) and the SLACS Team, [4] NASA, ESA, A. Bolton (Harvard-Smithsonian CfA) and the SLACS Team; p224: X-ray: NASA/CXC/CfA/M.Markevitch et al; Optical: NASA/STScI; Magellan/U.Arizona/D.Clowe et al; Lensing Map: NASA/STScI; ESO WFI; Magellan/U.Arizona/D.Clowe et al; p225: [1] X-ray(NASA/CXC/Stanford/S.Allen); Optical/Lensing(NASA/STScI/UC Santa Barbara/M.Bradac), [2] X-ray: NASA/CXC/UVic./A.Mahdavi et al. Optical/Lensing: CFHT/UVic./A.Mahdavi et al., [3] X-ray (NASA/CXC/IIA/C. Ma et al.); Optical (NASA/STScI/IIA/C. Ma et al.); p226: NASA, ESA, M.J. Jee and H. Ford (Johns Hopkins University); p227: [1] NASA, ESA, M.J. Jee and H. Ford (Johns Hopkins University); p228: NASA, ESA, S. Beckwith (STScI) and the HUDF Team; p229: [1] ESA & SPIRE Consortium & HerMES consortia; p230: NASA/WMAP Science Team; p232: NASA/JPL-Caltech/S. Stolovy (SSC/Caltech); p234: NASA, ESA, and K. Sahu (STScI); p236: NASA, ESA, and M. Livio and the Hubble 20th Anniversary Team (STScI).

For Elizabeth Grace, who sees castles among the stars – SC

And for Faye Zephyrine, who sees bananas – NC

First published in hardback in Great Britain in 2010 by Atlantic Books and Callisto, imprints of Atlantic Books Ltd.

Copyright © Stuart Clark, Nicolas Cheetham 2010

The moral right of Stuart Clark & Nicolas Cheetham to be identified as the authors of this work has been asserted in accordance with the Copyright, Designs and Patents Act of 1988.

All rights reserved. No part of this publication may be reproduced, stored in a retrieval system, or transmitted in any form or by any means, electronic, mechanical, photocopying, recording, or otherwise, without the prior permission of both the copyright owner and the above publisher of this book.

The picture credits constitute an extension of this copyright page.

Every effort has been made to trace or contact all copyright holders. The publishers will be pleased to make good any omissions or rectify any mistakes brought to their attention at the earliest opportunity.

A CIP catalogue record for this book is available from the British Library.

Callisto ISBN: 978 0 85740 021 5
Atlantic Export ISBN: 978 1 84887 946 1

Designed by Grade Design Consultants, www.gradedesign.com
Printed in China

10 9 8 7 6 5 4 3 2 1

Callisto and Atlantic Books
Imprints of Atlantic Books Ltd
Ormond House
26–27 Boswell Street
London
WC1N 3JZ

www.atlantic-books.co.uk